Programming the DRAGON12-Plus-USB™ in C and Assembly Language Using CodeWarrior™

Richard E. Haskell
Darrin M. Hanna

Oakland University, Rochester, Michigan

LBE Books
Rochester Hills, MI

ISBN 978-0-9824970-2-9

Published by LBE Books, LLC
1202 Walton Boulevard
Suite 214
Rochester Hills, MI 48307

www.lbebooks.com

Preface

Microcontrollers such as the Freescale MC9SDG256 are remarkable devices. They contain not only a sophisticated microprocessor with a rich set of instructions and addressing modes, but also contain built-in RAM, EEPROM, and flash memory as well as numerous useful I/O ports, including parallel I/O, several different types of serial I/O, timers, and A/D converters.

We will use a particular microcontroller, the Freescale MC9S12DG256, that it is one of the more powerful in the popular HCS12 family of microcontrollers from Freescale with lots of I/O capabilities. This microcontroller is available on the DRAGON12-Plus-USB™ development board from Wytec, Inc. The DRAGON12-Plus-USB™ has many built-in I/O devices including LEDs, switches, four 7-segment displays, a hex keypad, an LCD display, a hex keypad, a D/A converter chip, an on-board speaker, a built-in H-bridge for driving motors, convenient headers for connecting servos and an accelerometer board available from Wytec, and female headers for connecting to your circuits on the built-in protoboard.

A previous book from LBE Books, *Learning By Example Using C – Programming the DRAGON12-Plus™ Using CodeWarrior* showed how to write programs in C with a minimum of effort for this development board. We did this by providing you with a CodeWarrior stationery project that contained an assembly language file to do all the low-level interaction with the I/O registers. These assembly language routines become function calls for your C program. Thus, in this previous book you didn't have to learn any assembly language to get sophisticated programs to work on this development board.

This current book provides these same CodeWarrior Stationery projects so that you can write C programs easily for the DRAGON12-Plus-USB™ development board. However, in this book we look under the hood to see how all of the assembly language routines that are included in the stationery project work. This way you will learn how to program the HCS12 microcontroller in assembly language and how to call these assembly language routines from your top-level C program. You will therefore be able to write your own assembly language subroutines that you can call from your C program, and in this way get the maximum performance from the MC9SDG256 microcontroller.

In Chapter 1 we introduce the DRAGON12-Plus-USB™ development board. Chapter 2 will include examples of using the parallel ports for outputs and Chapter 3 will include examples of using the parallel ports for inputs. Liquid crystal displays are described in Chapter 4. The important topic of interrupts are introduced in Chapter 5. Examples using the two 8-channel A/D converters that are built into the MC9S12DG256 microcontroller are given in Chapter 6. Examples that show how to use pulse-width modulation (PWM) to control the speed of a DC motor or the position of a servo are presented in Chapter 7. Chapter 8 includes examples of using the serial communication interface (SCI) and Chapter 9 shows how to use the serial peripheral interface (SPI). Examples using the built-in timer module are given in Chapter 10 and an example of using the MC9S12DG256 microcontroller for fuzzy control is included in Chapter 11.

Many colleagues, students and reviewers have influenced the development of this book. Their stimulating discussions, probing questions, and critical comments are greatly appreciated. Special thanks go to Michael Latcha and Osamah Rawashdeh with whom we have had many useful discussions related to the contents of this book.

Richard E. Haskell
Darrin M. Hanna

Programming the DRAGON12-Plus-USB in C and Assembly Language Using CodeWarrior™

Table of Contents

Chapter 1

Introduction

The HCS12 is a family of Freescale microcontrollers and is a direct descendent of the original Motorola 68HC11 and the more recent 68HC12. In this book you will learn how to program the MC9S12DG256 microcontroller that is on the Wytec DRAGON12-Plus-USB™ board. You will learn to program this microcontroller in both assembly language and C using the industry-standard CodeWarrior development system. To make it as easy as possible we have provided a stationery project that you can build upon that includes a large collection of built-in assembly language routines to access all of the various I/O functions of the MC9S12DG256. You will access these routines through C function calls.

1.1 From Microprocessors to Microcontrollers

A major revolution in the computer industry has taken place in the past 25 years. The making of the first microprocessor was made possible by the remarkable development of integrated circuits during the 1960s. This technology allowed hundreds and then thousands of transistors to be etched onto a single piece of silicon. This led to the design of integrated circuits in which more and more logic elements were incorporated into a single chip. In 1969 Intel undertook a contract to develop a set of integrated circuits that could be used to make a programmable electronic calculator. Instead of developing yet another special purpose integrated circuit with only a limited function, Intel chose to produce a more general purpose device, the 4004 microprocessor, which could be programmed to perform many different functions. This first microprocessor had only four data lines over which both address information and data had to be sent to memory devices. Intel put this chip on the market in 1971 as part of a four chip set that formed a micro-programmable computer. The 4004 had many limitations and the following year Intel introduced the 8008 and two years later the 8080 which became widely used in a host of different applications. In 1975 Motorola produced its first microprocessor – the 6800.

The 6800 had 8 data lines (called a *data bus*) and 16 address lines (called an *address bus*). This means that it could address 2^{16} = 65,536 different memory addresses, each containing 8 bits, or one byte of data. The heart of the 6800 was its CPU, or central processing unit, sometimes referred to as an MPU, or microprocessor unit. The CPU contained the registers and logic to execute the instruction set of the 6800. The 6800 registers included two 8-bit accumulators (*A* and *B*), a 16-bit index register (*X*), a 16-bit stack pointer (*SP*), a 16-bit program counter (*PC*), and an 8-bit condition-code register (*CCR*).

Thus, the first microprocessors consisted only of a CPU that could address external memory as shown in Fig. 1.1.

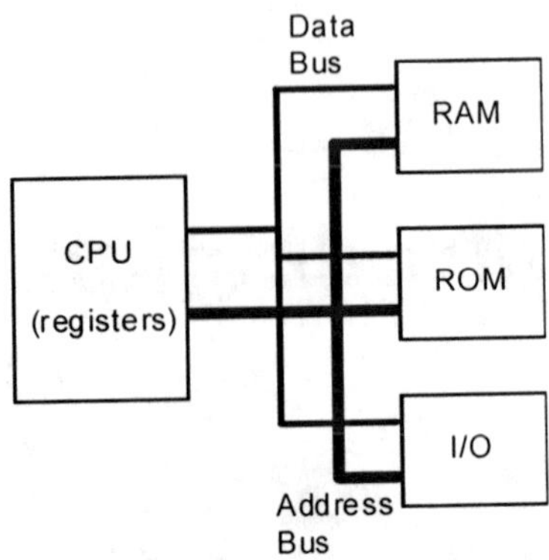

Figure 1.1 A microprocessor (CPU) connected to external memory

The external memory shown in Fig. 1.1 consists of read-write memory (RAM), read-only memory (ROM), and input/output memory (I/O). Typically the I/O memory consists of dedicated special-purpose devices for performing such operations as parallel I/O, serial I/O, timer functions, and analog-to-digital (A/D) conversion. These I/O devices contain registers that look like memory locations to the CPU. The RAM in Fig. 1.1 could be either static RAM (SRAM) or dynamic RAM (DRAM). Dynamic RAM can contain more bytes of memory than static RAM for the same size chip, but requires additional circuitry to refresh the data periodically to keep it from being lost. Other types of memory devices that might be connected to the address and data busses in Fig. 1.1 include erasable programmable read-only memory (EPROM), electrically-erasable programmable read-only memory (EEPROM), and flash EEPROM. Both flash EEPROM and EEPROM are non-volatile memory that will maintain their data when power is removed. Individual bytes can be erased and programmed in EEPROM while flash EEPROMs normally require erasing the entire memory array at one time.

As integrated circuit technology developed over the years one of the trends has been the development of faster and more complex microprocessors such as the Intel 80x86 and Pentium and the Motorola 680x0 and PowerPC. These microprocessors are in many of the popular desktop computers used in offices all over the world. Another trend has been to package more and more functionality onto a single chip. The Motorola 6801 was introduced in 1978 and included a small amount of RAM and ROM as well as parallel and serial I/O on a single chip. The following year Motorola introduced an EPROM version of the 6801, the 68701, as well as the first of the low-cost 6805 family of microcontrollers.

The first 68HC11 was introduced by Motorola in 1985. This 8-bit microcontroller (the A8 part) contained on a single chip the CPU11 microprocessor, 8 Kbytes of ROM, 256 bytes of RAM, 512 bytes of EEPROM, up to 38 parallel I/O lines, a 16-bit timer that included 3 input captures and 5 output compares, a synchronous serial peripheral interface (SPI), an asynchronous serial communications interface (SCI), and an 8-channel, 8-bit A/D converter. Since 1985 over five dozen different 68HC11 parts have been introduced by Motorola. These parts differ in the types and amounts of on-board resources that are included in the chip.

In 1997 Motorola introduced the 68HC12 as an enhanced 68HC11. It is upward compatible with the 68HC11 (but not at the object code level). It has a greatly enhanced central processing unit (CPU12) that has several new instructions and addressing modes designed to make it easier to support higher-level languages. Programs run significantly faster on a 68HC12 for several reasons. The typical clock speed was increased from 2 MHz on a 68HC11 to 8 MHz on a 68HC12. The number of clock cycles required to execute many of the instructions was reduced on the 68HC12. In addition, the new instructions and addressing modes require fewer instructions to perform the same task. This means that not only do programs run faster, but they also take up less memory space.

In 2002 Motorola introduced the HCS12 family of microcontrollers, which are a direct upgrade of the 68HC12 family. The Motorola Semiconductor Division was spun off as Freescale Semiconductor in 2004. The MC9S12DG256 microcontroller that is on the DRAGON12-Plus-USB board has 256K bytes of flash EEPROM, 12K bytes of RAM, 4K bytes of EEPROM, two 8-channel, 10-bit analog-to-digital (A/D) converters, two asynchronous serial communication interfaces (SCI), three serial peripheral interfaces (SPI), an 8-channel timer module that supports output compare and input capture, an 8-channel pulse-width modulator (PWM), 29 discrete digital I/O channels, and comprehensive interrupt functions. We will cover all of these I/O functions in this book. The MC9S12DG256 microcontroller has additional functions not covered in this book including two CAN 2.0 modules, an Inter-IC bus, and a digital Byte Data Link Controller (BDLC). The part can operate up to 25 MHz and we will run all of our programs at a clock speed of 24 MHz.

A block diagram of a typical HCS12 microcontroller is shown in Fig. 1.2. In the single-chip mode (which is what the DRAGON12-Plus-USB uses) the entire program is stored in the flash memory and the only contact with the outside world is through the various peripheral lines connected to the timer, parallel I/O, SPI, SCI, or A/D converter. An HCS12 microcontroller can also operate in an expanded multiplexed mode in which the parallel I/O lines become multiplexed address and data busses that can be used to address external memory.

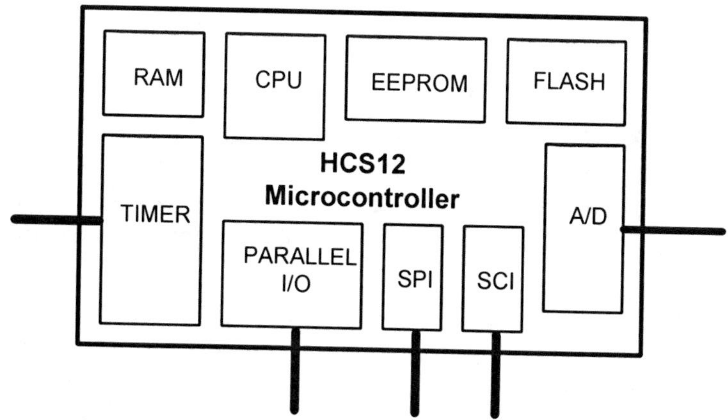

Figure 1.2 Block diagram of an HCS12 microcontroller

1.2 DRAGON12-Plus-USB™ Board

The DRAGON12-Plus-USB board from Wytec is shown in Fig. 1.3. This board contains the Freescale MC9S12DG256 microcontroller surrounded by four convenient female headers that bring out all of the I/O ports. This makes it easy to interface to your own I/O circuitry on the attached protoboard. In addition the board contains a four-digit 7-segment display, four pushbutton switches, an 8-position DIP switch, eight LEDs, a potentiometer for reading in an analog voltage between 0 and 5 volts, a liquid crystal display (LCD), a 4 x 4 keypad, a D/A converter chip, a temperature sensor, a light sensor, and an IR transmitter and receiver that can be used to detect the presence of an object. The DRAGON12-Plus-USB also has an on-board speaker, a built-in H-bridge for driving motors, and convenient headers for connecting servos and an accelerometer board available from Wytec.

Figure 1.3 The Wytec DRAGON12-Plus-USB board

1.3 The CodeWarrior Development Tools

Traditionally microcontrollers have been programmed in assembly language. The advantage of assembly language is that it is closest to the hardware and can execute programs most efficiently. The disadvantage of assembly language is that it is not portable. Every time you change to a different microcontroller you have to rewrite all of your programs. In addition, it generally takes longer to say something in assembly language than it does in a high-level language, and therefore it generally takes longer to write assembly language programs than it does to write high-level programs. For these reasons, the trend in recent years is to program microcontrollers in a high-level language – the most popular being C.

CodeWarrior Development Tools are available from Freescale for programming their microcontrollers in assembly language and C. The Special Edition is a free download that has certain code size restrictions, which will not be a concern for you. You will need to download the S12(X) microcontroller version from www.freescale.com.

One useful feature of CodeWarrior is the ability to create stationery projects upon which you can build your own programs. We have created a separate stationery project for the DRAGON12-Plus-USB. This project, called *LBE_DRAGON12_Plus*, is available to download from www.lbebooks.com. This stationery project contains over eighty assembly language routines that we have written to access all of the important I/O functions of the

Freescale MC9S12DG256 microcontroller. When you create your own project by following the tutorial in Appendix A, these assembly language routines will automatically be included in the file *main.asm* that will be part of your project. The top-level design in your project will be a C program that is stored in the file *main.c*. In this book, we will show you how to write your own assembly language routines that are stored in *main.asm* and how to call these routines as C function calls from your top-level C program stored in *main.c*.

To use CodeWarrior with the DRAGON12-Plus-USB-USB, the MC9S12DG256 microcontroller on these boards must contain the *Serial Monitor*. This *Serial Monitor* is 2 kbytes of code stored at addresses $F800 – $FFFF in the flash memory. This code is executed when you press the reset button on the board and allows CodeWarrior to communicate with your board through the serial port. If you're using a computer that does not have an RS232 serial port, you can use a USB port with a USB-to-Serial adapter cable. When you order one of the development boards from Wytec, make sure to specify that you want the *Serial Monitor* installed; otherwise, it will come with the Dbug monitor that is not compatible with CodeWarrior.

Getting the DRAGON12-Plus-USB board to do whatever you want is challenging and lots of fun. Therefore, let's get started!

Chapter 2

Parallel Ports - Outputs

In this chapter you will learn how parallel ports are used to turn on LEDs and the segments of a 7-segment display. As in all of our examples we will first show you how to do it entirely in C, and then we will show how to do it using C calls to our built-in assembly language routines. You will also learn how these assembly language routines work. Using these built-in assembly language routines will make your C programs much shorter and easier to write.

2.1 MC9S12DG256 Parallel I/O Ports

The MC9S12DG256 registers associated with parallel I/O are listed in Table 2.1. Each of these ports (except *PORTAD0* and *PORTAD1*) has a data register and a data direction register of the type shown in Fig. 2.1. Each pin of an I/O port can be either an input or an output depending on the bits in the corresponding data direction register as shown in Fig. 2.1.

Table 2.1 Parallel Ports in the MC9SDG256

Port	Port Name	DDR Name	DRAGON12-Plus-USB use
Port T	PTT	DDRT	Speaker
Port S	PTS	DDRS	SCI, SPI
Port M	PTM	DDRM	
Port P	PTP	DDRP	7-Seg enable, Servo
Port H	PTH	DDRH	Switches
Port J	PTJ	DDRJ	LED enable
Port AD0	PORTAD0	Input only	pot
Port AD1	PORTAD1	Input only	
Port A	PORTA	DDRA	Keypad
Port B	PORTB	DDRB	LEDs, 7-Seg, H-bridge
Port E	PORTE	DDRE	Mode, XIRQ
Port K	PORTK	DDRK	LCD

Most of the I/O ports listed in Table 2.1 have alternate or special optional functions many of which we will consider in later examples. When the pins of an I/O port are not being used for one of these alternate functions they can be used as general purpose I/O pins.

There are several different operating modes for the MC9S12DG256 including a single-chip mode and expanded external memory modes. In the expanded external memory modes, ports A and B are used for multiplexed address and data busses. The DRAGON12-Plus-USB board operates in the single-chip mode, so that ports A and B are available for parallel I/O. Port A is connected to the 4 x 4 keypad. On the DRAGON12-Plus-USB board Port B is connected to the red LEDs and to the segments of the 7-segment displays. You will also use Port B to control the direction of rotation of a motor using the H-bridge.

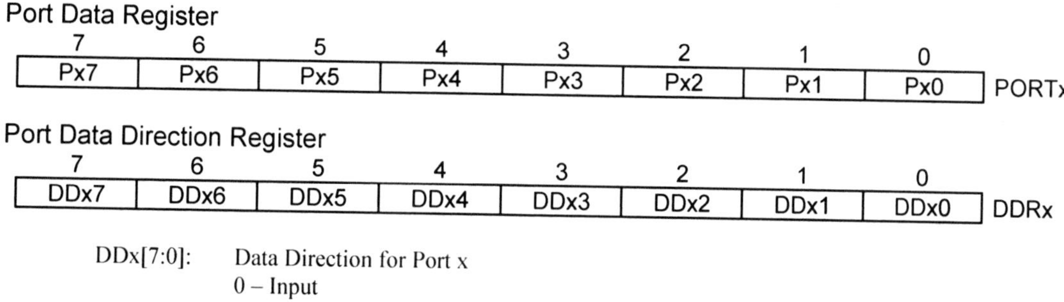

DDx[7:0]: Data Direction for Port x
0 – Input
1 – Output

Figure 2.1 Registers associated with parallel I/O ports

When using CodeWarrior the *Port Names* and *DDR Names* in Table 2.1 are associated with the specific register addresses given in Table 2.2. We will see in Examples 3 and 4 how you can use the CodeWarrior debugger to observe the contents of these register addresses change as you execute a program.

Table 2.2 Parallel Port Addresses when using CodeWarrior

Port	Port Name	Address	DDR Name	Address
Port T	PTT	0x0240	DDRT	0x0242
Port S	PTS	0x0248	DDRS	0x024A
Port M	PTM	0x0250	DDRM	0x0252
Port P	PTP	0x0258	DDRP	0x025A
Port H	PTH	0x0260	DDRH	0x0262
Port J	PTJ	0x0268	DDRJ	0x026A
Port AD0	PORTAD0	0x008F	ATD0DIEN	0x008D
Port AD1	PORTAD1	0x012F	ATD1DIEN	0x012D
Port A	PORTA	0x0000	DDRA	0x0002
Port B	PORTB	0x0001	DDRB	0x0003
Port E	PORTE	0x0008	DDRE	0x0009
Port K	PORTK	0x0032	DDRK	0x0033

The MC9S12DG256 contains phase-locked loop (PLL) circuitry that CodeWarrior uses to set the bus frequency to 24 MHz. Thus, when you download a program to the flash memory using CodeWarrior your program will be running at 24 MHz. However, when you move the LOAD-RUN switch to RUN and press the reset button, your program will normally run at a lower bus clock frequency that depends on the crystal on your board. To keep the frequency at 24 MHz when our programs are executed out of reset, we must include the statement *PLL_init( )* at the beginning of our programs, which will initialize the PLL to produce a PLL (oscillator) frequency of 48 MHz which results in a bus frequency of 24 MHz. The default stationery file *main.c* that comes up when you create a new project contains this *PLL_init( )* function at the beginning of the program. You should keep this function call in all of your programs so that your program will always run at 24 MHz even out of reset. Appendix F describes this *PLL_init*( ) function in more detail.

2.2 LEDs and 7-Segment Displays

Port B is connected to the eight red LEDs on the DRAGON12-Plus-USB board. A light emitting diode (LED) emits light when current flows through it in the positive direction as shown in Fig. 2.2. Current flows through the LED when the voltage on the *anode* side (the wide side of the triangle) is made higher than the voltage on the *cathode* side (the straight line connected to the apex of the triangle). When current flows through a lighted LED, the forward voltage across the LED is typically between +1.5 and +2.0 volts.

No light No current
$PORTB[x]=1$ LED R $PJ1=1$
+5V +5V

light
Current
$PORTB[x]=1$ LED R $PJ1=0$
+5V 0V

Figure 2.2 Turning on an LED

In the DRAGON12-Plus-USB board, the anode side of an LED is connected to one of the bits of Port B. The cathode side of each LED is connected through a resistor to bit 1 of Port J. If both *PORTB*[*x*] and *PJ*1 are 1 (+5V) then no current can flow through the LED and therefore no light will be emitted. On the other hand, if *PORTB*[*x*] = 1 and *PJ*1 = 0 (0V) then current will flow through the resistor *R* and the LED. The resistor is used to limit the amount of current that flows through the LED. The value of the LED resistors on the DRAGON12-Plus-USB board is 1.5 kΩ. Typical currents needed to light LEDs range from 2 to 15 milliamps.

Thus, to turn on certain LEDs the data direction registers of Port B and Port J must be set to all 1's (output), bit 1 of Port J must be set to 0, and the bits of Port B corresponding to the LEDs to be lit must be set to 1.

Seven LEDs can be arranged in a pattern to form different digits as shown in Fig. 2.3. Digital watches use similar 7-segment displays using liquid crystals rather than LEDs. The red digits on digital clocks are LEDs. Seven segment displays come in two flavors: *common cathode* and *common anode*. A common cathode 7-segment display has all of the cathodes tied together, while a common anode 7-segment display has all the anodes tied together.

The DRAGON12-Plus-USB board has four common-cathode 7-segment displays that are connected as shown in Fig. 2.3. The common cathodes of the four digits are connected to the lower four bits of Port P. These bits must be set to zero to enable the 7-segment displays. The output pins 6:0 of Port B are connected through 150 Ω current-limiting resistors to the anodes, *g* – *a*, of each of the four 7-segment displays. In this common-cathode case, an output 1 will turn on a segment and an output 0

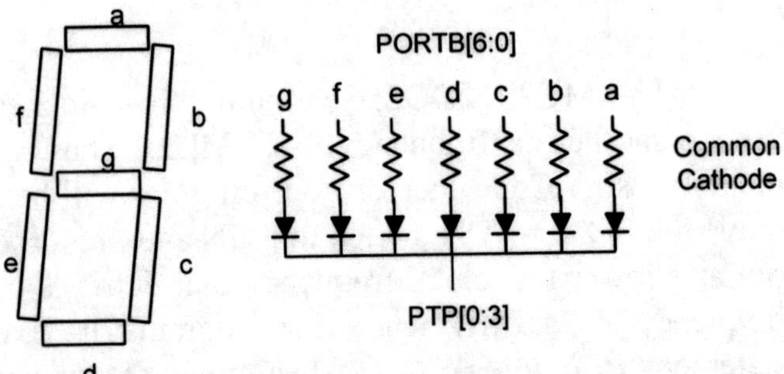

Figure 2.3 A 7-segment display contains seven light emitting diodes (LEDs)

will turn it off. If all four bits of *PTP*[0:3] are zero, then all four digits will display the same segment pattern given by the output of Port B. To display different digits on the four 7-segment displays, the displays must be multiplexed in time as will be shown in Example 6.

Example 1 – Writing to Ports

In this example, we will show how writing to ports can turn on the LEDs and 7-segment displays on the DRAGON12-Plus-USB.

Follow the steps in the tutorial in Appendix A to set up CodeWarrior and create a new project called *Example1* where you select the stationery file LBE_DRAGON12-Plus-USB. When you open the file *main.c* in the *Source* folder you should see the program shown in Listing 2.1. All text following a double slash // will be a comment to the end of the line.

The seven statements following the comment `/* put your own code here */` will do the following:

1. The statement *PLL_init*( ) will set the system clock frequency to 24 MHz as described above. This should be the first statement in all of your programs.

2. The statement *DDRB* = 0xFF will set all bits in data direction register *B* to 1 and therefore to all outputs. The notation 0*x* means that FF is a hexadecimal number equal to the binary number 11111111.

3. The statement *DDRJ* = 0xFF will set all bits in data direction register *J* to 1 and therefore to all outputs.

4. The statement *DDRP* = 0xFF will set all bits in data direction register *P* to 1 and therefore to all outputs.

5. The statement *PTJ* = 0x00 will set all bits of port *J* to zero and therefore will enable the LEDs.

6. The statement *PTP* = 0x00 will set all bits of port *P* to zero and therefore will enable the 7-segment displays.

7. The statement *PORTB* = 0x55 will set the bits in port B to 01010101 and therefore turn on segments *a*, *c*, *e*, and *g* shown in Fig. 2.3. (Recall that a 1 turn on a segment on the 7-segment display of the DRAGON12-Plus-USB.) The bits in port *B* are connected to the segments of the 7-segment display as shown in Fig. 2.4.

The statement *for*(;;) {} will just loop on itself forever. We will describe the use of the C *for* loop in more detail in Example 3.

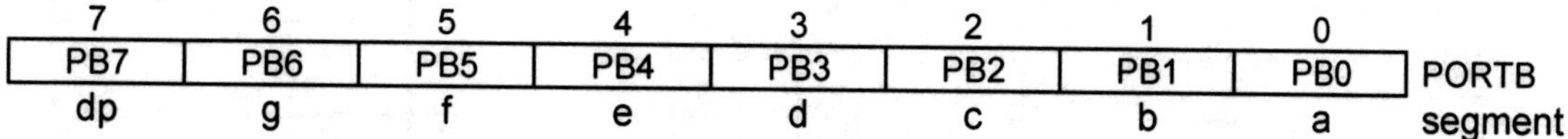

Figure 2.4 Connections of Port B to 7-segment display

Listing 2.1 Example 1: DRAGON12-Plus-USB

```
// Example 1: Turn on every other segment on 7-seg display
#include <hidef.h>       /* common defines and macros */
#include <mc9s12dg256.h>      /* derivative information */
#pragma LINK_INFO DERIVATIVE "mc9s12dg256b"

#include "main_asm.h" /* interface to the assembly module */

void main(void) {
  /* put your own code here */
  PLL_init();           // set system clock frequency to 24 MHz
  DDRB  = 0xff;         // Port B is output
  DDRJ  = 0xff;         // Port J is output
  DDRP  = 0xff;         // Port P is output
  PTJ = 0x00;           // enable LED
  PTP = 0x00;           // enable all 7-segment displays
  // turn on every other led and segment on 7-seg displays
  PORTB    = 0x55;

  for(;;) {} /* wait forever */
}
```

Run the program shown in Listing 2.1. Then re-run the program with the value of *PTJ* changed to 0x02. This should disable the LEDs. Next change *PTJ* back to 0x00 and change the value of *PTP* to 0x0A. This should disable digits 1 and 3 where digits are labeled 0 – 3 from left to right.

Example 2 – C Function Calls

In this example, we will show how to write assembly language subroutines that are called as C functions. The main C program is located in the file *main.c* and the assembly language subroutines are located in the file *main.asm*.

Instead of having to remember that the LEDs and 7-segment displays on the DRAGON12-Plus-USB are connected to Port B and controlled by bits in Port J and Port P, we have written six assembly language routines that are called by the six C function calls shown in Table 2.3. These assembly language routines are always available to you when you set up an LBE_DRAGON12-Plus-USB stationery project.

Table 2.3 C function calls for turning on the 7-segment display

C Function Call	Meaning
`led_enable();`	Sets DDRB and DDRJ to outputs, clears DJ1 to 0, and turns off all LEDs by clearing all bits of PORTB
`leds_on(int);`	Stores the lower 8 bits of the integer *int* in Port B
`led_disable();`	Sets DDRJ to outputs and sedts DJ1 to 1
`leds_off();`	Turn off all LEDs by clearing Port B
`seg7_enable();`	Sets DDRB and DDRP to outputs, clears the lower 4 bits of Port P, and clears all bits of PORTB
`seg7_disable();`	sets the lower 4 bits of Port P to 1
`seg7_on(int s, int b);`	Display the segments *s* on the 7-segment digit no. *b*
`seg7s_off();`	Turn off all 7-segment displays by clearing Port B

LEDs

Listing 2.2 will turn on every other LED while disabling the 7-segment displays. The function *seg7_disable*() will disable the four 7-segment displays by setting the lower 4 bits of Port P to 1 (see Fig. 2.3). The function *led_enable*() will enable the LEDs by setting the data direction registers for Port B and Port J to outputs, clearing *DJ1* to 0, and turning off all LEDs by clearing all bits in Port B to zero. Finally, the function *leds_on*(0x55) will write the hex value 0x55 to the Port B data register, thus turning on every other LED starting at the right.

Listing 2.2 Example 2a – DRAGON12-Plus-USB

```
// Example 2a: Turn on every other led
#include <hidef.h>       /* common defines and macros */
#include <mc9s12dg256.h>      /* derivative information */
#pragma LINK_INFO DERIVATIVE "mc9s12dg256b"

#include "main_asm.h" /* interface to the assembly module */

void main(void) {
  PLL_init();            // set system clock frequency to 24 MHz
  seg7_disable();        // disable 7-segment displays
  led_enable();          // enable leds
  leds_on(0x55);         // turn on every other led

  for(;;) {} /* wait forever */
}
```

Under the Hood

All of the C function calls used in this book are defined as assembly language routines in the file *main.asm*, located in the *source* folder of your CodeWarrior project. You should refer to Appendix B for a discussion of assembly language programming. The assembly language routines for the first six C function calls shown in Table 2.3 are shown in Listing 2.3. Note that the names of the C function calls must be the names of the labels for the corresponding assembly language routine. These labels end with a colon. The statements

```
XDEF led_enable, led_disable, leds_on, leds_off
XDEF seg7_enable, seg7_disable
```

must be included at the beginning of the file *main.asm*.

In the routine *led_enable* in Listing 2.3, the statement `movb #$FF,DDRB` will move the hex byte FF into the Port B data direction register, thus making all bits of Port B outputs. A similar statement also moves the hex byte FF into the Port J data direction register. The pound sign # indicates the immediate addressing mode (see Table B.1 in Appendix B) and the dollar sign $ indicates that FF is a hex value. The name *DDRB* is the address of the Port B data direction register, which, as shown in Table 2.2, has the hex value 0x0003. The addresses of all of these register names are defined using *equate* statements (*equ*) in the file *mc9s12dg256.inc*, which is located in the *libraries* folder in your CodeWarrior project. Examples of this *equate* statement are shown in Listing 2.4.

In the subroutine *led_enable* in Listing 2.3, the statement `bclr PTJ,$02` will clear bit 1 of the Port J data register. This *bit clear* statement will AND the complement of the mask $02 with PTJ. Since the complement of $02 = 00000010 is 11111101, this mask will clear bit 1 of PTJ, which enables all LEDs (see Fig. 2.2).

The next statement in the subroutine *led_enable* in Listing 2.8 is `clr PORTB`, which clears all bits of Port B to zero, and thus turns off all LEDs.

Listing 2.3 *led* and *seg7* Assembly Language Routines from *main.asm*

```
;             LEDs
led_enable:
          movb   #$FF,DDRB      ;   DataDirB -->all outputs
          movb   #$FF,DDRJ      ;   DataDirJ -->all outputs
          bclr   PTJ,$02        ;   enable leds PJ1 = 0
          clr    PORTB          ;   Turn-off all LEDS
          rts

leds_on:
          stab   PORTB          ; turn on selected led
          rts

leds_off:
          clr    PORTB          ; turn off all leds
          rts

led_disable:
          movb   #$FF,DDRJ      ;   DataDirJ -->all outputs
          bset   PTJ,$02        ;   enable leds PJ1 = 0
          rts


;             7-Segment Displays
seg7_enable:
          movb   #$FF,DDRB      ;   DataDirB -->all outputs
          movb   #$FF,DDRP      ;   DataDirP -->all outputs
          bclr   PTP,$0F        ;   enable 7-seg digits PTP[0:3] = 0000
          clr    PORTB          ;   Turn-off all 7-seg digits
          rts

seg7_disable:
          movb   #$FF,DDRP      ;   DataDirP -->all outputs
          bset   PTP,$0F        ;   disable 7-seg digits PTP[0:3] = 1111
          rts
```

The C function call *led_enable*( ) in Listing 2.2 gets compiled as a *jump to subroutine* (*JSR*) assembly language instruction that jumps to the subroutine `led_enable:` in Listing 2.8. The last statement in this subroutine is a *return from subroutine* (*RTS*) instruction, which will return to the statement following the *JSR led_enable* statement. This will be the C function call *leds_on*(0x55) in Listing 2.2, which will compile to a *JSR* to the subroutine *leds_on* in Listing 2.2. The first instruction in this subroutine is *stab PORTB*. The reason for this instruction is because the C function call *leds_on*(int) in Table 2.3 passes a 16-bit integer to the assembly language subroutine. If there is only one 16-bit integer passed to the subroutine, it is passed in accumulator *D*, the concatenation of accumulators *A* and *B*. Thus, the 8-bit byte 0x55, which is passed to the subroutine *leds_on* in Listing 2.2, will be in accumulator *B*. This value then gets stored in the Port *B* data register, *PORTB*, which will turn on every other LED starting at the right. The *RTS* instruction will return to the *for* loop in Listing 2.2, which gets compiled to an assembly language statement that branches on itself.

Listing 2.4 Register names are defined in *mc9s12dg256.inc*

```
;*** PORTB - Port B Register; 0x00000001 ***
PORTB:    equ    $00000001

;*** DDRB - Port B Data Direction Register; 0x00000003 ***
DDRB:     equ    $00000003

;*** PTJ - Port J I/O Register; 0x00000268 ***
PTJ:      equ    $00000268

;*** DDRJ - Port J Data Direction Register; 0x0000026A ***
DDRJ:     equ    $0000026A
```

The C function call *seg7_disable*( ) in Listing 2.2 gets compiled as a jump to the subroutine *seg7_disable* in Listing 2.3. The first statement in this subroutine is *movb* #$FF,*DDRP*, which will set the data direction register of Port *P* to all ones. The next statement is the *bit set* statement *bset PTP*,$0F, which will OR the mask $0F with *PTP* and thus set the lower 4 bits of the Port P data register to one. This will disable all four common-cathode 7-segment displays (see Fig. 2.3).

Follow Part 2 of the CodeWarrior tutorial in Appendix A to see how to single step through these assembly language instructions and watch exactly what is going on.

One last step is required to implement C function calls as assembly language routines. You must include a declaration of the function in the file *main_asm.h*. The declarations for the eight functions in Table 2.3 are shown in Listing 2.5.

Listing 2.5 Declarations added to *main_asm.h*

```
void led_enable(void);
void leds_on(int);
void led_disable(void);
void leds_off(void);
void seg7_enable(void);
void seg7_on(int, int);
void seg7_disable(void);
void seg7s_off(void);
```

7-Segment Displays

Listing 2.6 will turn on every other segment of the 7-segment display number 2 while disabling the LEDs. The digits are numbered 0 to 3 from left to right. Thus, digit 2 is the third digit from the left. Referring to Table 2.3, the function *led_disable*( ) will disable the eight red LEDs and the function *seg7_enable*( ) will enable the four 7-segment displays. The function *seg7_on*(0x55,2) will turn on segments *a*, *c*, *e*, and *g* of digit 2.

Under the Hood

The assembly language routines for the four *seg7* C function calls shown in Table 2.3 are shown in Listing 2.7. The statement

```
MASK:       DC.B     1,2,4,8,16,32,64,128
```

defines eight bytes that contain the constant hex values $01, $02, $04, $08, $10, $20, $40, and $80. Thus, each byte is a mask with only one of the eight bits set to 1. The label *MASK* is the address of the byte containing $01. Thus, *MASK* is a table that we can index into (with an index value of 0 – 7) to select one of the eight byte values.

Listing 2.6 Example 2b – DRAGON12-Plus-USB

```
// Example 2b: Turn on every other segment on digit 2
#include <hidef.h>          /* common defines and macros */
#include <mc9s12dg256.h>      /* derivative information */
#pragma LINK_INFO DERIVATIVE "mc9s12dg256b"

#include "main_asm.h" /* interface to the assembly module */

void main(void) {
  PLL_init();              // set system clock frequency to 24 MHz
  led_disable();           // disable leds
  seg7_enable();           // enable 7-segment displays
  seg7_on(0x55,2);         // turn on every other segment on digit 2

  for(;;) {} /* wait forever */
}
```

The function *seg7_on*(0x55,2) in Listing 2.6 gets compiled as a jump to the subroutine `seg7_on:` in Listing 2.7. Note that this C function needs to pass two parameters, 0x55 and 2, to the assembly language routine. We saw in Example 2a that if there is one integer value to pass to the subroutine, then it is passed in accumulator *D*. If there are more than one 16-bit integers to pass to a subroutine, then the last one in the list (2 in this case) is passed in accumulator *D*, while the rest of the parameters are pushed onto the stack before the subroutine is called. Recall from Appendix B that when a subroutine is called, its return address is pushed onto the stack. Thus, when the function *seg7_on*(0x55,2) is called, the 16-bit value $0055 is pushed onto the stack, the 16-bit value $0002 is put in accumulator *D*, the return address is pushed onto the stack, and the program jumps to the subroutine *seg7_on* in Listing 2.7. At this point, the stack looks like Fig. 2.5.

Listing 2.7 *seg7* Assembly Language Routines from *main.asm*

```
MASK:       DC.B    1,2,4,8,16,32,64,128

;           7-Segment Displays
seg7_enable:
        movb  #$FF,DDRB    ;  DataDirB -->all outputs
        movb  #$FF,DDRP    ;  DataDirP -->all outputs
        bclr  PTP,$0F      ;  enable 7-seg digits PTP[0:3] = 0000
        clr   PORTB        ;  Turn-off all 7-seg digits
        rts

seg7_disable:
        movb  #$FF,DDRP    ;  DataDirP -->all outputs
        bset  PTP,$0F      ;  disable 7-seg digits PTP[0:3] = 1111
        rts

;         display selected segments on one digit
; void seg7_on(int segs, int digit#);
; digit# is in D
; segs is at 2,sp  (hex value to store in Port B)
seg7_on:
           ldy     #MASK
           aby
           ldaa    0,y           ;A = mask
           coma
           staa    PTP           ;enable digit digit#
           ldd     2,sp          ;B = segs
           stab    PORTB
           rts

seg7s_off:
             clr  PORTB          ; turn off all 7-segment displays
             rts
```

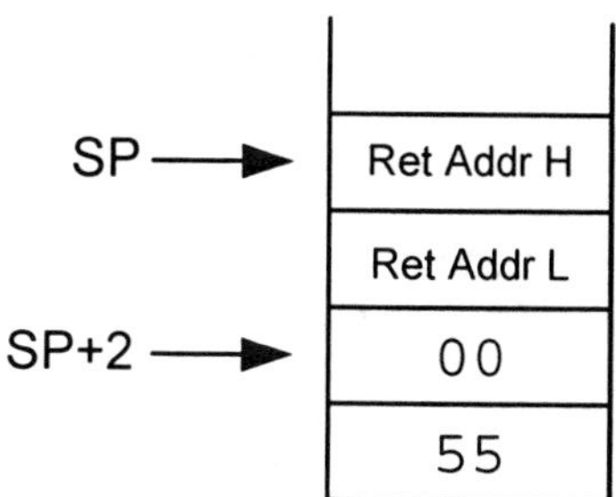

Figure 2.5 Passing subroutine parameters on the stack

The first instruction in the subroutine *seg7_on* in Listing 2.7 is `ldy #MASK`. This will load the address of the table *MASK* into register *Y*. The next instruction, `aby`, will add the value in accumulator *B* (which is 2, being passed in accumulator *D*) to the value in *Y*, leaving the sum in *Y*. Thus, *Y* now points to the third byte in the *MASK* table, which contains the constant \$04. The next instruction, `ldaa 0,y`, will load this value \$04 into accumulator *A*, and the next instruction, `coma`, will complement all bits of *A*, leaving the eight bits 11111011 in accumulator *A*. This value is then stored in the Port *P* data register, *PTP*, which will enable only digit 2 of the four 7-segment displays. To light the segments of this digit, we just need to store the hex value \$55 from Fig. 2.5 in *PORTB*. The statement `ldd 2,sp` will load accumulator *D* with the 16-bit value located at SP+2 as shown in Fig. 2.5. The byte \$55 will be in accumulator *B*, so now the instruction `stab PORTB` will store this value in the Port *B* data register, which will turn on segments *a*, *c*, *e*, and *g* of the 7-segment display on digit 2.

Example 3 – Delay Loops in C

We will generate a delay by making a simple software delay loop. A more accurate way of producing a delay is to use the timer module in the MC9S12DG256. We will look at how to do this in Chapters 4 and 9. Listing 2.8 shows how to make a software delay using two nested *for* loops in the function *delay*( ). The program in Listing 2.8 will blink on and off the seven right-most red LEDs plus all segments of the right-most 7-segment display.

The C *for* loop has the following general form

```
for(initial_index; terminal_index; increment) {
        statements;
}
```

In the inner *for* loop in the *delay*( ) function in Listing 2.8 the *initial_index* is defined by the statement $j = 0$, where *j* is a 16-bit integer declared along with *i* in the statement int *i*, *j*;.

The *terminal_index* in the inner *for* loop is defined by the statement $j < 5999$; and the *increment* is defined by the statement $j{+}{+}$. The statement $j{+}{+}$ is equivalent to $j = j + 1$ which just increments *j* by 1. Thus, in this *for* loop the index *j* starts at 0, the statements between the braces {...} are executed (there are no statements in the inner *for* loop in Listing 2.8), the index *j* is incremented by 1, and the statements between the braces are executed again. This process continues until the *terminal_index* is reached, or in this case when the statement $j < 5999$; is false, i.e. when *j* gets incremented to 5999. Thus, this *for* loop will execute 5999 times. We chose this number because it is the same as the number of times we go through the inner loop of the assembly language delay routine (described in Example 4) to produce a 1 millisecond delay. The delay in the C *for* loop will be somewhat longer because the *for* loop gets compiled to assembly language instructions that take a few more clock cycles than in the assembly language delay loop.

The inner *for* loop in the *delay*( ) function in Listing 2.8 will execute 500 times and, each time through this outer *for* loop, the inner *for* loop will execute 5999 times. Thus, the total number of times through the inner loop before the *delay*( ) function exits will be 500 x 5999 = 2,999,500. The bus clock frequency of the microcontroller is 24 MHz so, if the inner *for* loop took 4 clock cycles, then the total delay time will be
$4 \times 2{,}999{,}500 / 24{,}000{,}000 = 0.5$ seconds.

Before the main program in Listing 2.8 we have included the *delay*( ) function prototype declaration

```
void delay(void);
```

The first *void* in this statement indicates that this function does not return any value to the calling program. The second *void* in the parentheses indicates that there are no parameters to be passed from the calling program to the function. All functions that you use in your C programs must have a prototype declaration. These are often grouped together in a separate *.h* file, but you can also include them at the beginning of the program as we have done here.

Listing 2.8 Example 3 – DRAGON12-Plus-USB

```
// Example 3: Blinking 7-Segment Display
#include <hidef.h>              /* common defines and macros */
#include <mc9s12dg256.h>        /* derivative information */
#pragma LINK_INFO DERIVATIVE "mc9s12dg256b"

#include "main_asm.h"   /* interface to the assembly module */

void delay(void);

void main(void) {
  PLL_init();        // set system clock frequency to 24 MHz
  seg7_enable();           // enable 7-segment display
  while(1){
    seg7_on(0x7F,3);       // switch on all segments of digit 3
    delay();
    seg7s_off();           // switch off all segments
    delay();
  }
}

void delay() {
  int i,j;
  for(i = 0; i < 500; i++) {
    for(j = 0; j < 5999; j++) {
    }
  }
}
```

The main program in Listing 2.8 first enables the 7-segment displays and then enters a *while* loop. The C *while* loop has the following general form

```
while(expression) {
        statements;
}
```

When the *while* loop is executed the *expression* in the parentheses is evaluated, and if it is *true*, the statements between the braces {...} are executed, and then the *expression* in the parentheses is evaluated again. As long as the *expression* is true, the statements will be executed again. When the *expression* becomes false, the *while* loop is exited without executing the statements again. A value of zero for the expression is taken to be *false*, and a non-zero value is taken to be *true*. Therefore, in the statement *while*(1) in Listing 2.8 the expression is always true, so the *while* loop is never exited. We use this statement to continually execute the statements within the *while* loop forever.

Within the *while* loop, we first turn on all segments of the 7-segment display on the right-most 7-segment display on the DRAGON12-Plus-USB, delay approximately half a second, turn off all segments of the 7-segment display, and then delay approximately half a second again. This process repeats endlessly, causing the display to blink on and off about every second. Try it.

Example 4 – Delay Loops in Assembly: *ms_delay*(int *n*)

Instead of having to write your own delay loop in C we have written an assembly language routine that is called by the C function call shown in Table 2.4. This assembly language routine is always available to you when you set up an LBE_DRAGON12-Plus-USB stationery project. Listing 2.9 shows how you can modify the program in Listing 2.8 to produce the same result. Try it. Count the number of blinks in 10, 20, or 30 seconds, and verify that each blink takes exactly 1 second.

Table 2.4 C function call delaying *n* milliseconds

C Function Call	Meaning
`ms_delay(int n);`	Delay *n* milliseconds

Listing 2.9 Example 4 – DRAGON12-Plus-USB

```
// Example 4: Blinking 7-Segment Display using msdelay()
#include <hidef.h>           /* common defines and macros */
#include <mc9s12dg256.h>     /* derivative information */
#pragma LINK_INFO DERIVATIVE "mc9s12dg256b"

#include "main_asm.h"   /* interface to the assembly module */

void main(void) {
  PLL_init();          // set system clock frequency to 24 MHz
  seg7_enable();            // enable 7-segment display
  while(1){
    seg7_on(0x7F,3);        // switch on all segments of digit 3
    ms_delay(500);          // delay
    seg7s_off();            // switch off all segments
    ms_delay(500);          // delay
  }
}
```

Under the Hood

When the C function *ms_delay*(int *n*) is called, the assembly language subroutine *ms_delay* shown in Listing 2.10 is executed. The number of milliseconds to delay, *n*, is passed to the subroutine in accumulator *D*.

The first two instructions in the subroutine *ms_delay* push index registers *X* and *Y* on the stack. This is because we change the values of *X* and *Y* in this subroutine, which will destroy these values if they are being used by the program that called this subroutine. Since we can never know if this is the case, it is always important to save the contents of any register we use at the beginning of a subroutine, and then restore these values at the end of the subroutine. In Listing 2.10 the two instructions *puly* and *pulx* will pull (or pop) the values of *Y* and *X* from the stack. Note that the order of pulling values from the stack must be the opposite of pushing the values on the stack. For each push instruction, there must be a corresponding pull instruction, so that the return address will be left on the top of the stack for the *RTS* instruction to use to return to the next instruction in the calling program.

Listing 2.10 *ms_delay* Assembly Language Subroutine from *main.asm*

```
;         ms_delay
;         input: D = no. of milliseconds to delay
;         clock = 24 MHz
ms_delay:
          pshx
          pshy
          tfr      D,Y
md1:      ldx      #5999     ; N = (24000 - 6)/4
md2:      dex                ; 1 ccycle
          bne      md2       ; 3 ccycle
          dey
          bne      md1       ; Y ms
          puly
          pulx
          rts
```

The third instruction in the subroutine *ms_delay* transfers the value in *D* (the number of milliseconds to delay) to the index register *Y*. Index register *X* is then loaded with the decimal value 5999 (hex $176F). The loop

```
md2:      dex                ; 1 ccycle
          bne      md2       ; 3 ccycle
```

will then keep decrementing *X* until it becomes zero. Thus, each of these two instructions are executed a total of 5999 times. The instruction *dex* takes one clock cycle and the instruction *bne* takes 3 clock cycles. You can find these values in the CPU12 Reference Guide, available for download from www.freescale.com. Thus, the total number of clock cycles used to execute this *md2* loop is $5999 \times 4 = 23,996$. For a 24 MHz clock, each clock cycle will take $1/24,000,000 = 42 \times 10^{-9}$ seconds. Thus, the total time used to execute the *md2* loop is $23,996 \times 42 \times 10^{-9} = 0.99983$ milliseconds. The outer *md1* loop in Listing 2.10 loads index register *X* with 5999 (2 clock cycles), executes the *md2* loop (0.99983 ms), decrements *Y* (1 clock cycle), and, if *Y* is not equal to zero, branches back to *md1* (3 clock cycles). These extra six clock cycles take $6/24,000 = 0.00025$ milliseconds to execute. Thus, each time through the *md1* loop takes a total of $0.99983 + 0.00025 = 1.00008$ milliseconds. Therefore, to delay *n* milliseconds, we just need to execute this loop *n* times, but this is just the value that is in register *Y*.

Example 5 – Turning Single Bits On and Off

In this example we will show how to turn on and off individual LEDs on the DRAGON12-Plus-USB board. We will first show you how to do this entirely in C, and then we will provide new C function calls to do this.

Recall from Fig. 2.2 that setting a bit high in Port B will turn on the corresponding LED on the DRAGON12-Plus-USB. Thus, it will be important to be able to set a particular bit in a register to 1 or clear a particular bit to 0.

Suppose you want to set bit 3 of Port B to one, while leaving all other bits unchanged. You can do this by ORing *PORTB* with the mask shown in Fig. 2.6. Note that ORing a bit with a 0 will leave the bit unchanged, while ORing a bit with a 1 will force the bit to be 1. From Table 2.5, we can do this by using either the C statement

```
PORTB = PORTB | 0x08;                              (2.1)
```

where | is the C operator for a bitwise OR operation. That is, each bit in *PORTB* is ORed with the corresponding bit in the hex value 0x08. A shorthand way of writing the C statement (2.1) is

```
PORTB |= 0x08;                                     (2.4)
```

Thus, statements (2.1) and (2.2) are equivalent where |= is called a shorthand assignment operator. Other C operators and shorthand assignment operators are shown in Table 2.5.

Port B Register

7	6	5	4	3	2	1	0	
PB7	PB6	PB5	PB4	PB3	PB2	PB1	PB0	PORTB

7	6	5	4	3	2	1	0	
0	0	0	0	1	0	0	0	Mask

Figure 2.6 Setting a single bit to 1 by ORing with a mask

Suppose now you want to clear bit 3 of Port B to zero, while leaving all other bits unchanged. You can do this by ANDing *PORTB* with the mask shown in Fig. 2.7. Note that ANDing a bit with a 1 will leave the bit unchanged, while ANDing a bit with a 0 will force the bit to be 0. A C statement that will do this is

```
PORTB = PORTB & 0xF7;                                    (2.3)
```

or, using the shorthand assignment operator, we could use the equivalent statement

```
PORTB &= 0xF7;                                           (2.4)
```

Port B Register

7	6	5	4	3	2	1	0	
PB7	PB6	PB5	PB4	PB3	PB2	PB1	PB0	PORTB

7	6	5	4	3	2	1	0	
1	1	1	1	0	1	1	1	Mask

Figure 2.7 Clearing a single bit to 0 by ANDing with a mask

Table 2.5 Operators and Assignment Operators

Operator	Description	Assignment Operator
&	Bitwise AND	&=
|	Bitwise OR	|=
^	Bitwise XOR	^=
+	Addition	+=
-	Subtraction	-=
*	Multiplication	*=
/	Division	/=
%	Modulus	%=

Consider the C program shown in Listing 2.11 which first turns on LEDs 0, 2, and 4 in turn, and then turns them off in turn. We know that writing a 1 to the bit position in *PORTB* corresponding to a particular LED (see Fig. 2.9) will turn on that LED. For example, writing a 1 to PB0 in Fig. 2.9 will turn on LED 0 and writing a 0 to PB0 will turn off LED 0. As we have seen the way to turn on LED 0 while leaving all other LEDs unchanged is to first read *PORTB*, then OR it with the mask 00000001 (or 0x01), and finally write the resulting value back in *PORTB*. The C statement that will do this is

```
PORTB = PORTB | 0x01;
```

or, using the shorthand assignment operator from Table 2.5, we could use the equivalent statement

```
PORTB |= 0x01;
```

as shown in Listing 2.11. Similar statements are used to turn on LEDs 2 and 4.

To turn off LED 0, we would need to AND *PORTB* with 11111110 (or 0xFE). We can do this by using either the C statement

```
PORTB = PORTB & 0xFE;
```

or, using the shorthand assignment operator, we could use the equivalent statement

```
PORTB &= 0xFE;
```

as shown in Listing 2.11. Similar statements are used to turn off LEDs 2 and 4. Try this program.

Listing 2.11 Example 5a – DRAGON12-Plus-USB

```
// Example 5a: Single LEDs
#include <hidef.h>       /* common defines and macros */
#include <mc9s12dg256.h>      /* derivative information */
#pragma LINK_INFO DERIVATIVE "mc9s12dg256b"

#include "main_asm.h" /* interface to the assembly module */

void main(void) {
  PLL_init();             // set system clock frequency to 24 MHz
  led_enable();             // enable LEDs
  seg7_disable();           // disable 7-segment displays
  while(1){
    PORTB |= 0x01;            // turn on LED 0
    ms_delay(500);
    PORTB |= 0x04;            // turn on LED 2
    ms_delay(500);
    PORTB |= 0x10;            // turn on LED 4
    ms_delay(500);
    PORTB &= 0xFE;            // turn off LED 0
    ms_delay(500);
    PORTB &= 0xFB;            // turn off LED 2
    ms_delay(500);
    PORTB &= 0xEF;            // turn off LED 4
    ms_delay(500);
  }
}
```

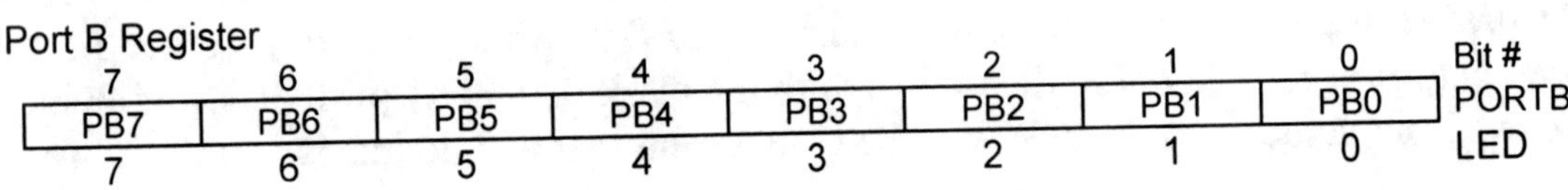

Figure 2.8 Connections of Port B to LEDs

C Function Calls for Turning On or Off a Single LED

Instead of having to figure out the hex value to OR and AND with *PORTB* in order to turn on or off a particular bit we have written two assembly language routines that are called by the C function calls shown in Table 2.6. These assembly language routines are always available to you when you set up an LBE_DRAGON12-Plus-USB stationery project. Listing 2.12 shows how you can modify the program in Listing 2.11 to produce the same result. Try it.

Table 2.6 C function calls for turning on or off a single bit of PORTB

C Function Call	Meaning
`led_on(int b);`	Sets bit *b* of PORTB high
`led_off(int b);`	Sets bit *b* of PORTB low

Listing 2.12 Example 5b – DRAGON12-Plus-USB

```
// Example 5b: Single LEDs
#include <hidef.h>      /* common defines and macros */
#include <mc9s12dg256.h>     /* derivative information */
#pragma LINK_INFO DERIVATIVE "mc9s12dg256b"

#include "main_asm.h" /* interface to the assembly module */

void main(void) {
  PLL_init();              // set system clock frequency to 24 MHz
  led_enable();            // enable LEDs
  seg7_disable();          // disable 7-segment displays
  while(1){
    led_on(0);              // turn on LED 0
    ms_delay(500);          // half-second delay
    led_on(2);              // turn on LED 2
    ms_delay(500);          // half-second delay
    led_on(4);              // turn on LED 4
    ms_delay(500);          // half-second delay
    led_off(0);             // turn off LED 0
    ms_delay(500);          // half-second delay
    led_off(2);             // turn off LED 2
    ms_delay(500);          // half-second delay
    led_off(4);             // turn off LED 4
    ms_delay(500);          // half-second delay
  }
}
```

Under the Hood

When the C function *led_on*(int *n*) is called, the assembly language subroutine *led_on* shown in Listing 2.13 is executed. The LED number to turn on, *n*, is passed to the subroutine in accumulator *D*, and therefore in accumulator *B*.

The first instruction in the subroutine *led_on* in Listing 2.13 is *ldy #MASK*. This will load the address of the table *MASK* into register *Y*. The next instruction, *aby*, will add the value in accumulator *B* (which is the bit number, being passed in accumulator *D*) to the value in *Y*, leaving the sum in *Y*. Thus, *Y* now points to a byte in the *MASK* table, which has only the bit number *n* set to 1. The next instruction, *ldaa 0,Y*, will load this value into accumulator *A*, and the next instruction, *oraa PORTB*, will OR this value with the contents of *PORTB*, leaving the result in accumulator *A*. This value is then stored in the Port B data register, *PORTB*, which will now have bit *n* of Port B high.

Listing 2.13 *led* Assembly Language Subroutines from *main.asm*

```
MASK:     DC.B    1,2,4,8,16,32,64,128

;       led_on( b# )
;       set bit number b# of PORTB to 1
led_on:
        pshy
        ldy     #MASK
        aby
        ldaa    0,Y
        oraa    PORTB               ;OR mask with PORTB
        staa    PORTB               ;store back in PORTB
        puly
        rts

;       led_off( b# )
;       clear bit number b# of PORTB to 0
led_off:
        pshy
        ldy     #MASK
        aby
        ldaa    0,Y
        coma                        ;complement mask
        anda    PORTB               ;AND mask with PORTB
        staa    PORTB               ;store back in PORTB
        puly
        rts
```

When the C function *led_off*(int *n*) is called, the assembly language subroutine *led_off* shown in Listing 2.13 is executed. The bit number to set low, *n*, is passed to the subroutine in accumulator *D*, and therefore in accumulator *B*.

The first three instructions in the subroutine *led_off* in Listing 2.13 are the same as the first three instructions in the subroutine *led_on*. Thus, at this point, the value in accumulator *A* will contain a *MASK* value with a single bit set to 1. The next statement, *coma*, will complement all bits, so that all bits in accumulator *A* will be 1 except bit number *n*, which will be 0. This value in accumulator *A* is then ANDed with the contents of *PORTB*, leaving the result in accumulator *A*. All bits in *PORTB* that are ANDed with 1 will remain unchanged. However, the bit value that is ANDed with 0 will be forced to be 0. This resulting value in accumulator *A* is then stored back in *PORTB*, which will cause bit *n* in *PORTB* to go low.

Example 6 – Hex Counter

In this example we will show how to have the each of the 7-segment displays on the DRAGON12-Plus-USB board count in hex from 0 to F continually. We will first show you how to do this entirely in C, and then we will provide a new C function to display any hex digit.

We have seen in Fig. 2.3 that the DRAGON12-Plus-USB board has a *common-cathode* 7-segment display connected to Port B. This means that on the DRAGON12-Plus-USB a 1 turns a segment *on* and a 0 turns a segment *off*.

The table shown in Fig. 2.9 shows the output values for each segment *a* – *g* needed to display all hex digits, *D*, from 0 – F, for the DRAGON12-Plus-USB board.

D	g	f	e	d	c	b	a	code
0	0	1	1	1	1	1	1	3F
1	0	0	0	0	1	1	0	06
2	1	0	1	1	0	1	1	5B
3	1	0	0	1	1	1	1	4F
4	1	1	0	0	1	1	0	66
5	1	1	0	1	1	0	1	6D
6	1	1	1	1	1	0	1	7D
7	0	0	0	0	1	1	1	07
8	1	1	1	1	1	1	1	7F
9	1	1	0	1	1	1	1	6F
A	1	1	1	0	1	1	1	77
b	1	1	1	1	1	0	0	7C
C	0	1	1	1	0	0	1	39
d	1	0	1	1	1	1	0	5E
E	1	1	1	1	0	0	1	79
F	1	1	1	0	0	0	1	71

Figure 2.9 Segment values required to display hex digits 0 – F

Listing 2.14 shows how we can create a table of the hex codes in Fig. 2.9 by using a constant character array called *seg7tbl*[]. The type declaration *char* defines each element of the array *seg7tbl*[] to be an 8-bit byte. The type qualifier *const* defines each of these array elements to be a constant that can't be changed in the program. Note how the braces {..} are used in the array definition to define the 16 constant hex codes given in Fig. 2.9. Also note that the type declarations for *seg7tbl*[] and the integer *i* used in the *for* loop must precede the function call *PLL_init*( ).

In the *while* loop in Listing 2.13 there is a *for* loop with an index *i* that goes from 0 to 15. Each time through this *for* loop the output of Port B is set to *seg7tbl*[*i*], which will output the proper hex code corresponding to the hex digit *i*. Note that the square brackets [ ] are used to indicate array elements in C. The second statement in the *for* loop is a half-second delay before the next digit is displayed. Once all 16 digits have been displayed the *while*(1) loop will just keep counting again. Try it. Note that all four 7-segment displays count from 0 – F in unison. We will next see how to display a hex values on a single 7-segment display and then, in Example 7, show how to display different values on each of the 7-segment displays.

A C function call to display hex digits

Instead of having to make your own 7-segment decoder table, we have written an assembly language routine that is called by the C function call *seg7dec*(int *i*, int *b*) shown in Table 2.7. This assembly language routine is always available to you when you set up an LBE_DRAGON12-Plus-USB stationery project. Note that this function will display the hex value *i* on the 7-segment display number *b*, where *b* = 0 is the left-most 7-segment display and $b = 3$ is the right-most 7-segment display. Listing 2.15 shows a program that has the right-most 7-segment display count from 0 to F. Try it.

Listing 2.14 Example 6a – DRAGON12-Plus-USB

```
// Example 6a: 7-Segment Decoder - C version
#include <hidef.h>              /* common defines and macros */
#include <mc9s12dg256.h>        /* derivative information */
#pragma LINK_INFO DERIVATIVE "mc9s12dg256b"

#include "main_asm.h"      /* interface to the assembly module */

void main(void) {
    const char seg7tbl[] = {
        0x3F,0x06,0x5B,0x4f,
        0x66,0x6D,0x7D,0x07,
        0x7F,0x6F,0x77,0x7C,
        0x39,0x5E,0x79,0x71
  };

  int i;

  PLL_init();              // set system clock frequency to 24 MHz
  seg7_enable();           // enable 7-segment display
  led_disable();           // disable LEDs
  while(1){
    for(i = 0; i < 16; i++) {
       PORTB = seg7tbl[i];
       ms_delay(500);
    }
  }
}
```

Table 2.7 C function call for 7-segment displays

C Function Call	Meaning
`seg7_enable();`	Enables the 7-segment displays
`seg7_disable();`	Disables the 7-segment displays
`seg7_on(int s, int b);`	Display the segments *s* on the 7-segment digit no. *b*
`seg7dec(int i, int b);`	Display the hex value *i* on the 7-segment digit no. *b*

Listing 2.15 Example 6b – DRAGON12-Plus-USB

```
// Example 6b: Single Digit 7-Segment Decoder
#include <hidef.h>       /* common defines and macros */
#include <mc9s12dg256.h>     /* derivative information */
#pragma LINK_INFO DERIVATIVE "mc9s12dg256b"

#include "main_asm.h" /* interface to the assembly module */

void main(void) {
  int i;
  PLL_init();              // set system clock frequency to 24 MHz
  seg7_enable();           // enable 7-segment display
  led_disable();           // disable LEDs
  while(1){
    for(i = 0; i < 16; i++) {
       seg7dec(i,3);
       ms_delay(500);
    }
  }
}
```

Under the Hood

When the C function *seg7dec*(int *i*, int *b*) is called, the assembly language subroutine *seg7dec* shown in Listing 2.16 is executed. Recall from Example 2b that if there are more than one 16-bit integer to pass to a subroutine, then the last one in the list (the digit number *b* in this case) is passed in accumulator *D*, and therefore in accumulator *B*, while the rest of the parameters are pushed onto the stack before the subroutine is called. The hex digit, *i*, is therefore passed to the subroutine on the stack, above the return address, at *SP*+2.

The first three instructions in the subroutine *seg7dec* in Listing 2.16 are the same as the first three instructions in the subroutine *led_on* in Listing 2.13. Thus, at this point, the value in accumulator *A* will contain a *MASK* value with a single bit set to 1. The next statement, *coma*, will complement all bits, so that all bits in accumulator *A* will be 1 except bit number *b*, which will be 0. This value in accumulator *A* is then stored in *PTP*, which will enable the 7-segment display, digit *b*.

The next instruction, *ldd 2,sp*, will load the load the value of the hex digit, *i*, into accumulator *D*, and therefore into accumulator *B*. The next three instructions in the subroutine *seg7dec* in Listing 2.16 will use this hex digit value (between 0 and F) as an index into the table *SEG7TBL*, and load the corresponding 7-segment code into accumulator *A*. This value is then stored in *PORTB*, which will now display the hex digit *i* on digit *b* of the 7-segment displays.

Listing 2.16 *seg7dec* Assembly Language Subroutine from *main.asm*

```
MASK:       DC.B     1,2,4,8,16,32,64,128

SEG7TBL:    DC.B     $3F,$06,$5B,$4f
            DC.B     $66,$6D,$7D,$07
            DC.B     $7F,$6F,$77,$7C
            DC.B     $39,$5E,$79,$71

;       7-segment decoder
; void seg7dec(int digit, int digit#);
; digit# is in D
; digit is at 2,sp   (index into SEG7TBL)
seg7dec:
            pshy
            ldy      #MASK
            aby
            ldaa     0,y            ;A = mask
            coma
            staa     PTP            ;enable digit digit#
            ldd      2,sp           ;B = digit
            ldy      #SEG7TBL
            aby                     ;y -> 7-seg code
            ldaa     0,y
            staa     PORTB
            puly
            rts
```

Example 7 – Multiplexing the 7-Segment Displays

We have seen that the contents of Port B determine the segments $a - g$ that are displayed on the 7-segment displays and that Port P determines which of the four digits are enabled. Up to this point there doesn't seem to be any way to display different hex values on different 7-segment displays at the same time. However, we do have the function call *seg7dec*(int *i*, int *b*) in Table 2.7 that will enable one digit *b* at a time and display the hex value *i* on that digit.

We can use this function to first display a hex value on the left-most 7-segment display ($b = 0$) and wait a few milliseconds. Then we can display a different hex value on the next 7-segment display ($b = 1$) and wait a few milliseconds. Next we can display yet a different hex value on the third 7-segment display ($b = 2$) and wait a few milliseconds. Finally we can display a fourth hex value on the right-most 7-segment display ($b = 3$) and wait a few milliseconds. If we repeat this process endlessly at a fast enough rate, all four of the 7-segment displays will appear to be on all the time, because our eyes are unable to see that each digit is blinking at a fast rate.

Listing 2.17 shows a program that will display the digits 1234 on the four 7-segment displays. Note that we delay 5 ms after displaying each digit. Thus, each digit is on for 5 ms and off for 15 ms. The blinking time of each digit is therefore 20 ms, which corresponds to a blinking rate of 50 Hz. Your eyes can't see things blinking at that rate. Try out the program.

Listing 2.17 Example 7

```
// Example 7: Display 4 different digits
#include <hidef.h>      /* common defines and macros */
#include <mc9s12dg256.h>     /* derivative information */
#pragma LINK_INFO DERIVATIVE "mc9s12dg256b"

#include "main_asm.h" /* interface to the assembly module */

void main(void) {
  const char digits[] = {
  1,2,3,4
  };
  int i;
  PLL_init();              // set system clock frequency to 24 MHz
  seg7_enable();           // enable 7-segment display
  led_disable();           // disable LEDs
  while(1){
    for(i = 0; i < 4; i++) {
       seg7dec(digits[i],i);
       ms_delay(5);
    }
  }
}
```

PROBLEMS

2.1 Modify Listing 2.1 to turn on all segments and all LEDs but enable only the two center 7-segment displays.

2.2 Modify Listing 2.1 to turn on the four left-most LEDs.

2.3 Modify Listing 2.1 to turn on the two LEDs on each end.

2.4 Modify Listing 2.6 to turn on all segments.

2.5 Modify Listing 2.6 to display the letter L.

2.6 Modify Listing 2.6 to display the letter H.

2.7 Modify Listing 2.6 to display the letter P.

2.8 Modify Listing 2.6 to display the letter A.

2.9 Modify Listing 2.6 to display the letter E.

2.10 Modify Listing 2.9 to blink a 2 on digit 3 every 2 seconds.

2.11 Modify Listing 2.9 to blink a 5 on digit 0 every 0.5 seconds.

2.12 Modify Listing 2.9 to blink a 1 on digit 2 every 0.25 seconds.

2.13 Modify Listing 2.9 to blink a 3 on digit 1 every 3 seconds.

2.14 Modify Listing 2.9 to blink a 5 on digit 3 every 0.2 seconds.

2.15 Modify Listing 2.9 to blink a 4 on digit 1 every 4 seconds.

2.16 Modify Listing 2.12 to turn on LEDs 1, 3, 5 in sequence and then turn them off in the same sequence.

2.17 Modify Listing 2.12 to turn on LEDs 7, 6, 5 in sequence and then turn them off in the same sequence.

2.18 Modify Listing 2.12 to turn on LEDs 0, 3, 4, 7 in sequence and then turn them off in the same sequence.
2.19 Modify Listing 2.12 to turn on and off each LED in sequence from right to left.
2.20 Modify Listing 2.12 to turn on and off each LED in sequence from left to right.
2.21 Modify Listing 2.15 to count only the even hex digits.
2.22 Modify Listing 2.15 to count only the odd hex digits.
2.23 Modify Listing 2.15 to count down from F to 0.
2.24 Modify Listing 2.15 to count down only the even hex digits.
2.25 Modify Listing 2.15 to count down only the odd hex digits.
2.26 Modify Listing 2.15 to count only hex digits that are divisible by 3.
2.27 Modify Listing 2.17 to display the hex number 93AF on the 7-segment displays.
2.28 Modify Listing 2.17 to display the word HELP on the 7-segment displays.
2.29 Write a program that will have the LEDs on the DRAGON12-Plus-USB board count in binary in steps of 1 every 0.5 seconds.
2.30 Write a program that will have the LEDs on the DRAGON12-Plus-USB board count in binary in steps of 5 every 1.0 second.
2.31 Write a program that will have the LEDs on the DRAGON12-Plus-USB board count in binary in steps of 10 every 0.5 seconds.
2.32 Write a program that will have the LEDs on the DRAGON12-Plus-USB board count in binary in steps of 2 every 0.25 seconds.
2.33 Write a program that will have the LEDs on the DRAGON12-Plus-USB board count in binary in steps of 4 every 0.5 seconds.
2.34 Write a program that will have the LEDs on the DRAGON12-Plus-USB board count in binary in steps of 1 every 0.2 seconds.
2.35 Write a program that will have the LEDs on the DRAGON12-Plus-USB board count in binary in steps of 8 every 0.4 seconds.

Chapter 3

Parallel Ports - Inputs

In this chapter we will see how to read bits from parallel ports in order to read the status of pushbutton and DIP switches. We will also learn how to decode a hex keypad.

3.1 Pushbuttons and DIP Switches

The DRAGON12-Plus-USB board contains four pushbuttons and eight DIP switches. Pushbutton switches S2 – S5 on the DRAGON12-Plus-USB board are connected to bits 3 – 0 of Port H as shown in Fig. 3.1. If the switches are not being pressed the 100 kΩ pullup resistors will cause the voltages at pins 3 – 0 to be 5 volts and therefore a read of Port H will read these bits as 1. Closing a switch will cause the input to that bit of Port H to be grounded and therefore that bit will read 0 when Port H is read.

The DIP switch SW1 is connected to the same Port H as shown in Fig. 3.2. Note that the rightmost four DIP switches share the same lower four bits of Port H with the four pushbutton switches. Also note that the DIP switches are connected to ground through 4.7 kΩ resistors. These are low enough compared with the 100 kΩ pullup resistors that a closed switch will still read a zero.

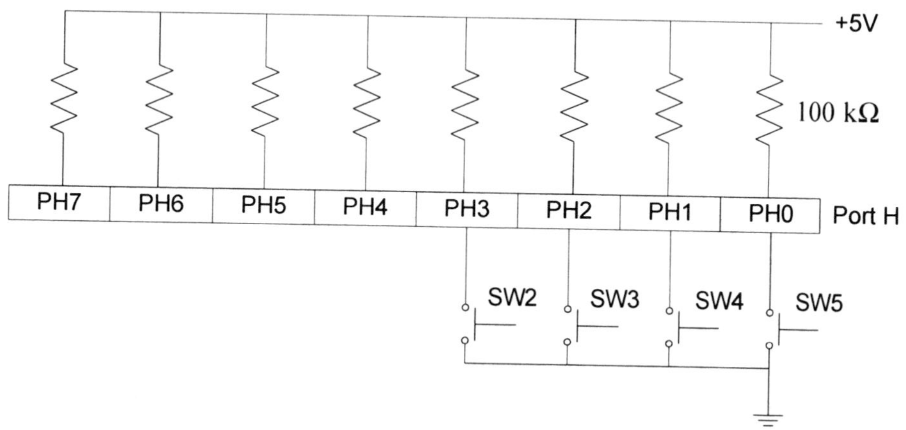

Figure 3.1 DRAGON12-Plus-USB pushbutton connections to Port H

In Example 8 we will show how to read the DIP switch SW1 and the four pushbutton switches, SW2, SW3, SW4 and SW5, on the DRAGON12-Plus-USB board. We will first show you how to do this in C, and then we will provide new C function calls to do this.

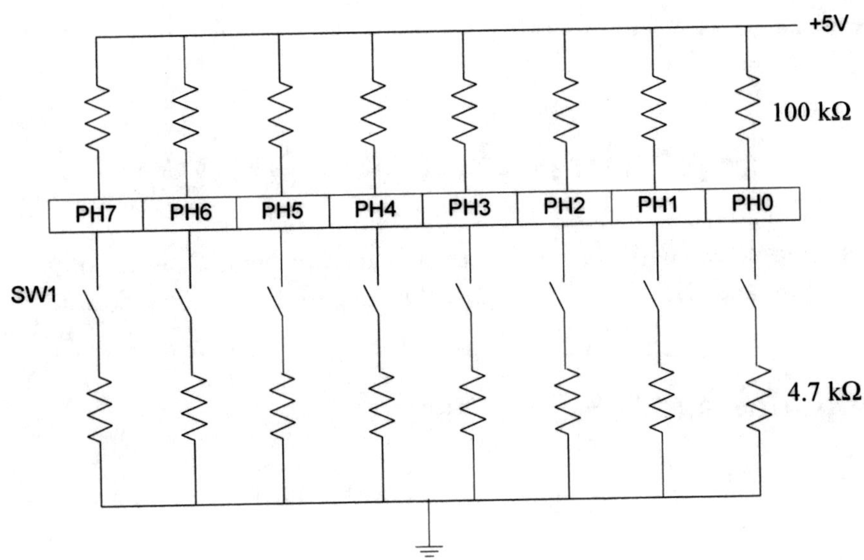

Figure 3.2 DRAGON12-Plus-USB DIP switch SW1 connections to Port H

Example 8 – Switches on the DRAGON12-Plus-USB

The pushbuttons and DIP switches on the DRAGON12-Plus-USB board are connected to Port H (*PTH*) as shown in Figs. 3.1 and 3.2. The program in Listing 3.1 will read *PTH*, complement (i.e. flip) each bit by using the bitwise NOT operator ~, and write the resulting value to the red LEDs. Thus, if the DIP switches are all open (in the up position) and you are not pressing any pushbutton, reading *PTH* will read all 1's or hex $FF. Complementing this value will give hex 00 and thus all LEDs will be off. Pressing any pushbutton will ground the corresponding bit of Port H, which, when complemented, will become 1 and turn on the corresponding LED. Thus, if you run the program in Listing 3.1, then pressing any of the four pushbutton switches will light up the corresponding LED. Closing any of the DIP switches will also light up the corresponding LED. Try it. Note that all bits of Port H must be programmed as inputs by setting the data direction register *DDRH* to 0x00.

To tell if pushbutton switch SW2 is being pressed we must first read the *PTH* register and then test to see if bit 3 is a 1 (SW2 open) or 0 (SW2 closed). We can do this by ANDing the value read from *PTH* with the mask 00001000 (0x08). If the switch is open (not being pressed), then the result of this AND operation will be 0x08. On the other hand, if the switch is closed (being pressed), then the result of this AND operation will be 0x00. Similar masks can be used to test the pressing of pushbutton switches SW3, SW4, and SW5.

The C program shown in Listing 3.2 will display a 2 on the 7-segment display number 0 while switch SW2 is being pressed, display a 3 on the 7-segment display number 1 while switch SW3 is being pressed, display a 4 on the 7-segment display number 2 while switch SW4 is being pressed, and display a 5 on the 7-segment display number 3 while switch SW5 is being pressed.

Listing 3.1 Example 8a – DRAGON12-Plus-USB

```
// Example 8a: Pushbutton Switches - DRAGON12-Plus-USB
#include <hidef.h>      /* common defines and macros */
#include <mc9s12dg256.h>     /* derivative information */
#pragma LINK_INFO DERIVATIVE "mc9s12dg256b"

#include "main_asm.h" /* interface to the assembly module */

void main(void) {
  PLL_init();         // set system clock frequency to 24 MHz
  seg7_disable();     // disable 7-segment display
  led_enable();       // enable LEDs
  DDRH = 0x00;        // Port H inputs
  while(1){
      leds_on(~PTH);
  }
}
```

Listing 3.2 Example 8b – DRAGON12-Plus-USB

```
// Example 8b: Pushbutton Switches -> 7-segment displays
//             - DRAGON12-Plus-USB
#include <hidef.h>      /* common defines and macros */
#include <mc9s12dg256.h>     /* derivative information */
#pragma LINK_INFO DERIVATIVE "mc9s12dg256b"

#include "main_asm.h" /* interface to the assembly module */

void main(void) {
  PLL_init();         // set system clock frequency to 24 MHz
  seg7_enable();      // enable 7-segment display
  led_disable();      // disable LEDs
  DDRH = 0x00;        // Port H inputs
  while(1){
     while((PTH & 0x01) == 0){  // while pressing SW5
         seg7dec(5,3);          //   display 5 on digit 3
     }
     seg7s_off();               // turn off all 7-seg displays
     while((PTH & 0x02) == 0){  // while pressing SW4
         seg7dec(4,2);          //   display 4 on digit 2
     }
     seg7s_off();               // turn off all 7-seg displays
     while((PTH & 0x04) == 0){  // while pressing SW3
         seg7dec(3,1);          //   display 3 on digit 1
     }
     seg7s_off();               // turn off all 7-seg displays
     while((PTH & 0x08) == 0){  // while pressing SW2
         seg7dec(2,0);          //   display 2 on digit 0
     }
     seg7s_off();               // turn off all 7-seg displays
  }
}
```

Note that the expression

```
(PTH & 0x01) == 0
```

will be true if bit 0 of *PTH* is 0, i.e., if switch SW5 is being pressed. Similarly, the expression

```
(PTH & 0x04) == 0
```

will be true if bit 2 of *PTH* is 0, i.e., if switch SW3 is being pressed.

If you download the program in Listing 3.2 to the DRAGON12-Plus-USB board and press any of the pushbutton switches S1 then the number of that pushbutton switch will be displayed on the corresponding 7-segment display. Try it. Make sure that all eight DIP switches SW1 are in the open, or up, position.

Note the use of the equality operator == in Listing 3.2. The C operators for equality and inequality are shown in Table 3.1.

Table 3.1 Equality and Inequality Operators

Operator	Description
==	Test for equality
!=	Test for inequality

C Function Calls for Reading DRAGON12-Plus-USB Switches

Instead of having to remember which bits in which register the switches on the DRAGON12-Plus-USB are connected to, we have written assembly language routines that are called by the C function calls shown in Table 3.2. These assembly language routines are always available to you when you set up an *LBE_DRAGON12_Plus* stationery project. Listing 3.3 shows how you can modify the program in Listing 3.2 to produce the same result. Try it.

Table 3.2 C function calls for reading switches SW1 – SW5

C Function Call	Meaning
`SW_enable();`	Enable switches SW1 – SW5
`SW1_dip();`	Returns 8-bit reading of SW1
`SW2_down();`	Returns **true** if SW2 is down
`SW3_down();`	Returns **true** if SW3 is down
`SW4_down();`	Returns **true** if SW4 is down
`SW5_down();`	Returns **true** if SW5 is down
`SW2_up();`	Returns **true** if SW2 is up
`SW3_up();`	Returns **true** if SW3 is up
`SW4_up();`	Returns **true** if SW4 is up
`SW5_up();`	Returns **true** if SW5 is up

Listing 3.3 Example 8c – DRAGON12-Plus-USB

```
// Example 8c: Pushbutton Switches -> 7-segment displays
//              - DRAGON12-Plus-USB
#include <hidef.h>      /* common defines and macros */
#include <mc9s12dg256.h>     /* derivative information */
#pragma LINK_INFO DERIVATIVE "mc9s12dg256b"
#include "main_asm.h" /* interface to the assembly module */

void main(void) {
  PLL_init();          // set system clock frequency to 24 MHz
  seg7_enable();           // enable 7-segment display
  led_disable();           // disable LEDs
  SW_enable();             // enable switches
  while(1){
     while(SW5_down()){           // while pressing SW5
         seg7dec(5,3);            //   display 5 on digit 3
      }
      seg7s_off();                // turn off all 7-seg displays
     while(SW4_down()){           // while pressing SW4
         seg7dec(4,2);            //   display 4 on digit 2
      }
      seg7s_off();                // turn off all 7-seg displays
     while(SW3_down()){           // while pressing SW3
         seg7dec(3,1);            //   display 3 on digit 1
      }
      seg7s_off();                // turn off all 7-seg displays
     while(SW2_down()){           // while pressing SW2
         seg7dec(2,0);            //   display 2 on digit 0
      }
      seg7s_off();                // turn off all 7-seg displays
  }
}
```

Under the Hood

As shown in Figs. 3.1 and 3.2, the four pushbutton switches, S2 – S5, and the DIP switch, S1, on the DRAGON12-Plus-USB are connected to Port H (*PTH*). The assembly language routines for the ten *SW1-SW5* C functions shown in Table 3.2 are shown in Listing 3.4. Note that the first subroutine, *SW_enable*, will clear all bits in the data direction register for Port H, thereby all bits of Port H inputs. The subroutine *SW1_dip* will read the status of the DIP switches by returning the contents of *PTH* in accumulator *D*.

The subroutine *SW2_down* in Listing 3.4 will return a *true* value ($FFFF) in accumulator *D* when switch SW2 is being pressed, i.e., when the switch is closed. The first two instructions will clear accumulator *D*, making its value *false* ($0000). The next instruction is

```
brset   PTH,#$08,SW2end1
```

This *branch on set* instruction will AND the complement of the bits in *PTH* with the mask, $08 = 00001000, and branch to *SW2end1* if the result is zero. That is, if the original bit 3 of *PTH* is 1, meaning pushbutton switch SW2 is open and not being pressed, then the program branches to *SW2end1*, which is an *rts* instruction that returns the value $0000 (*false*) in accumulator *D*. On the other hand, if SW2 is being pressed, then bit 3 of *PTH* will be 0, and the ANDing of the complement of the bits in *PTH* with the mask, $08 = 00001000 will not be zero, so the branch will not be taken and the next instruction, *ldd* #$FFFF, will be executed. This instruction will load the value $FFFF (*true*) into accumulator *D* before returning to the calling program.

The subroutine *SW2_up* in Listing 3.4 will return a *true* value ($FFFF) in accumulator *D* when pushbutton switch SW2 is *not* being pressed, i.e., when the switch is open. This subroutine is very similar to the *SW2_down* subroutine except that the *brset* instruction is replaced by the *branch on clear* instruction

```
brclr   PTH,#$08,SW2end1
```

As you might expect, this instruction will AND the bits in *PTH* with the mask, $08 = 00001000, and branch to *SW2end1* if the result is zero. That is, if bit 3 of *PTH* is 0, meaning pushbutton switch SW2 is closed and being pressed, then the program branches to *SW2end1*, which is an *rts* instruction that returns the value $0000 (*false*) in accumulator *D*. On the other hand, if SW2 is being pressed, then the instructions following the *brclr* instruction will be executed, returning a value of $FFFF (*true*) in accumulator *D* to the calling program.

The remaining subroutines in Listing 3.4 work exactly the same ways as the subroutines *SW2_down* and *SW2_up* except that the masks used in the *brset* and *brclr* instructions are different, corresponding to bits 2, 1, and 0 of *PTH*.

Listing 3.4 *SW1-5* Assembly Language Subroutines from *main.asm*

```
; Pushbutton and DIP switches
SW_enable:
            clr   DDRH    ;Port H inputs
            rts

SW1_dip:
            clra
            ldab  PTH     ;Read Port H
            rts

SW2_down:               ;return true is SW2 is down
            clra
            clrb
            brset  PTH, #$08,SW2end1
            ldd    #$FFFF
SW2end1:    rts

SW2_up:                 ;return true is SW2 is up
            clra
            clrb
            brclr  PTH, #$08,SW2end2
            ldd    #$FFFF
SW2end2:    rts
```

Listing 3.4 (cont.) ***SW1-5*** **Assembly Language Subroutines from *main.asm***

```
SW3_down:            ;return true is SW3 is down
          clra
          clrb
          brset  PTH, #$04,SW2end1
          ldd    #$FFFF
SW3end1:  rts

SW3_up:              ;return true is SW3 is up
          clra
          clrb
          brclr  PTH, #$04,SW2end2
          ldd    #$FFFF
SW3end2:  rts

SW4_down:            ;return true is SW4 is down
          clra
          clrb
          brset  PTH, #$02,SW4end1
          ldd    #$FFFF
SW4end1:  rts

SW4_up:              ;return true is SW4 is up
          clra
          clrb
          brclr  PTH, #$02,SW4end2
          ldd    #$FFFF
SW4end2:  rts

SW5_down:            ;return true is SW5 is down
          clra
          clrb
          brset  PTH, #$01,SW5end1
          ldd    #$FFFF
SW5end1:  rts

SW5_up:              ;return true is SW5 is up
          clra
          clrb
          brclr  PTH, #$01,SW5end2
          ldd    #$FFFF
SW5end2:  rts
```

3.2 Hex Keypad

The DRAGON12-Plus-USB has a built-in 4×4 hex keypad that is connected to Port A of the microcontroller as shown in Fig. 3.3. Note that pins *PA0–PA3* are configured as outputs and pins *PA4–PA7* are configured as inputs. These four inputs are pulled up to 5 volts with four internal pull-up resistors. The C statement *PUCR* = 0x01 will enable these pull-up resistors. Thus, if all the key switches are open, the four bits *PA4–PA7* will all be read as 1's. If a zero is written to only one of the inputs *PA0–PA3* (one column in Fig. 3.3), then a key in that column that is pressed will cause the input connected to its row to go low. This can be read by the MCU to determine which key has been pressed.

For example, in Fig. 3.3, suppose that *PA1* is brought low while *PA0*, *PA2*, and *PA3* are high. That is, a 1101, or 0xD, is written to the low nibble (lower 4 bits) of Port A. If Port A is then read and the high nibble, *PA4–PA7*, is not 0xF, then either key 2, 5, 8, or 0, must have been pressed. If *PA4* is low, i.e. Port A reads 0xED, then key 2 was pressed. If *PA5* is low, i.e. Port A reads 0xDD, then key 5 was pressed. If *PA6* is low, i.e. Port A reads 0xBD, then key 8 was pressed. If *PA7* is low, i.e. Port A reads 0x7D, then key *0* was pressed. In a similar way we could determine the key codes for all 16 keys and store them in a table called *keycodes* as shown in Table 3.3.

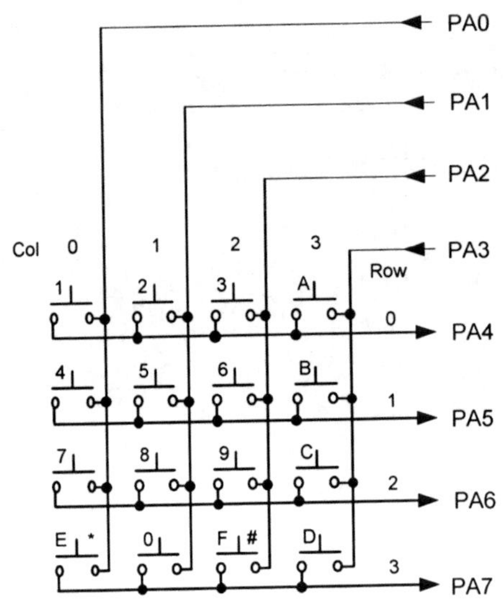

Figure 3.3 Connecting the 4 x 4 keypad on the DRAGON12-Plus-USB to Port A

Table 3.3 Keycodes for 4 x 4 hex keypad in Fig. 3.5b

key	0	1	2	3	4	5	6	7	8	9	A	B	C	D	* E	# F
code	7D	EE	ED	EB	DE	DD	DB	BE	BD	BB	E7	D7	B7	77	7E	7B

Example 9 – Hex Keypad in C

The C function *key_scan*( ) given in Listing 3.5 reads each of the 16 codes in the table *keycodes*, stores the code in *PORTA*, and then reads back the contents of *PORTA*. The key value is found when the read back value is equal to the key code. Note that *key_scan*( ) returns a value of 16 if no key is being pressed. The constant *keycodes*[ ] array given in Listing 3.5 is from Table 3.3. The C function *get_key*( ) shown in Listing 3.6 will wait for a key to be pressed and return the hex value of the key pressed. Note that it does this by using the C *do-while* looping statement that will continue to loop as long as *key_scan*( ) returns a value of 16; i.e. as long as no key is being pressed.

Once you obtain a keypad value using the word *get_key*( ) you usually want to do something with this value such as display the hex digit on a liquid crystal display (LCD) that will be described in Chapter 4. If, for example, you want to display the value of the first key pressed at the current cursor position on an LCD, and then display the value of the second key pressed at the next cursor position, you could run into a problem. After displaying the first value, if your finger was still pressing the key, the program would display this same value at the next cursor position. In fact, the first digit would streak across the LCD display as long as you keep your finger down! You need to be able to wait until you have released your finger before waiting to press another key. The C function *wait_for_keyup*( ) in Listing 3.6 will do this. The C program *main*( ) shown in Listing 3.7 will display any key you press on the right-most 7-segment display of the DRAGON12-Plus-USB.

Listing 3.5 C function *key_scan*( )

```
int key_scan(void){
  const char keycodes[] = {
         0x7D,0xEE,0xED,0xEB,
         0xDE,0xDD,0xDB,0xBE,
         0xBD,0xBB,0XE7,0xD7,
         0xB7,0x77,0x7E,0x7B
  };
  int i,j, key;
  char readback;
  int found;
  i = 0;
  key = 16;                        // return 16 if no key pressed
  found = 0;
  while((i < 16) && (found == 0)){
    PORTA = keycodes[i];           // write keycode to PORTA
    for(j = 0; j<10; j++){
    }                              // wait a bit
    readback = PORTA;
    if(readback == keycodes[i]){   // read back PORTA, if same
      key  = i;                    //   get key number
      found = 1;                   //     and exit loop
    }
    else
      i++;                         // else check next key
  }
  return key;                      //     return key
}
```

Listing 3.6 C functions *get_key()* and *wait_for_keyup*( )

```
int get_key(void){
  int key;
  do {
    key = key_scan();
  }
  while(key == 16);
  return key;
}

void wait_for_keyup(void){
  while(key_scan() != 16){
  }
}
```

Listing 3.7 Example 9 – DRAGON12-Plus-USB

```
// Example 9: 4 x 4 keypad in C - DRAGON12-Plus-USB
#include <hidef.h>      /* common defines and macros */
#include <mc9s12dg256.h>     /* derivative information */
#pragma LINK_INFO DERIVATIVE "mc9s12dg256b"

#include "main_asm.h" /* interface to the assembly module */

int key_scan(void);
int get_key(void);
void wait_for_keyup(void);

void main(void) {
  int c;
  PLL_init();         // set system clock frequency to 24 MHz
  seg7_enable();      // enable 7-segment display
  led_disable();      // disable LEDs
  DDRA = 0x0F;        // Port A: A7:A4 inputs, A3:A0 outputs
  PUCR = 0x01;        // enable pullup resistors
  while(1){
      c = get_key();
      seg7dec(c,3);
      wait_for_keyup();
  }
}
```

Example 10 – Keypad C Function Calls

Sometimes the switches making up a keypad will have a tendency to bounce when they are pressed. That is, when contact is first made, it may open momentarily before closing for good. This could lead to thinking that the key was up (and therefore continuing the program) when it really wasn't. In such a situation a digit might inadvertently get displayed twice. To solve this problem, key switches are debounced, either in hardware or software. The software solution is to delay for about 10 ms after a key pressing is sensed. If the key is read again, and it is the same value as before, then you can conclude that the key has stopped bouncing and the correct value has been read.

We have written assembly language routines for reading the 4×4 keypad, which include the debounce delays. (The assembly language routines to read pushbutton switches SW2 to SW5 described in Example 8 also include debounce delays.) The C function calls to access these routines are shown in Table 3.4. The *keypad_enable*( ) routine will properly set the data direction register and enable the pull-up resistors of Port A. An example of using these routines to display the key value pressed on the right-most 7-segment display of the DRAGON12-Plus-USB is given in Listing 3.8.

Table 3.4 C function calls for reading a 4 x 4 keypad

C Function Call	Meaning
`keypad_enable();`	Enable the keypad
`int getkey();`	Waits to press key and returns value
`void wait_keyup();`	Waits until key is not being pressed
`int keyscan();`	Returns 16 if no key is being pressed Returns key value if key is being pressed

Listing 3.8 Example 10 – DRAGON12-Plus-USB

```
// Example 10: 4 x 4 keypad using C function calls
//              - DRAGON12-Plus-USB
#include <hidef.h>      /* common defines and macros */
#include <mc9s12dg256.h>     /* derivative information */
#pragma LINK_INFO DERIVATIVE "mc9s12dg256b"

#include "main_asm.h" /* interface to the assembly module */

void main(void) {
  char c;
  PLL_init();           // set system clock frequency to 24 MHz
  led_disable();        // disable leds
  seg7_enable();        // enable 7-segment displays
  keypad_enable();      // enable keypad
  while(1){
    c = getkey();
    seg7dec(c,3);
    wait_keyup();
  }
}
```

Under the Hood

The assembly language routines for the four hex keypad C functions shown in Table 3.4 are shown in Listing 3.9. The first instruction in the subroutine *keypad_enable* will store the hex value $0F in data direction register A. This will make PA7 – PA4 inputs and PA3 – PA0 outputs as shown in Fig. 3.3. The pull-up control register (*PUCR*) shown in Fig. 3.4 can be used to enable internal pull-up resistors on pins that have been configured as inputs on Ports A, B, E, and K. (This register affects only pins 7, 4 – 0 on Port E). Thus, to enable pull-up resistors on the inputs PA7 – PA4 in Port A, we need to write a 1 to bit 0 of *PUCR*. We can do this with the instruction

```
bset  PUCR, $01
```

The subroutine *keyscan* in Listing 3.9 is the assembly language version of the C function *key_scan*( ) in Listing 3.5, which will scan all 16 keys on the 4×4 keypad. If no key is being pressed, a value of 16 ($10) is left in accumulator *D* to be returned as the value of the C function *keyscan*( ) in Table 3.6. If a key is being pressed, then the value returned in accumulator *D* will be the hex value of the key being pressed.

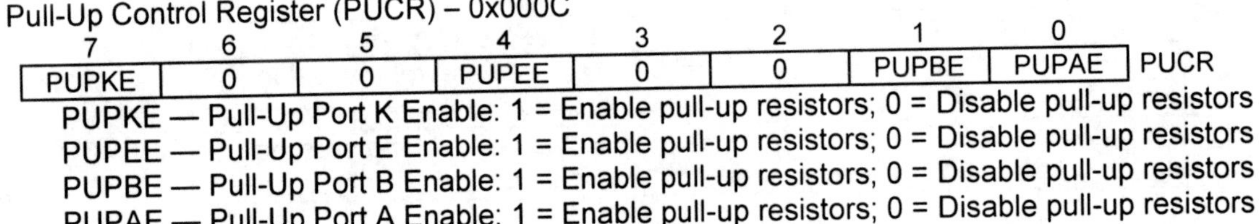

Pull-Up Control Register (PUCR) – 0x000C
7 6 5 4 3 2 1 0
PUPKE 0 0 PUPEE 0 0 PUPBE PUPAE PUCR
PUPKE — Pull-Up Port K Enable: 1 = Enable pull-up resistors; 0 = Disable pull-up resistors
PUPEE — Pull-Up Port E Enable: 1 = Enable pull-up resistors; 0 = Disable pull-up resistors
PUPBE — Pull-Up Port B Enable: 1 = Enable pull-up resistors; 0 = Disable pull-up resistors
PUPAE — Pull-Up Port A Enable: 1 = Enable pull-up resistors; 0 = Disable pull-up resistors

Figure 3.4 Pull-up control register (PUCR)

Listing 3.9 *keypad* Assembly Language Subroutines from *main.asm*

```
; Enable keypad
keypad_enable:
          movb    #$0f,DDRA     ;A7:A4 inputs, A3:A0 outputs
          bset    PUCR, $01     ;enable pullup resistors
          rts

;  scan all keys;  B = key pressed
;  if B = #$10, no key pressed
keyscan:
          clrb                  ; B = index
          ldx     #keycodes
ks1       ldaa    b,x
          staa    PORTA         ;write next code
          anda    #$F0          ;save high nibble
          staa    temp
          ldaa    #10           ;wait to settle down
ks2       deca
          bne     ks2
          ldaa    PORTA         ;read it back
          anda    #$F0          ; check high nibble
          cmpa    temp          ;if key pressed,
          beq     ks3           ; B = key
          incb                  ;else, inx index
          cmpb    #$10          ; and scan all keys
          bne     ks1           ;if no key pressed
ks3       clra                  ; B = #$10
          rts                   ;B = key value

;  wait to press a key
;  B = key value
keypad:
          bsr     keyscan       ;scan keypad
          cmpb    #$10          ;until key pressed
          beq     keypad
          rts
```

Listing 3.9 (cont.) *keypad* Assembly Language Subroutines from *main.asm*

```
;  debounced key input
;  B = key value
getkey:
gk1        bsr    keypad         ;wait for key
           pshb                  ;save key value
           ldd    #10
           jsr    ms_delay       ;delay ~10 ms
           bsr    keypad         ;wait for key
           pula                  ;get 1st value
           sba                   ;if not same as 2nd
           bne    gk1            ;repeat
           rts                   ;D = key value

;  wait to lift finger from key (with debounce)
wait_keyup:
           bsr    keyscan        ;scan keypad
           cmpb   #$10           ;while key is pressed
           bne    wait_keyup
           ldd    #10
           jsr    ms_delay       ;delay ~10 ms
           bsr    keyscan        ;scan keypad
           cmpb   #$10           ;if key is pressed
           bne    wait_keyup     ;repeat
           rts
```

The next instruction in the subroutine, *keyscan*, in Listing 3.9 is *ldaa b,x*. This will load into accumulator *A* the byte at the address formed by adding *B* to *X*. This will be the first byte in the *keycodes* table. The *keycode* is stored in *PORTA* and the upper four bits of this code are saved in the variable *temp*. This byte variable is defined at the beginning of the file *main.asm* using the statement

```
temp:  rmb 1
```

The directive *rmb* means *reserve memory byte*, and will reserve 1 byte in memory to hold the value of *temp*. You can reserve any number of bytes using *rmb*. For example,

```
buff:  rmb  12
```

will define a buffer containing 12 bytes with *buff* being the address of the first byte in the buffer.

The *ks2* loop in Listing 3.9 is a short delay of about 40 clock cycles to allow the voltages on Port A to stabilize before reading back the contents of *PORTA*. This value is then ANDed with $F0 and compared with the upper four bits of the *keycode* that was saved in the variable *temp*. If the value read from PA7 – PA4 is equal to the value in *temp*, then the program jumps to *ks3* where accumulator *A* is cleared and *B* will contain the hex value of the key being pressed. On the other hand, if the value read from PA7 – PA4 is *not* equal to the value in *temp*, then the value of *B* is incremented, and if it is not equal to 16 ($10), the program branches back to *ks1* where the next *keycode* in the table is tested. Note that if no key is being pressed, all *keycodes* will be tested before the subroutine exits with a value in *B* equal to 16 ($10).

The subroutine *keypad* in Listing 3.9 continually calls the subroutine *keyscan* until the value in *B* is something other than 16 ($10), i.e., until a key has been pressed. The subroutine *getkey* in Listing 3.9 is the assembly language version of the C function *get_key*( ) in Listing 3.6, except that we have debounced the keys by adding a 10 ms delay. We first wait until a key has been pressed by calling *keypad,* and then we save the key value by pushing *B* onto the stack. After delaying 10 ms, we call *keypad* again. If the key has stopped bouncing, the value in *B* should be the same as the first value we pushed on the stack. We can compare these two values by pulling this first value into *A*, and subtracting *B* from *A*. If the result is zero, we have our debounced key value still in *B* and we exit the subroutine. If the values are not equal, we go back and repeat the process until they are equal.

Finally, the subroutine *wait_keyup* in Listing 3.9 is a debounced assembly language version of the C function *wait_for_keyup*( ) in Listing 3.6. This subroutine continually calls the subroutine *keyscan* until the value in *B* is 16 ($10), i.e., until a key has been released. After delaying 10 ms, the subroutine then checks to make sure that the key is still up.

PROBLEMS

3.1 Modify Listing 3.1 to have the DIP switches on the DRAGON12-Plus-USB turn on the corresponding segments of the 7-segment displays. Hint: Enable the 7-segment displays and disable the LEDs in Listing 3.1.

3.2 Write a program that will toggle a 5 on and off on digit 3 of the 7-segment displays when pushbutton SW5 is pressed on the DRAGON12-Plus-USB. That is, the first time the button is pressed a 5 is displayed on the 7-segment display and stays displayed when the button is released. The second time the button is pressed, the display goes off. The third time the button is pressed the 5 is displayed again.

Chapter 4

Liquid Crystal Displays

In this chapter we will show how to write characters to the liquid crystal display (LCD) on the DRAGON12-Plus-USB board. We will provide new C function calls to make it easy to do this.

4.1 Liquid Crystal Displays

A liquid crystal display (LCD) is a common type of display used in a variety of applications such as watches, calculators, and laptop computers. Its big advantage is that it uses much less power than an LED and therefore can be used in battery-powered applications. An LCD consists of a liquid crystal material sandwiched between two conducting plates. An AC voltage applied between the two conductors will cause the reflectance (or transmittance) of the liquid crystal to change, making a character visible. LCD displays come in a variety of configurations.

For example, the Sanyo DM1623 displays 2 lines of 16 characters. This display and many other common ones use a built-in Hitachi HD44780 LCD Controller/Driver that performs all of the functions needed to drive the LCD and provides an easy interface to a microcontroller using an 8-bit data bus, *DB0-DB7*, and three control signals, *RS*, *R/W*, and *E*. It is also possible to communicate with the Hitachi HD44780 LCD Controller/Driver over a 4-bit data bus. This is what the DRAGON12-Plus-USB does. The relationships between *RS*, *R/W*, and *E* are shown in Fig. 4.1.

RS	R/W	E	Operation
0	0	↘ (falling edge)	Write instruction code
0	1	⎍ (pulse)	Read busy flag and address counter
1	0	↘ (falling edge)	Write data
1	1	⎍ (pulse)	Read data

Figure 4.1 Relationships between RS, R/W, and E

The signal, *RS*, can be thought of as a register select signal that selects either the LCD control register (*RS* = 0) or the LCD data register (*RS* = 1). The read/write signal *R/W* is 1 for a read operation and 0 for a write operation. Data or instruction codes are written on the falling edge of *E*, and *E* must be high for a read operation.

The HD44780 has its own instruction set shown in Table 4.1. (For a complete data sheet go to *http://www.hitachi.com/*.) The first eight are instruction codes that are written to the LCD control register with *RS* = 0 and *R/W* = 0 as shown in Fig. 4.1. The last entry in Table 4.1 shows the format of the *busy flag* and *address counter* when reading from the LCD control register with *RS* = 0 and *R/W* = 1 as shown in Fig. 4.1.

Table 4.1 HD44780 Instruction Set

Instruction	DB7	DB6	DB5	DB4	DB3	DB2	DB1	DB0	Description
Clear display	0	0	0	0	0	0	0	1	Clears display & returns cursor to home. Sets I/D=1 in Entry Mode.
Return home	0	0	0	0	0	0	1	x	Returns cursor to home position (Address 0) Set DD RAM address to zero.
Entry mode set	0	0	0	0	0	1	I/D	S	I/D=1: increment cursor; S=0: normal ; I/D=0: decrement cursor; S=1 shift display.
Display ON/OFF control	0	0	0	0	1	D	C	B	Sets ON/OFF all display (D), cursor (C), and blink of cursor (B).
Cursor or display shift	0	0	0	1	S/C	R/L	x	x	S/C=1: display shift; S/C=0: cursor move; R/L=1: shift right; R/L=0: shift left.
Function set	0	0	1	DL	N	F	x	x	DL=1: 8 bits; DL=0: 4 bits; N=1: 2 line; N=0: 1 line; F=1: 5x10 dots; F=0; 5x7 dots.
Set the CG RAM address	0	1	CG RAM address						Sets the CG RAM address, after which CG RAM data is sent and received.
Set the DD RAM address	1	DD RAM address							Sets the DD RAM address, after which DD RAM data is sent and received.
Read busy flag & address	BF	Address counter							Read busy flag (BF) and address counter contents.

The HD44780 contains a 128-byte data display memory (DD RAM) that contains the ASCII codes of the characters being displayed on the LCD display. This DD RAM address is set (address 0 is the display home position) using the *Set the DD RAM address* instruction. After this is done, subsequent data writes will write the ASCII code of the character to be displayed to the DD RAM address (and display the character) and then increment the DD RAM address so that the next character will be displayed in the next location.

The HD44780 also contains a 64-byte character-generator memory (CG RAM) that can be used to change the font of up to 16 different characters. If you are interested in doing this you can consult an HD44780 data sheet.

The data bus *DB0-DB7* on the HD44780 can be connected directly to a microcontroller's data bus and the controller can be wired up to respond to reads and writes to a particular series of addresses. The HD44780 can also be connected to the parallel I/O ports on a microcontroller and then software can be written to produce the control signals shown in Fig. 4.1. This is the approach taken on the DRAGON12-Plus-USB board.

The diagram in Fig. 4.2 shows how the LCD connector on the DRAGON12-Plus-USB board is connected to Port K of the MC68HCS912DG256. Note that only the upper 4 bits of the LCD controller data bus are connected to *PTK*[5:2] while the enable signal *E* is connected to *PK1* and the register select signal *RS* is connected to *PK0*. The read/write line is connected to *PK7* through the header J5 on the DRAGON12-Plus-USB board. This J5 header can also connect the read/write line directly to ground to provide write-only operation of the LCD display. In this case, you will not be able to read the busy flag. This is not a disadvantage because reading this flag is often problematic and an alternative is to simply delay after writing to the LCD. This is what we will do.

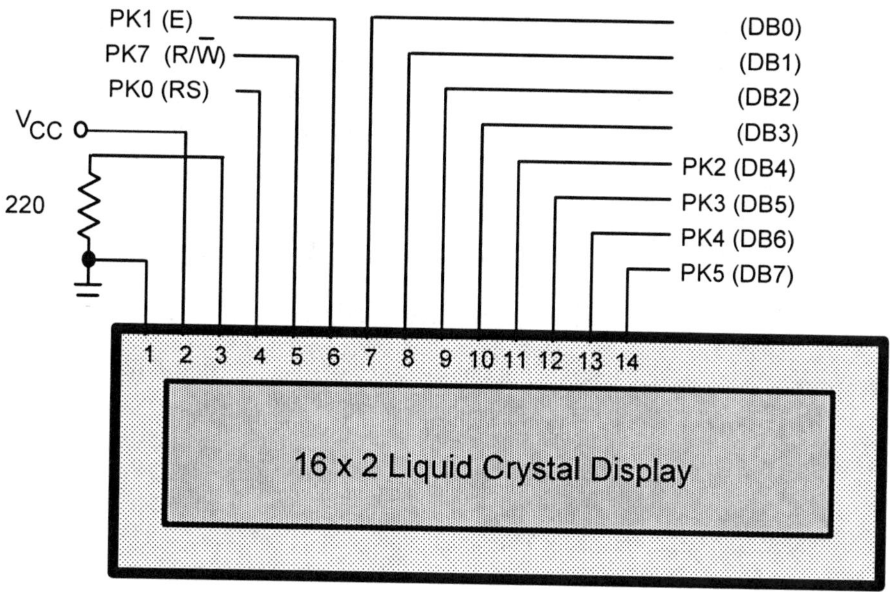

Figure 4.2 Interfacing to a Liquid Crystal Display on the DRAGON12-Plus-USB board

Before you can write to the LCD you must initialize it. We have provided the C function call *LCD_init*( ) to do this. This function initializes it for 4-bit, 2 line, 5 x 7 dot operation, display on, cursor off, no blinking, then clears the display and sets the cursor to the home position.

You can set the cursor to any position on the display by calling the built-in C function call *set_lcd_addr*(char *ad*) where *ad* is an 8-bit hex address whose display position is shown in Fig. 4.3. Note that there is a gap between the end of the first line and the beginning of the second line.

00	01	02	03	04	05	06	07	08	09	0A	0B	0C	0D	0E	0F
40	41	42	43	44	45	46	47	48	49	4A	4B	4C	4D	4E	4F

Figure 4.3 Hex addresses of 16 x 2 LCD display

Example 11 – Writing a Message on the LCD

A list of all the C function calls that we have provided assembly language routines for are shown in Table 4.2. Listing 4.1 shows how to display a message on each line of the display. Try it.

The statement *char** $q1$; in Listing 4.1 defines $q1$ to be a *pointer*, i.e., an address to a memory location of type *char* (i.e., a byte). The statement $q1$ = "*Microcontrollers*"; then gives the value of $q1$ to be the address of the first character in the string "*Microcontrollers*". The C function *lcd_init*( ) will initialize the LCD. You must call this function before the LCD can be used. The statement *set_lcd_addr*(0x00) will move the cursor to the beginning of the first row of the LCD as shown in Fig. 4.3. The function *type_lcd*($q1$) will then write the entire string $q1$ on the LCD.

Table 4.2 C Function calls for LCD display

Function	Description
`void lcd_init(void);`	Initialize LCD display (clears display)
`void set_lcd_addr(char);`	Set cursor address (see Fig. 4.3)
`void data8(char);`	Write ASCII character to display at cursor location
`void instr8(char);`	Write instruction to display (see Table 4.1)
`void clear_lcd(void);`	Clear LCD display
`void hex2lcd(char);`	Write hex digit (0 – F) to LCD display
`char hex2asc(char);`	Convert hex digit (0 – F) to ASCII code
`void type_lcd(char*);`	Display ASCIIZ string on LCD display at cursor location

Listing 4.1 Example 11

```
// Example 11: LCD Display
#include <hidef.h>        /* common defines and macros */
#include <mc9s12dg256.h>      /* derivative information */
#pragma LINK_INFO DERIVATIVE "mc9s12dg256b"

#include "main_asm.h" /* interface to the assembly module */

void main(void) {
  char* q1;
  char* q2;
  q1 = "Microcontrollers";
  q2 = "are FUN";
  PLL_init();        // set system clock frequency to 24 MHz

  lcd_init();                // enable lcd
  set_lcd_addr(0x00);
  type_lcd(q1);              // write q1
  set_lcd_addr(0x44);
  type_lcd(q2);              // write q2
  for(;;){
  }                          // wait forever
}
```

The function *data8*(char *c*) in Table 4.2 will display the character whose ASCII code is passed as a parameter. The ASCII codes of all characters are shown in Table 4.3. In this table, the upper nibble of the ASCII code is given by the column heading, and the lower nibble is given by the row number. For example, the hex ASCII code for upper-case *A* is 0x41 and the ASCII code for lower-case *k* is 0x6B. Thus, the function call *data8*(0x41) will display an upper-case *A* at the current cursor position. The cursor is automatically incremented when this function is called.

The function *hex2lcd*(char *c*) in Table 4.2 will display the hex digit passed as the parameter on the LCD display. For example, *hex2lcd*(0xA) will display the *A* on the LCD display by first converting 0xA to the ASCII code 0x41 using the built-in function *hex2asc*(char *c*). The cursor is automatically incremented when this function is called.

Table 4.3 Standard ASCII Codes

Dec	→	0	16	32	48	64	80	96	112
↓	Hex	0	1	2	3	4	5	6	7
0	0	NUL	DLE	Blank	0	@	P		p
1	1	SOH	DC1	!	1	A	Q	a	q
2	2	STX	DC2	“	2	B	R	b	r
3	3	ETX	DC3	#	3	C	S	c	s
4	4	EOT	DC4	$	4	D	T	d	t
5	5	ENQ	NAK	%	5	E	U	e	u
6	6	ACK	SYN	&	6	F	V	f	v
7	7	BEL	ETB	‘	7	G	W	g	w
8	8	BS	CAN	(	8	H	X	h	x
9	9	HT	EM	)	9	I	Y	i	y
10	A	LF	SUB	*	:	J	Z	j	z
11	B	VT	ESC	+	;	K	[	k	{
12	C	FF	FS	,	<	L	\	l	|
13	D	CR	GS	-	=	M	]	m	}
14	E	SO	RS	.	>	N	^	n	~
15	F	SI	US	/	?	O	_	o	DEL

Under the Hood

The assembly language routines for the eight LCD C functions shown in Table 4.2 are given in Listing 4.2. To initialize the LCD for the 4-bit mode, a sequence of 12 instructions from Table 4.1 must be written to the LCD. This unusual sequence can be found in the HD44780 datasheet. These twelve 4-bit instruction codes are listed in the *init_codes* table in Listing 4.2 as the high nibble of each byte in the table. Note that we use the assembly language directive *fcb* (form constant byte) to define the contents of this table. The first byte in the table is the number of instruction codes that follow (12). The subroutine *lcd_init* in Listing 4.2 will write these twelve instruction codes to the LCD.

In the subroutine *init_lcd* in Listing 4.2, the instruction *ldx #init_codes* will load index register *X* with the address of the table *init_codes*. The instruction *ldab* 1,*x*+ will load *B* with the byte pointed to by *X* (12 = $0C) and then increment *X* by 1. The index register *X* is now pointing to the first LCD instruction in the table, namely, \$30. The instruction *ldaa 1,x+* will then load this value into accumulator *A* and increment *X* again to point to the next byte in the table. The instruction *jsr write_instr_nibble* jumps to the subroutine *write_instr_nibble*, which will shift the 4-bit nibble 2 bits to the right so that it will end up in *PK*5 – *PK*2 as required in Fig. 4.2. The *write_instr_nibble* subroutine then brings *E* (*PK*1) high and then low (after a short delay) with *RS* (*PK*0) equal to zero. This satisfies the instruction write condition in Fig. 4.1.

The rest of the subroutine *init_lcd* in Listing 4.2 loops through the entire *init_codes* table, writing each instruction to the LCD with a 5 ms delay between writes. While this delay is longer than required for some of the instructions, it will satisfy the worst case condition, and makes the programming easier by using a simple loop.

Listing 4.2 *LCD* Assembly Language Subroutines from *main.asm*

```
;  Initialize LCD
lcd_init:
            ldaa  #$ff
            staa  DDRK                    ; port K = output
            ldx   #init_codes             ; point to init. codes.
            pshb                          ; output instruction command.
            ldab  1,x+                    ; no. of codes
lcdi1:      ldaa  1,x+                    ; get next code
            jsr   write_instr_nibble      ; initiate write pulse.
            pshd
            ldd   #5
            jsr   ms_delay                ;delay 5 ms
            puld                          ; in reset sequence
            decb                          ; to simplify coding
            bne   lcdi1
            pulb
            rts

; Initialization codes for 4-bit mode
; uses only data in high nibble
init_codes:
            fcb   12          ; number of high nibbles
            fcb   $30         ; 1st reset code, must delay 4.1ms
            fcb   $30         ; 2nd reste code, must delay 100us
            ;  following 10 nibbles must delay 40us each after sending
            fcb   $30         ; 3rd reset code,
            fcb   $20         ; 4th reste code,
            fcb   $20         ; 4 bit mode, 2 line, 5X7 dot
            fcb   $80         ; 4 bit mode, 2 line, 5X7 dot
            fcb   $00         ; cursor incr, disable display shift
            fcb   $60         ; cursor incr, disable display shift
            fcb   $00         ; display on, cursor off, no blinking
            fcb   $C0         ; display on, cursor off, no blinking
            fcb   $00         ; clear display, set cursor to home pos
            fcb   $10         ; clear display, set cursor to home pos

; write instruction upper nibble
write_instr_nibble:
            anda  #$F0
            lsra
            lsra              ; nibble in PK2-PK5
            oraa  #$02        ; E = 1 in PK1; RS = 0 in PK0
```

Listing 4.2 (cont.) ***LCD*** **Assembly Language Subroutines from** ***main.asm***

```
          staa   PORTK
          ldy    #10
win       dey
          bne    win
          anda   #$FC          ; E = 0 in PK1; RS = 0 in PK0
          staa   PORTK
          rts

; write data upper nibble
write_data_nibble:
          anda   #$F0
          lsra
          lsra                 ; nibble in PK2-PK5
          oraa   #$03          ; E = 1 in PK1; RS = 1 in PK0
          staa   PORTK
          ldy    #10
wdn       dey
          bne    wdn
          anda   #$FD          ; E = 0 in PK1; RS = 1 in PK0
          staa   PORTK
          rts

; write instruction byte
write_instr_byte:
          psha
          jsr    write_instr_nibble
          pula
          asla
          asla
          asla
          asla
          jsr    write_instr_nibble
          rts

;write data byte
write_data_byte:
          psha
          jsr    write_data_nibble
          pula
          asla
          asla
          asla
          asla
          jsr    write_data_nibble
          rts

;   write instruction byte B to LCD
instr8:
          tba
          jsr    write_instr_byte
          ldd    #10
          jsr    ms_delay
          rts
```

Listing 4.2 (cont.) *LCD* Assembly Language Subroutines from *main.asm*

```
;   write data byte B to LCD
data8:
          tba
          jsr   write_data_byte
          ldd   #10
          jsr   ms_delay
          rts

;   set address to B
set_lcd_addr:
          orab  #$80
          tba
          jsr   write_instr_byte
          ldd   #10
          jsr   ms_delay
          rts

;   clear LCD
clear_lcd:
          ldaa  #$01
          jsr   write_instr_byte
          ldd   #10
          jsr   ms_delay
          rts

;   display hex value in B on LCD
hex2lcd:
          bsr   hex2asc       ;convert to ascii
          jsr   data8         ;display it
          rts

;       Hex to ascii subroutine
;       input: B = hex value
;       output: B = ascii value of lower nibble of input
hex2asc:
          andb  #$0f          ;mask upper nibble
          cmpb  #$9           ;if B > 9
          bls   ha1
          addb  #$37          ; add $37
          rts                 ;else
ha1       addb  #$30          ; add $30
          rts

;   display asciiz string on LCD
;   D -> asciiz string
type_lcd:
          pshx                          ;save X
          tfr   D,X                     ;X -> asciiz string
next_char ldaa  1,X+                    ;get next char
          beq   done                    ;if null, quit
          jsr   write_data_byte         ;else display it
          ldd   #10
          jsr   ms_delay
          bra   next_char               ;and repeat
done      pulx                          ;restore X
          rts
```

The subroutine *write_data_nibble* in Listing 4.2 is similar to the subroutine *write_instr_nibble* except that the value of *RS* (*PK*0) is set equal to 1. This satisfies the data write condition in Fig. 4.1. The subroutines *write_instr_byte* and *write_data_byte* will write an instruction byte and a data byte to the LCD by calling the subroutines *write_instr_nibble* and *write_data_nibble* twice, first by writing the upper nibble, and then shifting the lower nibble to the upper nibble position.

When the C function *instr*8(char *b*) in Table 4.2 is called, the subroutine *instr*8 in Listing 4.2 is executed. The LCD instruction byte *b* is passed in accumulator *B*. The first instruction in the subroutine *instr*8 transfers this value to accumulator *A*, and then the subroutine *write_instr_byte* is called followed by a 10 ms delay. This delay is necessary to allow the LCD to complete its operation. The C function *data*8(char *b*) in Table 4.2 behaves in a similar way by calling the subroutine *write_data_byte* in the subroutine *data*8.

When the C function *set_lcd_addr*(char *ad*) in Table 4.2 is called, the subroutine *set_lcd_addr* in Listing 4.2 is executed. The display address *ad* is passed in accumulator *B*. The first instruction in the subroutine *set_lcd_addr* ORs this value with $80, which sets bit DB7 in Table 4.1, thus executing the LCD instruction *Set the DD RAM address*. Similarly, the C function *clear_lcd*( ) in Table 4.2 executes the subroutine *clear_lcd* in Listing 4.2. This subroutine writes the instruction byte $01 to the LCD, which is the *Clear display* instruction in Table 4.1.

The function *hex2lcd*(char *c*) in Table 4.2 will display the hex digit passed in accumulator *B* on the LCD display. The subroutine *hex2lcd* in Listing 4.2 does this by executing the subroutine *hex2asc* followed by *data*8. Note that the algorithm for converting a hex digit (0 – F) to the corresponding ASCII code ($30 – $39, $41 – $46) is: *if* hex digit is greater than 9, *then* add $37, *else*, add $30.

Finally, when the C function *type_lcd*(char* *q*) in Table 4.2 is called, the subroutine *type_lcd* in Listing 4.2 is executed. The address *q* of the first byte in the string to display on the LCD is passed in accumulator *D* to the subroutine *type_lcd*. After transferring this address to the index register *X*, each character in the string is written to the LCD by calling the subroutine *write_data_byte*. This string is an ASCIIZ string, which means that the last byte in the string contains a 0. This is used to tell when to stop displaying characters on the LCD. Note the use of the instruction *ldaa 1,X+* to increment through the characters in the string using the post-increment, indexed addressing mode.

4.2 Binary Number to ASCII String Conversion

In this section we will show how a binary number can be converted to an ASCII string that can be displayed on an LCD display. To display the value of a 16-bit integer (*int*) or a 32-bit long integer (*long*) on a computer screen or LCD display it is first necessary to convert this integer to a string of ASCII characters. The steps used to create this string of ASCII characters are illustrated in Fig. 4.4. Note that the algorithm consists of dividing the number by the base, and converting the remainder to an ASCII character.

Figure 4.5 shows the algorithm for a routine called *sharps* which will convert a 32-bit double number to an ASCII string according to the steps in Fig 4.4. Note that the index *pad* starts at the end of the buffer, *buff*, and gets decremented before storing each ASCII code in the buffer. When the entire double number has been converted *buff*[*pad*] will contain the first ASCII character in the number string.

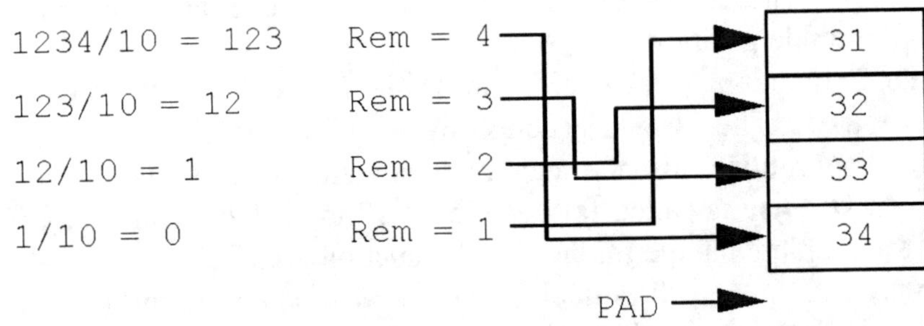

Figure 4.4 Steps for creating an ASCII number string

SHARPS: convert the double number *val32* to an ASCII string in a given *base*. The digits are converted least significant digit first and stored in memory starting at the end of the string. If the base is 16 then 0x37 must be added to the remainder to obtain the ASCII codes for A – F.

```
void sharps(long val32, int base) {
        unsigned char c;
        int rem;
        long quot;
        int pad;
        unsigned char buff[12];
        pad = 12;
        do{
          quot = val32/base;
          rem = val32 % base;
          if(rem > 9){
            rem = rem + 7;
          }
          c = 0x30 + rem;
          pad--;
          buff[pad] = c;
          val32 = quot;
        } while(quot != 0);
}
```

Figure 4.5 Algorithms to convert a double number to an ASCII string

Example 12 – Displaying Integers on the LCD

We have written assembly language routines called *sharp*, *sharps*, and *ddiv* to implement the algorithm in Fig. 4.5 and have included them in the *main.asm* file. We call the routine *sharp* in the two C function calls *write_int_lcd*(int *n*) and *write_long_lcd*(long *d*) shown in Table 4.3. The function *write_int_lcd(int)* will display a 16-bit integer, right-justified in a field of 5 digits. The function *write_long_lcd(long)* will display a 32-bit long integer, right-justified in a field of 10 digits. Listing 4.3 shows an example of using these functions. Try it.

Listing 4.3 Example 12

```
// Example 12: Writing INTs and LONGs to LCD
#include <hidef.h>      /* common defines and macros */
#include <mc9s12dg256.h>     /* derivative information */
#pragma LINK_INFO DERIVATIVE "mc9s12dg256b"

#include "main_asm.h" /* interface to the assembly module */

int val16;
long val32;

void main(void) {
  PLL_init();        // set system clock frequency to 24 MHz
  lcd_init();                    // enable lcd
  val16 = 54321;
  set_lcd_addr(0x00);            // display 5-digit int
  write_int_lcd(val16);
  val32 = 2345678123;
  set_lcd_addr(0x40);            // display 10-digit long
  write_long_lcd(val32);
  while(1) {
  }
}
```

Table 4.3 C function calls for writing integers to the LCD

C Function Call	Meaning
void **write_int_lcd**(int);	Display a 16-bit integer right-justified in a field of 5 digits
void **write_long_lcd**(long);	Display a 32-bit integer right-justified in a field of 10 digits

Under the Hood

The assembly language routines for the two integer display C functions shown in Table 4.3 are given in Listing 4.4. The constant *bas*10 is equal to the base 10. Four bytes are reserved for the 32-bit variable dnum, and 12 bytes are reserved for the buffer *buff*. The address *pad* is the first address after the end of the buffer *buff*.

When the C function *write_int_lcd*(int *n*) in Table 4.3 is called, the subroutine *write_int_lcd* in Listing 4.4 is executed. The integer *n* to display on the LCD is passed to the subroutine in accumulator *D*. After filling the buffer (called *pad*) with blanks (ASCII $20), the integer in *D* is stored in the lower two bytes of *dnum*, with the upper two bytes filled with zeros. Then the binary number to ASCII string conversion is performed by pointing to the address *pad* with index register *X*, and calling the subroutine *sharps*.

Listing 4.4 ***Write Integer*** **Assembly Language Subroutines from** ***main.asm***

```
bas10:          equ   10
dnum:           rmb   4
buff:           rmb   12
pad:            rmb   1

;   write an integer to the LCD display
;   write_int_lcd(int);
write_int_lcd:
                pshd                ;save D
                bsr   blank_pad     ;fill pad with blanks
                puld                ;get D
                std   dnum+2
                clr   dnum
                clr   dnum+1
                ldx   #pad
                jsr   sharps
                ldx   #pad-5
wl1             ldab  1,x+
                jsr   data8         ;display the ascii string
                cpx   #pad
                blo   wl1
                rts

;   write an integer to the LCD display
;   write_long_lcd(long);
write_long_lcd:
                pshd                ;save D
                pshx                ;save X
                bsr   blank_pad     ;fill pad with blanks
                pulx                ;get X
                puld                ;get D
                std   dnum+2
                stx   dnum
                ldx   #pad
                jsr   sharps
                ldx   #pad-10
wll1            ldab  1,x+
                jsr   data8         ;display the ascii string
                cpx   #pad
                blo   wll1
                rts

;   blank pad
blank_pad:
                ldx   #buff
                ldab  #13
                ldaa  #$20          ;ascii blank
bp1:            staa  1,x+
                decb
                bne   bp1
                rts
```

Listing 4.4 (cont.) ***Write Integer*** **Assembly Language Subroutines from *main.asm***

```
; double division  32 / 16 = 32  16 rem
; numH:numL / denom = quotH:qoutL  remL
; Y:D / X = Y:D  rem X    use EDIV twice  Y:D / X = Y   rem D
ddiv:
        pshd                ;save numL
        tfr   y,d           ;d = numH
        ldy   #0            ;0:numH / denom
        ediv                ;y = quotH, d = remH
        bcc   dd1           ;if div by 0
        puld
        ldd   #$FFFF        ;quot = $FFFFFFFF
        tfr   d,y
        tfr   d,x           ;rem = $FFFF
        rts
dd1     sty   2,-sp         ;save quotH on stack
        tfr   d,y           ;y = remH
        ldd   2,sp          ;d = numL
        ediv                ;remH:numL/denom  Y = quotL  D = remL
        tfr   d,x           ;x = remL
        tfr   y,d           ;d = quotL
        puly                ;y = quotH
        leas  2,sp          ;fix stack
        rts

;   Binary number to ASCII string conversion    x -> ascii buffer
sharp:
        pshd                ;save regs
        pshy
        pshx                ;save ptr
        ldy   dnum
        ldd   dnum+2
        ldx   #bas10
        jsr   ddiv          ;dnum/base rem in X
        sty   dnum          ; => dnum
        std   dnum+2
        tfr   x,d           ;b = rem
        cmpb  #9            ;if rem > 9
        bls   shp1
        addb  #7            ; add 7
shp1    addb  #$30          ;conv to ascii
        pulx                ;restore ptr
        stab  1,-x          ;store digit
        puly                ;restore regs
        puld
        rts

; input: x -> pad (ascii buffer)
; output: x -> first char in ascii string
sharps:
        bsr   sharp         ;do next digit
        ldd   dnum          ;repeat until
        bne   sharps        ; quot = 0
        ldd   dnum+2
        bne   sharps
        rts
```

The subroutine *sharps* in Listing 4.4 implements the algorithm shown in Fig. 4.5. It does this by repeatedly calling the subroutine *sharp* until the quotient left in dnum is equal to zero. The subroutine *sharp* converts the next digit in the conversion by dividing *dnum* by the base, converting the remainder to ASCII, and storing this ASCII code in the next location in the buffer, which is being pointed to by *X* (see Fig. 4.4). The division is carried out using the subroutine *ddiv* in Listing 4.4. This division divides a 32-bit double integer (long) by a 16-bit integer, leaving a 32-bit quotient and a 16-bit remainder. Recall from Appendix C that the unsigned division instruction *ediv* will divide the unsigned 32-bit number (Y:D) by the unsigned 16-bit number X, and store the unsigned 16-bit quotient in Y and the unsigned remainder in D. The problem is, that if the divisor in X is too small then the quotient won't fit in Y, but could be as large as 32 bits. We solve this problem by using ddiv, which calls ediv twice, first by dividing

$$(0:numH)/denom = quotH \quad remH$$

and then dividing

$$(remH:numL)/denom = quotL \quad remL$$

Note in the subroutine *ddiv* the value of *quotH*, which is in *Y* after the first *ediv* instruction, is saved on the stack using the instruction *sty* $2,-sp$. This pre-decrement, indexed addressing will first decrement the stack pointer, *sp*, by 2 and then store the value of *Y* in memory at the address pointed to by *sp*. At the beginning of the subroutine we pushed *D* on the stack so that we could access *numL* later. When we need it later, the value of *Y* is on the top of the stack, so we use the instruction *ldd* $2,sp$ to get the value of D from the stack. At the end of the subroutine, we pull the value of Y from the top of the stack (which contains the value of quotH), but the original value of D is still on the stack. We can't just remove this value from the stack by pulling it into D, because D now contains the correct value of quotL. We need to add 2 to the stack pointer so that it will be pointing to the subroutine return address. We can do this using the *load effective address* instruction *leas* 2,*sp*, which loads into the stack pointer, sp, the effective address of the addressing mode used. In this case, 2,*sp* adds 2 to *sp*, so the effective address is $sp+2$. Thus, the instruction *leas* 2,*sp* is equivalent to $sp = sp+2$.

After calling the subroutine *sharps* in the subroutine *write_int_lcd* in Listing 4.4, there will be a maximum of five ASCII codes stored at the end of the buffer, *buff*. This is because the largest 16-bit unsigned number is 65535. Thus, the first character in the number string will be located at $pad-5$. We load this address into *X* and then load each ASCII code in turn into *B* using the instruction *ldab* 1,*x*+, and then display it on the LCD using the subroutine *data8*. Note that *X* gets incremented by 1 each time we load *B* with the next ASCII code. We stop the loop when *X* is no longer less than *pad*. Note that we use the branching instruction *blo* rather than *bne*, because we want to compare *unsigned* addresses and *bne* would treat the addresses as signed numbers and could therefore not exit the loop properly.

When the C function *write_long_lcd*(long *d*) in Table 4.3 is called, the subroutine *write_long_lcd* in Listing 4.4 is executed. The 32-bit long integer *d* to display on the LCD is passed to the subroutine in *X*:*D*. That is, the high 16-bits of *d* are passed in index register *X*, and the low 16-bits of *d* are passed in accumulator *D*. The operation of this subroutine is very similar to the subroutine *write_int_lcd*, except that a maximum of 10 digits are stored in the buffer, *pad*, and displayed on the LCD. This is because the largest unsigned value that can be stored in 32 bits is 4294967295.

4.3 ASCII Number String to Binary Conversion

In this section we will show how an ASCII number string can be converted to a binary number and use it to enter binary numbers from a keyboard or keypad. As an example we will design a simple calculator.

When you enter a number (such as 34671) from the keyboard, the characters in the number are stored in a buffer as an ASCII string. If you were to type such a number on a hex keypad of the type we described in Section 3.2, then you could form an ASCII string by first converting each digit to an ASCII value using the function *hex2asc*(char) (see Table 4.2 and Listing 4.2). If we want to store the *value* of this number as an integer or long integer variable we must convert the ASCII number string to a binary number. After performing some calculation, it will be necessary to convert the binary number to an ASCII number string before the result can be displayed on the LCD display as shown in Section 4.2.

The decimal value 34671 can be represented as

$$
\begin{aligned}
34671 &= 3\times10^4 + 4\times10^3 + 6\times10^2 + 7\times10 + 1 \\
&= 1 + 10\Big(7 + 10\big(6 + 10\big(4 + 10(3)\big)\big)\Big)
\end{aligned} \tag{4.1}
$$

This form of representing a number can be used to convert an ASCII number string to a binary number using the algorithm *number* shown in Fig. 4.6. Note that this algorithm begins by setting the value of the long integer *dnum* to zero. It then starts with the first digit in the string, and adds it to the value of *dnum* times the base (10 in this case). This result becomes the new value of *dnum*. This process continues for each digit in the string.

```
long number(char*):
      char c;
      long dnum;
      dnum = 0;
      while(1){
        c = get_next_digit();
        if(digit_valid())
          dnum = dnum*base + c;
        else
          break;
      }
      return dnum;
```

Figure 4.6 Algorithm to convert an ASCII string to a double number

We have implemented this algorithm in assembly language, which you can call using the C function call shown in Table 10.1. In your C program you will have an ASCII number string stored in an array pointed to by the pointer *ptr*. This ASCII number string will be terminated by some character other than the ASCII codes for 0 – 9 (0x30 - 0x39). The algorithm continues to convert the ASCII string to a long integer as long as valid digits are in the string. It terminates with the first invalid digit. Thus, if you call *number(ptr)* it will return a long integer (32 bits) whose value is equal to the ASCII number string.

Table 4.4 C Function call for converting ASCII number string to binary

Function	Description
`long number(char* ptr);`	Return 32-bit binary number equal to ASCII number string

Under the Hood

When the C function *number*(char* *ptr*) shown in Table 4.4 is called, the subroutine *number* shown in Listing 4.5 is executed. When this subroutine is called, accumulator *D* contains the value of the pointer *ptr*, i.e., it contains the address of the first ASCII character in the ASCII number string. This value is transferred to index register *Y*. The value of the base, 10, is then stored in the 16-bit word, *bas*, which is located just before the 32-bit double word, *dnum*, in memory. Index register *X* points to *bas*, and the contents of dnum is initialized to zero as shown in Fig. 4.7.

Listing 4.5 *number* Assembly Language Subroutines from *main.asm*

```
bas:    rmb   2
dnum:   rmb   4

; input: A = ascii code of char
; output: if carry=0 A=valid hex value of char
;         if carry=1 A=invalid char in current base
;
digit:
        pshb
        psha
        suba  #$30          ;ascii codes < 30
        blo   dgt2          ; are invalid
        cmpa  #9            ;char between
        bls   dgt1          ; 9 and A
        cmpa  #17           ; are invalid
        blo   dgt2          ;fill gap
        suba  #7            ; between 9&A
dgt1    cmpa  bas+1         ;digit must be
        bhs   dgt2          ; < base
        andcc #$FE          ;clear carry (valid)
        pulb                ;pop old A
        pulb                ;restore B
        rts
dgt2    pula                ;restore A
        pulb                ;restore B
        orcc  #$01          ;set carry (invalid)
        rts
```

Listing 4.5 (cont.) ***number*** **Assembly Language Subroutines from *main.asm***

```
; input:  D -> ascii number string buffer
; output: X:D is long int number
number:
        pshy
        tfr   d,y           ;y -> kbuf
        ldd   #bas10
        std   bas           ;base = 10
        ldx   #bas          ;x -> base
        ldd   #0
        std   2,x           ;clear dnum
        std   4,x
num1    ldaa  1,y+          ;get next digit
        jsr   digit         ;conv to value
        bcs   num2
        jsr   dumul         ;mult dnum by base
        adda  5,x           ;add digit value
        staa  5,x
        ldaa  4,x
        adca  #0
        staa  4,x
        ldaa  3,x
        adca  #0
        staa  3,x
        ldaa  2,x
        adca  #0
        staa  2,x
        bra   num1          ;do until invalid digit
num2    ldx   dnum
        ldd   dnum+2        ; X:D = dnum
        puly
        rts

; 32 x 16 = 32 unsigned multiply
; A:B x C = pH:pL   A x C = ACH:ACL  (drop ACH)    B x C = BCH:BCL
; pL= BCL       pH = ALC + BCH
; C     rmb   2        A    rmb   2           B    rmb   2

dumul:
        psha                ;save A
        pshy                ;save Y
        ldd   0,x           ;D = C
        ldy   2,x           ;Y = A
        emul                ;Y = ACH, D = ACL
        std   2,x           ;save ACL
        ldd   0,x           ;D = C
        ldy   4,x           ;Y = B
        emul                ;Y = BCH, D = BCL
        std   4,x           ;save pL = BCL
        tfr   y,d           ;D = BCH
        addd  2,x           ;D = BCH+ACL = pH
        std   2,x           ;save pH
        puly                ;restore Y
        pula                ;restore A
        rts
```

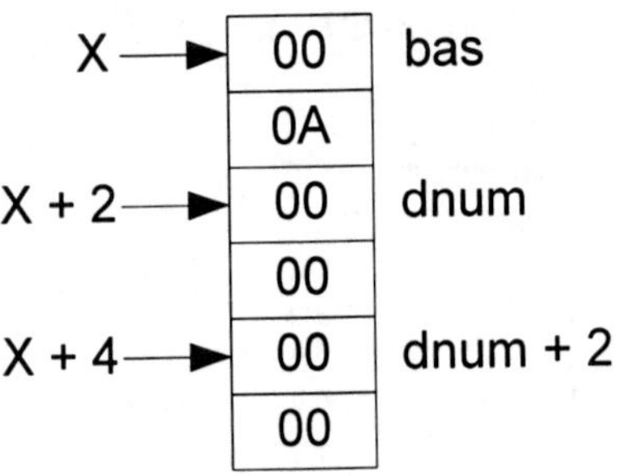

Figure 4.7
Layout of variables *bas* and *dnum*

In the *num1* loop in the subroutine *number* in Listing 4.5, the next ASCII code pointed to by *Y* is loaded into accumulator *A*, and then the subroutine *digit* is called. The *digit* subroutine checks to see if the ASCII code is a valid digit in the current base. This subroutine will work for both decimal and hex digits, even though we have set the base to 10 in *main.asm*. If the ASCII code is valid, the subroutine *digit* will return the valid hex value (0 – 9, A – F) in accumulator *A* with the carry flag, *C*, cleared to zero. If the ASCII code is *not* a valid digit in the current base, the subroutine *digit* will return an invalid character in accumulator *A* with the carry flag, *C*, set to 1. The subroutine *number* will use this carry flag to tell when to exit the *num1* loop. If the digit was valid, then the subroutine *dumul* is called, which multiplies the 32-bit *dnum* by the 16-bit base in *bas* (see Fig. 4.7). The digit value in accumulator *A* is then added to the resulting product in *dnum*. Note that when we add *A* to *dnum*+3 ($X+5$), there may be a carry, which could propagate to all of the higher bytes in *dnum*. We take care of this by adding with carry (*adca*) the value 0.

Example 13 – Calculator

As an example of using the conversion routine, *number*(*ptr*), we will write a C program for a simple calculator as shown in Listing 4.6. Note in Listing 4.6, we define a character array called *kbuf* that contains room for 12 characters. A 32-bit integer can have a maximum of 10 decimal digits (largest unsigned value is 4,294,967,295). We must leave space for a terminating invalid character and we might want to include a negative sign, so we will reserve 12 bytes for *kbuf*.

Listing 4.6 Example 13

```
// Example 13: Calculator with ASCII string to number conversion
#include <hidef.h>      /* common defines and macros */
#include <mc9s12dg256.h>     /* derivative information */
#pragma LINK_INFO DERIVATIVE "mc9s12dg256b"
#include "main_asm.h" /* interface to the assembly module */

void main(void) {
  long op1, op2;                 // 32-bit operands
  char* ptr;                     // pointer to keypad buffer
  char* blanks;
  char  kbuf[12];                // keypad buffer
  char  c, a;
  int  i;
  ptr = kbuf;
  blanks = "            ";
```

Listing 4.6 (cont.) Example 13

```
PLL_init();                     // set system clock frequency to 24 MHz
  lcd_init();                   // enable lcd
  keypad_enable();              // enable keypad
  set_lcd_addr(0x00);           // display on 1st line
  i = 0;                        // kbuf index = 0
  while(1) {
    c = getkey();               // read keypad
    a = hex2asc(c);             // convert to ascii
    kbuf[i] = a;                //   and store in kbuf
    if(c < 10){                 // if 0 - 9
      data8(a);                 //   display on LCD
      wait_keyup();             //   wait to release key
      i++;                      // inc index
    } else {
      switch(c){
        case 0xE:                     // if enter (*) key
          op1 = number(ptr);          // convert to binary
          set_lcd_addr(0x40);         // display on 2nd line
          write_long_lcd(op1);
          set_lcd_addr(0x00);         // clear 1st line
          type_lcd(blanks);
          wait_keyup();               // wait to release key
          i = 0;                      // reset kbuf index
          set_lcd_addr(0x00);         // display on 1st line
          break;
        case 0xA:                     // if key A
          op2 = number(ptr);          // convert to binary
          op1 = op1 + op2;            // compute sum
          set_lcd_addr(0x40);         // display on 2nd line
          write_long_lcd(op1);
          set_lcd_addr(0x00);         // clear 1st line
          type_lcd(blanks);
          wait_keyup();               // wait to release key
          i = 0;                      // reset kbuf index
          set_lcd_addr(0x00);         // display on 1st line
          break;
        case 0xF:                     // if clear (#) key
          clear_lcd();                // clear lcd display
          wait_keyup();               // wait to release key
          i = 0;                      // reset kbuf index
          break;
        default:
          break;
      }
    }
  }
}
```

We define a pointer called *ptr* to this keypad buffer using the statement

```
char* ptr;
```

and then set this pointer to the address of the first character in *kbuf* using the statement

```
ptr = kbuf;
```

After initializing the LCD and enabling the keypad we enter an infinite *while* loop. We first wait for a key on the keypad to be pressed (using *getkey*( ))and then return the value in *c*. This hex value is converted to ASCII using *hex2asc*( ) and the result (in *a*) is stored at the next location in *kbuf*. If the hex value *c* read from the keypad was less than 10 (i.e. 0 – 9), then it is displayed on the LCD using *data8*(*a*) and the program waits for you to lift your finger from the keypad. The *kbuf* index *i* is then incremented and you can continue to type in additional digits that will be displayed on the LCD and the ASCII values stored in *kbuf*.

If you type a key other than 0 – 9 (i.e. A – F) then the *else* part of the *if* statement will be executed. This contains the C *switch* statement, which behaves like a *case* statement that executes one of several possible cases depending on the value of the *switch* expression, in this case the value of the hex value *c*. Note that the last statement in each of the cases is a *break* statement that terminates the *switch* statement.

If *c* is equal to 0xE (i.e. you pressed the E or * key) then the first case is executed. The first statement in this case is

```
op1 = number(ptr);
```

which will convert the ASCII string that you typed from the keypad to the long integer *op*1. Note that the ASCII value for E (0x45) was stored in *kbuf* when you pressed *E* and became the invalid digit that wasn't between 0 and 9. The next two statements will write this long integer, right-justified in a field of 10, on the second line. The following two statements will clear the first line. After waiting for you to lift your finger, the program then resets the *kbuf* index *i* to zero, sets the LCD address to the beginning of the first line, and then executes a *break* statement that will break out of the *switch* statement.

After typing in one number and entering it by pressing *E*, you can type in another number, but instead of pressing *E* you should press *A* this time, which will add the two numbers together and display the sum.

The second case in the *switch* statement will execute if you press the *A* key. It begins by displaying *op*1 again on line two. The first statement will convert the second number you typed to binary and store the result in *op*2. Then the sum of *op*1 and *op*2 is stored back in *op*1 and displayed on the second line. The first line is erased by overwriting it with blanks and then the program waits for you to lift your finger.

The LCD address is reset to the beginning of the first line and you can now enter another number. If you press *A* again, the old sum will be added to your third number, and the new sum will be displayed on the second line. You can continue to add numbers in this fashion. Pressing the F (or #) key will clear the display. Try it.

Note that when you call *lcd_init*( ), the cursor is not displayed. This was useful when we just want to display text or numbers as in Examples 11 and 12. However, in the case of the calculator, it would be useful to display a cursor. You can do this by adding the C statement *instr8*(0x0F), which will display a blinking cursor, or *instr8*(0x0E), which will display a non-blinking cursor (see Table 4.1). Try it.

PROBLEMS

4.1 Modify Listing 4.1 to display your name centered on the first two rows.

4.2 Modify Listing 4.1 to display the digits 0 – 9 in a row using a *for* loop.

4.3 Modify Listing 4.1 to display the following figure made of $ signs centered on the display.

```
$$$$$$
$    $
```

4.4 Modify Listing 4.3 to display the 16-bit integer 123 in the center of the second row of the LCD display. Remember that *write_int_lcd(int)* will display leading blanks in a field of 5.

4.5 Modify Listing 4.3 to display the 32-bit long integer 1234567 in the center of the first row of the LCD display. Remember that *write_long_lcd(long)* will display leading blanks in a field of 10.

4.6 The algorithm shown in Fig. 4.5 will work for any base. If you want to display hex values on the LCD you can open the file *main.asm* and change the statement

```
bas10:   equ   10
```

to

```
bas10:   equ   16
```

Then, if you re-compile and re-run the program shown in Listing 4.3 the value 54321 will be displayed as its hex equivalent D431 and the value 2345678123 will be displayed as its hex equivalent 8BD0352B. Try it. Don't forget to change the value of *bas10* back to 10.

4.7 Modify Listing 4.6 to

a) display the result of subtracting the second number from the first number when you press the B key.
b) display the result of multiplying two numbers when you press the C key.
c) display the result of dividing the second number into the first number when you press the D key.

Chapter 5

Interrupts

In this chapter we will introduce the idea of interrupts and show how to use the real-time interrupt to create a count variable that increments every 10 milliseconds. We will use this count variable to blink a 7-segment display, implement a traffic light controller, and blink the Morse code SOS.

5.1 Hardware Interrupts

Hardware interrupts allow external events to interrupt the normal execution of a program and instead execute an interrupt service routine, after which the execution of the original program picks up where it left off. The addresses of the interrupt service routines are called *interrupt vectors*. These interrupt vectors are stored in a special table in memory. When a particular interrupt occurs, the address of the interrupt service routine is looked up in the interrupt vector table and control is transferred to that address.

There are over 50 different sources of interrupts on a MC9S12DG256 and their interrupt vectors are stored in memory between the hex addresses $FF80 and $FFFF. The most important interrupt vector is the reset vector that is located at addresses $FFFE and $FFFF. When the *RESET* pin on an HCS12 microcontroller goes low, normal microprocessor functions are suspended. When this pin returns high the microprocessor will disable hardware interrupts and start executing instructions starting at the address stored at $FFFE-$FFFF. HCS12 microcontrollers have a power-on reset (POR) circuit that causes the reset signal to be asserted internally after power (5 volts) has been applied to the processor.

It is necessary for addresses $FFFE-$FFFF to be in some type of non-volatile memory (ROM, EPROM, or Flash memory) so that a valid reset vector will be at that address. Of course, the memory it points to must also be in non-volatile memory so that some meaningful code will be executed when you turn on the processor. In the DRAGON12-Plus-USB, the memory between $F800 and $FFFF is in protected flash memory and contains the Serial Monitor in addition to the table of interrupt vectors.[1] The reset vector at $FFFE - $FFFF contains the address $F800 which is the beginning of the Serial Monitor. If the left slide switch SW7 on the DRAGON12-Plus-USB is set to LOAD, then when you press the reset button, the Serial Monitor at $F800 will be executed. When you download your program to the flash memory using CodeWarrior the Serial Monitor maps the interrupt vector table between $FF80 - $FFFF to unprotected flash memory between $F780 - $F7FF and stores the starting address of your program at $F7FE - $F7FF.

[1] You must order the DRAGON12-Plus-USB with the Serial Monitor included; otherwise, by default, it comes with a Debug12 monitor installed.

If the left slide switch SW7 is set to RUN, then when you press the reset button your program whose address is at $F7FE - $F7FF will be executed.

A hardware interrupt is an unexpected event that can occur at any time during the execution of a program. It might result from pressing a key, having a byte received in the SCI port, or when some timer has timed out. When a hardware interrupt occurs, a series of events takes place. The current instruction is completed, and then the programming registers (see Fig. B.1 in Appendix B) are pushed on the stack. The return address will be the value in the program counter; i.e., the address of the instruction following the one being executed when the interrupt occurs. This will be the address returned to after the interrupt service routine is executed. After all registers in Fig. B.1 are pushed on the stack, both the *I* bit and the *X* bit in the condition code register *CCR* are set This means that another interrupt cannot get serviced during the execution of the interrupt service routine. The address of the interrupt service routine is loaded from the interrupt vector table into the program counter so that the first instruction in the interrupt service routine will be executed. The last instruction of an interrupt service routine is the *RTI* instruction, which will pop the registers shown in Fig. B.1 off the stack, including the *CCR* register which will have its *I* bit cleared. At that point a new interrupt can occur including one that might have occurred during the processing of the previous interrupt.

A list of all interrupt sources available on the MC9S12DG256 is given in Table D.1 in Appendix D. Note that each interrupt source has a vector number (between 0 and 57) associated with it. The address of the interrupt vector for each interrupt source is also shown in Table D.1.

5.2 Real-Time Interrupts

A *real-time interrupt* produces an interrupt at periodic intervals. To use an interrupt, it is first necessary to write an interrupt service routine that will be executed when the interrupt occurs. To write a real-time interrupt routine in C and tell it where the interrupt vector is stored you would use the following form

```
void interrupt 7 handler(){
  << your C code goes here >>
}
```

The word *interrupt* tells the C compiler that this is an interrupt service routine and the number 7 is the interrupt vector number from Table D.1. In this case the 7 is the vector number for a *real-time interrupt* with the interrupt vector stored in addresses $FFF0 - $FFF1. The name of the interrupt service routine is *handler*( ). The compiler will automatically assign the address of this interrupt routine to the proper interrupt vector address. When using the Serial Monitor and CodeWarrior, these interrupt vector addresses have been mapped to $F780 - $F7FF. Thus, you will find the address of the real-time interrupt service routine *handler*( ) at addresses $F7F0 - $F7F1.

We have written three assembly language routines for real-time interrupts that can be called using the C functions shown in Table 5.1. The routine *RTI_init*( ) enables a real-time interrupt that produces an interrupt every 10.24 milliseconds. When an interrupt occurs, it sets a flag in one of the RTI registers. You must clear this flag in the interrupt service routine so as not to cause another interrupt immediately upon leaving the interrupt service routine. The C function *clear_RTI_flag*( ) will do this. The C function *RTI_disable*( ) will disable real-time interrupts. We will give three examples of using the real-time interrupt.

Table 5.1 C Function calls for the real-time interrupt

Function	Description
`void RTI_init(void);`	Initialize real-time interrupts every 10.24 ms
`void clear_RTI_flag(void)`	Clear the RTI flag
`void RTI_disable(void)`	Disable real-time interrupts

Example 14 – Blinking 7-Segment Display

An example of using the real-time interrupt in a C program is shown in Listing 5.1. In this program, two global variables, *ticks* and *ticks*0, are defined as unsigned short (16-bit) integers. The interrupt service routine is

```
// RTI Interrupt Service Routine
void interrupt 7 handler(){
  ticks++;
  clear_RTI_flag();
}
```

which just increments the variable *ticks* every 10.24 ms and then clears the RTI flag.

Note in Listing 5.1 we have defined the function *half_second_delay*( ) that first reads the current value of *ticks* (that is being incremented every 10.24 ms by the real-time interrupt routine) and stores this value in *ticks*0. It then stays in the *while* loop as long as (*ticks* – *ticks*0) is less than 49. Thus, the *while* loop will exit after 49 interrupts which will take 49 x 10.24 ms = 0.502 seconds. Remember that *ticks* is being incremented in the background by the real-time interrupt routine. Once you enable this real-time interrupt by calling *RTI_init*( ), the value of *ticks* gets incremented every 10.24 ms. The main program in Listing 5.1 blinks the digit 8 on the 7-segment display on and off every second.

Under the Hood

The registers associated with real-time interrupts are shown in Fig. 5.1. The *RTICTR* register determines the timeout period. In the formula for the timeout period in Fig. 5.1, the three bits *RTR*[6:4] can have values from 1 – 7, and the four bits *RTR*[3:0] can have values from 0 – 15. This means that the numerator in the *timeout_period* formula can range from 1×2^{10} to 16×2^{16}. The value of *OSCCLK* in the formula is the oscillator, or crystal, clock frequency, which is 8 MHz on the DRAGON12-Plus-USB. To set the timeout period to 10.24 ms, you would store the hex value $54 in *RTICTR* on the DRAGON12-Plus-USB. The following is the calculation.

$$timeout\_period = 5\times2^{14}/8\times10^{6} = 0.01024 \text{ sec.}$$

To enable real-time interrupts, you would write a 1 to bit 7 (*RTIE*) of the *CRGINT* register. The assembly language instruction

```
bset  CRGINT, #$80
```

will do this. To disable real-time interrupts, you would write a 0 to bit 7 (*RTIE*) of the *CRGINT* register. The assembly language instruction to do this is

```
bclr  CRGINT, #$80
```

When a real-time interrupt times out, bit 7 (*RTIF*) in the *CRGFLG* register gets set to 1. If real-time interrupts have been enabled by setting bit 7 in the *CRGINT* register, then a real-time interrupt will occur. To clear the *RTIF* bit, you must write a 1 to this bit. This may seem strange, but this is the way that most flags are cleared. Writing a 0 to a flag bit has no effect. Therefore, to clear the flag in bit 7 of the *CRGFLG* register, you could store the hex value $80 in this register using the statement

```
movb  #$80, CRGFLG
```

Note that all of the zeros that are written to the other bits in the *CRGFLG* register will have no effect on the flags that may be set in these other bits.

Listing 5.1 Example 14a – DRAGON12-Plus-USB

```
// Example 14a: Real-time interrupt
#include <hidef.h>        /* common defines and macros */
#include <mc9s12dg256.h>     /* derivative information */
#pragma LINK_INFO DERIVATIVE "mc9s12dg256b"
#include "main_asm.h" /* interface to the assembly module */
void half_sec_delay(void);
unsigned short ticks, ticks0; // RTI interrupt counts
// RTI Interrupt Service Routine
void interrupt 7 handler(){
  ticks++;
  clear_RTI_flag();
}

void main(void) {
  PLL_init();               // set system clock frequency to 24 MHz
  seg7_enable();            // enable 7-segment displays
  led_disable();            // disable LEDs
  RTI_init();
  while(1) {
    seg7dec(8,3);           //  display 8 on 7seg display #3
    half_sec_delay();
    seg7s_off();            //  turn off 7seg display
    half_sec_delay();
  }
}

void half_sec_delay(void){     // delay for 0.5 seconds
  ticks0 = ticks;
  while((ticks-ticks0)<49) {
  }
}
```

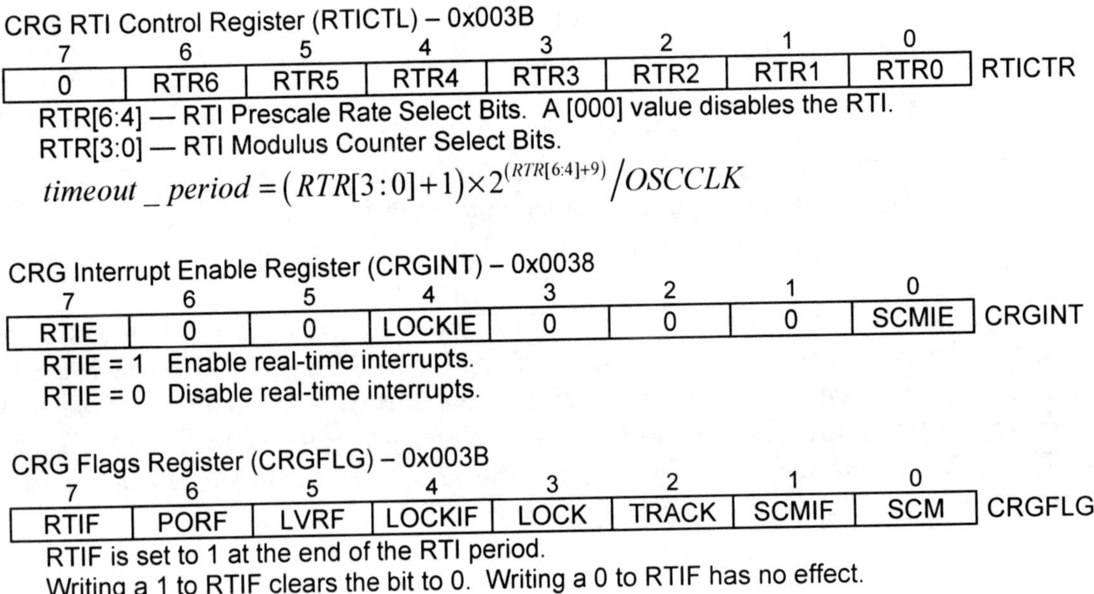

Figure 5.1 Registers associated with real-time interrupts

Listing 5.2 shows the assembly language subroutines that correspond to the three C function calls shown in Table 5.1. Note that the first instruction, *sei*, in the subroutine *RTI_init* disables hardware interrupts by setting the I-bit in the condition code register (*CCR*) to 1. Hardware interrupts are then enabled at the end of this subroutine by clearing this I-bit in the *CCR* using the instruction *cli*. It is always a safe procedure to disable interrupts while setting up a hardware interrupt, and then enable hardware interrupts using *cli* after all setup has occurred.

Listing 5.2 *RTI* Assembly Language Subroutines from *main.asm*

```
;    Real-time interrupt
;    RTI_init();
RTI_init:
        sei                           ;disable interrupts
        movb  #$54, RTICTL            ;set rti to 10.24 ms
        bset  CRGINT, #$80            ;enable rti
        cli                           ;enable interrupts
        rts

;    clear_RTI_flag();
clear_RTI_flag:
        movb  #$80, CRGFLG            ;clear rti flag
        rts

;    disable RTI
;    RTI_disable():
RTI_disable:
        bclr  CRGINT, #$80            ;disable rti
        rts
```

Writing Your Own Interrupt Service Routines (ISR) in *main.asm*

In Listing 5.1, we used the C statements

```
// RTI Interrupt Service Routine
void interrupt 7 handler(){
  ticks++;
  clear_RTI_flag();
}
```

to write the interrupt service routine. When these statements are compiled, the address of the compiled interrupt service routine, called *handler*, is automatically stored in the flash memory address, $F7F0, which is the mapped interrupt vector address of the RTI type 7 interrupt, $FFF0, which is in protected memory.

It is sometimes useful to be able to write the interrupt service routine in assembly language in the file *main.asm*. When you do this, the address of your interrupt service routine must end up in the mapped interrupt vector table in flash. For the RTI interrupt, this will be at $F7F0. The way to do this is to include the following statements at the end of the *main.asm* file.

```
org $FFF0
dc.w rti_intser
```

where *rti_intser* is the name of your assembly language interrupt service routine. Note that these statements will try to store the address of *rti_intser* at the address $FFF0, which is the real interrupt vector location for an RTI interrupt from the table in Appendix D, but is in protected memory. CodeWarrior will automatically map this address to $F7F0 and store the address of *rti_intser* at this flash memory location. Listing 5.3 shows an example that illustrates this process.

The interrupt service routine, *rti_intser*, in Listing 5.3 will blink an 8 on the right-most 7-segment display on the DRAGON12-Plus-USB once per second. The 16-bit variable *ticks* must be defined in the *MY_EXTENDED_RAM* section of *main.asm*. The interrupt service routine, *rti_intser*, and the subroutine, *blink_rti*, should be placed following *asm_main*: in the *MyCode* section.

When the interrupt service routine, *rti_intser*, is executed (once every 10.24 ms), the value of *ticks* is decremented by 1. If the result is equal to zero, then the state of the segments on the 7-segment display is toggled by complementing Port B on the DRAGON12-Plus-USB. The value of *ticks* is then reset to *ticks_max*, which is 49. If the result of decrementing *ticks* at the beginning of *rti_intser*, is not zero, then the *RTIF* flag is cleared before returning from the ISR.

To run this program, the subroutine *blink_rti* is called from the C program in Listing 5.4 using the function call *blink_rti*( ). Note that after calling this function, the main program just waits forever while the interrupt service routine, *rti_intser*, does all the work in the background.

The subroutine *blink_rti* in Listing 5.3 initializes the appropriate ports, sets the initial value of ticks to 1 (so a blink will occur on the first interrupt), and then enables RTI and hardware interrupts. Once this subroutine is called, an RTI interrupt will occur every 10.24

ms, and the interrupt service routine, *rti_intser*, will do all of the work in blinking the 7-segment display.

Listing 5.3 DRAGON12-Plus-USB ISR in *main.asm*

```
MY_EXTENDED_RAM: SECTION

ticks_max:   equ 49
ticks:       rmb 2

MyCode:      SECTION
asm_main:

rti_intser:
          ldd   ticks
          subd  #1
          std   ticks                 ;decrement ticks
          bne   rt1                   ;if ticks = 0
          com   PORTB                 ;  toggle display
          movw  #ticks_max,ticks      ;  reset ticks to 49
rt1:      movb  #$80,CRGFLG           ;clear rtif
          rti

blink_rti:
          sei                         ;disable interrupts
          movb  #$FF,DDRB             ;port B outputs
          movb  #$FF,DDRP             ;port P outputs
          movb  #$FF,DDRJ             ;port J outputs
          movw  #1,ticks              ;ticks = 1
          bset  PTJ,$02               ;disable leds
          movb  #$07,PTP              ;enable digit 3
          clr   PORTB                 ;turn 7seg off
          movb  #$54,RTICTL           ;set rti to 10.24 ms
          bset  CRGINT,#$80           ;enable rti
          cli                         ;enable interrupts
          rts

;at the end of main.asm add
          org $FFF0
          dc.w rti_intser

          end
```

Listing 5.4 Example 14b – Calling blink_rti( )

```
// Example 14b: Turn on every other segment on 7-seg display
#include <hidef.h>        /* common defines and macros */
#include <mc9s12dg256.h>     /* derivative information */
#pragma LINK_INFO DERIVATIVE "mc9s12dg256b"
#include "main_asm.h" /* interface to the assembly module */

void main(void) {
  PLL_init();            // set system clock frequency to 24 MHz
  blink_rti();           // blink 7seg display using rti
  while(1) {}          /* wait forever */
}
```

Example 15 – Interrupt-Driven Traffic Light

It is often useful to be able to sequence through an arbitrary number of states, staying in each state an arbitrary amount of time. For example, consider the set of traffic lights shown in Fig. 5.2. The lights are assumed to be at a four-way intersection with one street going north-south and the other road going east-west.

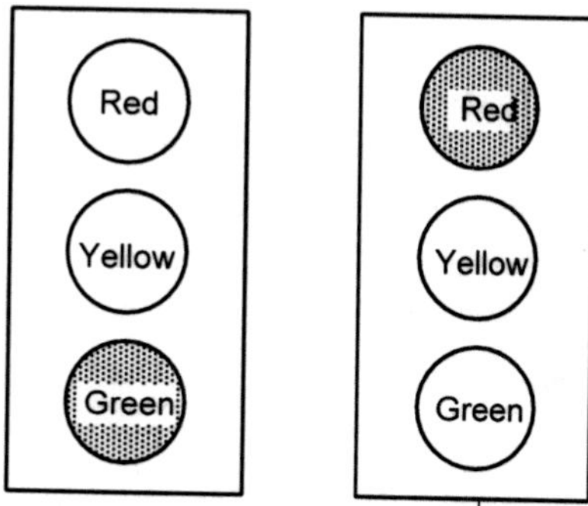

Figure 5.2 Six colored LEDs can represent a set of traffic lights

To simulate these traffic lights you could plug colored LEDs into the protoboard and connect them to Port M as shown in Fig. 5.3. When the pin output is low the output of the inverter is high (+5 volts) and no current can flow through the LED and therefore no light will be emitted. If you bring the port output pin high, the output of the inverter goes low (assume about 0.2 volts) and current will flow from the +5 volt power supply through the resistor *R* and the LED. The resistor is used to limit the amount of current that flows through the LED. A typical current would be 15 milliamps or 15 x 10^{-3} amps. Using Ohm's law we can compute the resistor size needed as shown in Fig. 5.3. You could, for example, connect the east-west lights to *PM0–PM2* and the north-south lights to *PM3–PM5*.

We can use real-time interrupts (see Example 14) to continually cycle through the six states shown in Table 5.2. Note that when the light on one street is red and the light on the other street is green, we will delay 5 seconds. (Assume very fast cars so that you won't have to wait all day!) We will delay 1 second on a yellow-red or red-red combination.

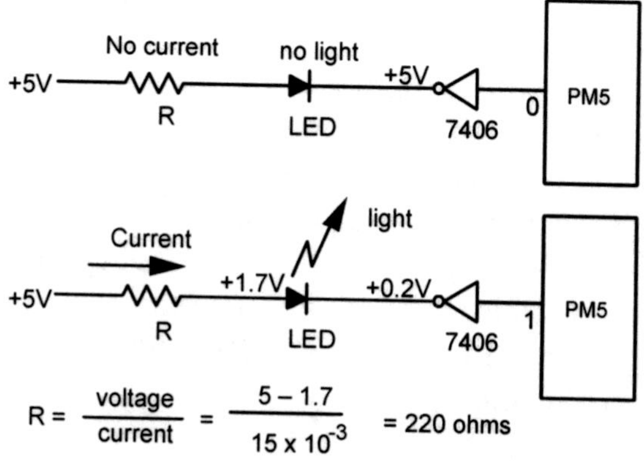

Figure 5.3 Turning on an LED by storing a 1 in PM5

Table 5.2 Traffic Light States

State	North - South	East - West	Delay (sec.)
0	Green	Red	5
1	Yellow	Red	1
2	Red	Red	1
3	Red	Green	5
4	Red	Yellow	1
5	Red	Red	1

The idea is to use interrupts so that the entire operation will be carried out in the background with no need for the CPU to intervene to keep the traffic lights going. The same idea can be used to cycle through any set of states, which you can change by writing to an output port.

We begin by defining two arrays that represent the six states shown in Table 5.2. These arrays are called *lights*[ ] and *delay*[ ] in the program shown in Listing 5.5. The first byte in the array *lights*[ ] is the hex value 0x0C. This is the binary value 00001100 which will be written out to Port M. The bits in Port M will be assigned to the "colored" LEDs according to the bit positions --RYGRYG. Thus the hex value 0x0C will turn on the green north-south light and the red east-west light.

The first entry in the array *delay*[ ] is the delay time measured in *ticks*. A tick will be the time between interrupts, which is 10.24 ms. Therefore, a delay of 1 second will be 488 ticks and a delay of 5 seconds will be 98 ticks. The rest of the entries in the *lights*[ ] array store the values to be written to Port M for each state, and the corresponding entries in the *delay*[ ] array contain the delay time for that state.

The variable *dtime* defined at the beginning of the program in Listing 5.5 is used to hold the number of *ticks* before a timeout that will move to the next state. This value will be initialized to 1 so that a state change will occur on the first interrupt. The variable *ix* will be the index into the states.

The interrupt service routine, *handler()*, shown in Listing 5.5 starts by decrementing the value of *dtime*. If the decremented value is not zero then the *IF* statement is skipped and the *RTIF* flag is cleared. If the decremented value of *dtime* is equal to zero in the interrupt service routine, then the *IF* statement is executed. The first statement turns on the next set of lights by writing the value of *lights*[*ix*] to Port M. The next statement stores the corresponding delay time for that state in *dtime*. The state index *ix* is then incremented and when it equals the number of states (6) it is reset to zero.

In the main program, Port M is set as output, the real-time interrupts are enabled, *ix* is set to 0, and *dtime* is set to 1. The main program then just enters an infinite *while* loop. The interrupt routine takes care of changing the traffic lights on schedule. The main program could go on and do useful things while the traffic light is changing all on its own!

Listing 5.6 is a version of this traffic lights program that will run directly on the DRAGON12-Plus-USB using its red LEDs as the traffic lights. You will have to pretend that some of them are yellow and green!

Listing 5.5 Example 15a

```
//  Example 15a  Traffic Lights
#include <hidef.h>      /* common defines and macros */
#include <mc9s12dg256.h>     /* derivative information */
#pragma LINK_INFO DERIVATIVE "mc9s12dg256b"

#include "main_asm.h" /* interface to the assembly module */

int dtime;                      // delay time
int ix;                         // index into states
const int numstates = 6;
const char lights[] = {         // --RYGRYG
     0x0C,                      // 00001100
     0x14,                      // 00010100
     0x24,                      // 00100100
     0x21,                      // 00100001
     0x22,                      // 00100010
     0x24,              // 00100100
};
const int delay[] = {
     488,                       // 5 sec delay
     98,                // 1 sec delay
     98,                        // 1 sec delay
     488,                       // 5 sec delay
     98,                        // 1 sec delay
     98,                        // 1 sec delay
};

void interrupt 7 handler(){
  dtime--;
  if(dtime == 0){
    PTM = lights[ix];          // turn on next lights
    dtime = delay[ix];         // get next delay time
    ix++;                      // increment index
    if(ix == numstates){       // after going through all states
      ix = 0;                  //  reset index to 0
    }
  }
  clear_RTI_flag();
}

void main(void) {
  PLL_init();            // set system clock frequency to 24 MHz
  DDRM = 0xFF;           // all bits of Port M are outputs
  RTI_init();            // initialize RTI to 10.24 ms interrupts
  ix = 0;                       // reset index into states
  dtime = 1;                    // start traffic light right away
  while(1) {             // do nothing while traffic light goes
  }
}
```

Listing 5.6 Example 15b – DRAGON12-Plus-USB

```
//  Example 15b  Traffic Lights
#include <hidef.h>      /* common defines and macros */
#include <mc9s12dg256.h>     /* derivative information */
#pragma LINK_INFO DERIVATIVE "mc9s12dg256b"
#include "main_asm.h" /* interface to the assembly module */

int dtime;                    // delay time
int ix;                       // index into states
const int numstates = 6;
const char leds[] = { // --RYGRYG
     0x0C,                    // 00001100
     0x14,                    // 00010100
     0x24,                    // 00100100
     0x21,                    // 00100001
     0x22,                    // 00100010
     0x24,              // 00100100
};
const int delay[] = {
     488,                     // 5 sec delay
     98,                // 1 sec delay
     98,                      // 1 sec delay
     488,                     // 5 sec delay
     98,                      // 1 sec delay
     98,                      // 1 sec delay
};

void interrupt 7 handler(){
  dtime--;
  if(dtime == 0){
    leds_on(leds[ix]);              // turn on next lights
    dtime = delay[ix];        // get next delay time
    ix++;                     // increment index
    if(ix == numstates){      // after going through all states
      ix = 0;                 //  reset index to 0
    }
  }
  clear_RTI_flag();
}

void main(void) {
  PLL_init();           // set system clock frequency to 24 MHz
  led_enable();               // enable LEDs
  seg7_disable();             // disable 7-segment displays
  RTI_init();           // initialize RTI to 10.24 ms interrupts
  ix = 0;                     // reset index into states
  dtime = 1;                  // start traffic light right away
  while(1) {            // do nothing while traffic light goes
  }
}
```

Example 16 – Interrupt-Driven Blinking SOS

As a second example of an interrupt-driven controller, let's write a program to blink the Morse Code for SOS on the rightmost 7-segment display on the DRAGON12-Plus-USB, while displaying the letters SOS. The Morse Code for S is *dot-dot-dot* and that for O is *dash-dash-dash*. We will therefore blink an S three times quickly to indicate *dot-dot-dot* and then blink an O about 3 times slower to indicate *dash-dash-dash* and then blink an S again three times quickly to indicate another *dot-dot-dot*. This sequence will then be repeated endlessly.

A program for doing this is shown in Listing 5.7. Note that it follows the same pattern that we used for the traffic light example in Listings 5.5 and 5.6. In this case, there are a total of 18 states: 6 to turn the S on and off three times; 6 to turn the O on and off three times; and 6 to turn the S on and off three times again. The on and off delay time for the dot is 12 x 10.24 ms = 0.123 seconds and the on and off delay time for the dash is 36 x 10.24 ms = 0.369 seconds. A slightly longer delay is used at the end of the first three dots and an even longer delay is used at the end of the entire SOS sequence. Try this program.

Listing 5.7 Example 16 – DRAGON12-Plus-USB

```
// Example 16: Interrupt-Driven Controller: SOS
#include <hidef.h>      /* common defines and macros */
#include <mc9s12dg256.h>     /* derivative information */
#pragma LINK_INFO DERIVATIVE "mc9s12dg256b"

#include "main_asm.h" /* interface to the assembly module */

unsigned short dtime;     // delay time
int ix;                   // index into states
const int numstates = 18;
const char seg7[] = {
  0x6D, 0x00, 0x6D, 0x00, 0x6D, 0x00,    // S
  0x3F, 0x00, 0x3F, 0x00, 0x3F, 0x00,    // O
  0x6D, 0x00, 0x6D, 0x00, 0x6D, 0x00     // S
};
const char delay[] = {
  0x0C, 0x0C, 0x0C, 0x0C, 0x0C, 0x18,    // dots
  0x24, 0x24, 0x24, 0x24, 0x24, 0x24,    // dashes
  0x0C, 0x0C, 0x0C, 0x0C, 0x0C, 0x30     // dots
};

void interrupt 7 handler(){
  dtime--;
  if(dtime == 0){
    seg7_on(seg7[ix],3);     // turn on next display
    dtime = delay[ix];       // get next delay time
    ix++;                    // increment index
    if(ix == numstates){     // after going through all states
      ix = 0;               //  reset index to 0
    }
  }
  clear_RTI_flag();
}

void main(void) {
  PLL_init();         // set system clock frequency to 24 MHz
  led_disable();      // disable LEDs
  seg7_enable();      // enable 7-segment displays
  RTI_init();
  ix = 0;             // reset index into states
  dtime = 1;          // start display right away
  while(1) {          // do nothing while display goes
  }
}
```

Chapter 6

Analog-to-Digital Converter

In this chapter we will show how to use the two 8-channel analog-to-digital (A/D) converters that are part of the MC9S12DG256 microcontroller. We will use the A/D converter to read the potentiometer value, read the values of an *x-y-z* accelerometer, and measure the temperature in Fahrenheit and Centigrade.

6.1 Analog-to-Digital Conversion

A/D converters transform an analog voltage within a given voltage range into a corresponding digital number. For example, you might convert a voltage between 0 and 5 volts to an 8-bit binary number between 00000000 and 11111111. This represents a decimal number between 0 and 255. In this case, a change in the least-significant bit (LSB) of 1 corresponds to a change in voltage of 5V/256 = 19.5 mV. This quantization error, or step size, is inherent in any type of A/D conversion. We can minimize this error by using more bits. For example, a 10-bit A/D converter will have a step size between 0 and 5 volts of $5V/2^{10}$ = 5V/1024 = 4.9 mV. The MC9S12DG256 A/D converters can be programmed to do either 8-bit or 10-bit conversions. We will provide C functions to do 10-bit A/D conversions.

There are several different methods used for performing A/D conversions. One of the most popular, and the one used in the HCS12 microcontrollers, is the method of successive approximation. We will illustrate this method by using a 4-bit conversion in which the step size between 0 and 5 volts will be $5V/2^4$ = 5V/16 = 0.3125 V. For *n* bits the method of successive approximation requires *n* steps. The method is essentially a binary search as shown in Fig. 6.1 for four bits.

Suppose that the input analog voltage to convert is V_{in} = 3.5V. The first step is to guess the mid-range voltage of 2.5V corresponding to the binary number 1000. That is, we just set the most-significant bit. If this voltage (2.5V) is less than the voltage V_{in}, then we want to keep this bit, because we know the input voltage is greater than 2.5V. We then add the next most-significant bit and try 1100, or 3.75V, in step 2. This voltage is greater than 3.5V, so we have overshot the mark and must discard this bit. Setting the next bit means that we will try the value 1010, or 3.125V is step 3. This value is less than 3.5V so we will keep this bit. Finally, we will set the last (least-significant) bit and try 1011, or 3.4375V in step 4. This is still less than 3.5V so we keep this bit. We are now done and our converted value is 1011, which really represents 3.4375V, but is within our error margin of 0.3125V.

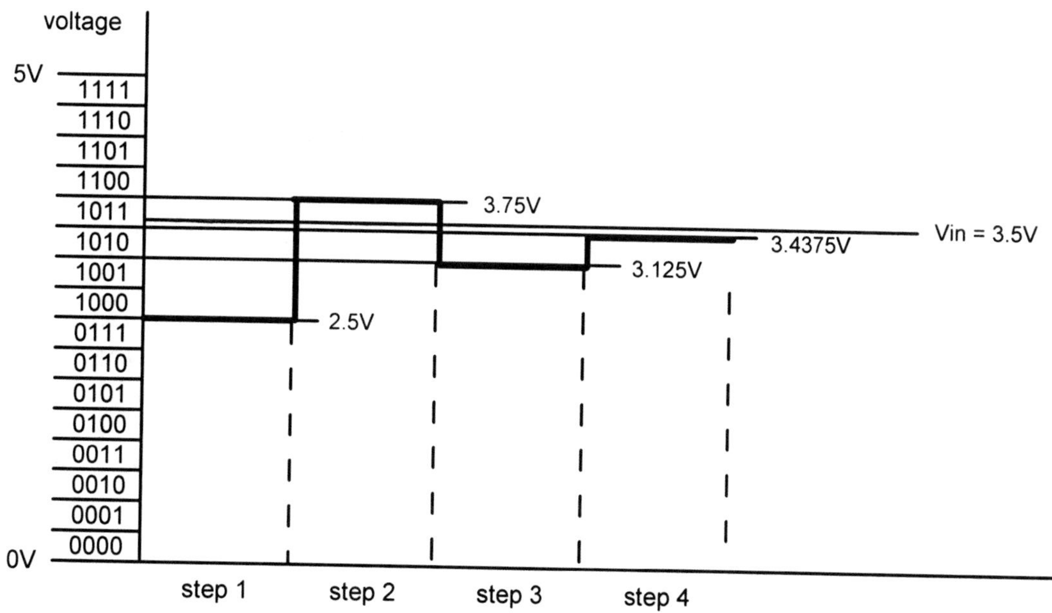

Figure 6.1 Illustrating the method of successive approximation

The successive approximation method illustrated in Fig. 6.1 can be implemented using a comparator and D/A converter as shown in Figure 6.2. Assuming a 4-bit A/D converter as shown in Figure 6.1, the control circuit will first put out the binary value 1000. The D/A converter will convert this value to V_{DA} = 2.5V. Because this value is less than V_{in} = 3.5V, the output, *C*, of the comparator will be 1. This tells the control circuit to keep this bit and output the value 1100 in the second step, as shown in Fig. 6.1. This time the value of V_{DA} = 3.75V is greater than V_{in} = 3.5V, and therefore the output, *C*, of the comparator will be 0. This tells the control circuit to throw away this bit and to output the value 1010 in step 3. This bit is kept as is the last bit as shown in Figure 6.1.

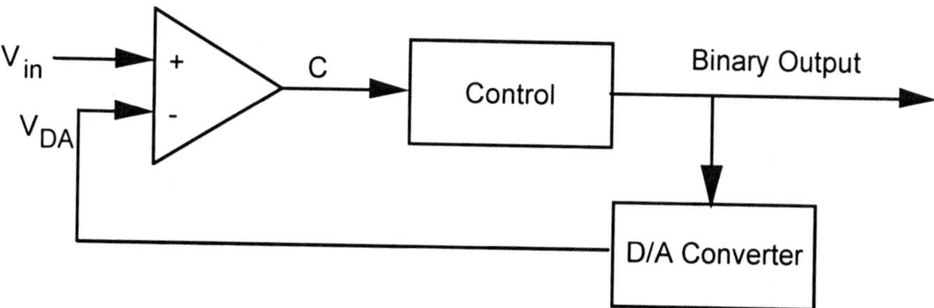

Figure 6.2 Implementing the method of successive approximation

6.2 Using the MC9S12DG256 A/D Converters

The MC9S12DG256 microcontroller has two 8-channel A/D converters, called *ATD*0 and *ATD*1, which can produce either 8-bit or 10-bit conversions. These A/D converters share the same input pins as *PORTAD*0 and *PORTAD*1, which can be used for digital inputs when the A/D converter is not being used. Pin 7 of *PORTAD*0 is connected to the center tap of the potentiometer on the DRAGON12-Plus-USB board. This input will vary between 0 and 5 volts as the white cap of the potentiometer (pot) is turned with a small screw driver. We will use this input to illustrate the use of *ATD*0.

There are lots of registers associated with the use of the A/D converters. We will look at these in the *Under the Hood* section below. To make it easy, we have written several assembly language routines that are called by the C functions shown in Table 6.1.

The pinouts of the two A/D converters are shown in Table 6.2. On the DRAGON12-Plus-USB, channel 7 of *ATD*0 is connected to the potentiometer, channel 5 of *ATD*0 is connected to a temperature sensor, and channel 4 of *ATD*0 is connected to the output of a phototransistor. The DRAGON12-Plus-USB has a 10-pin header that is connected to Channels 0-2 of ATD1. This header is convenient for connecting an x-y-z accelerometer or the GP2D12 distance sensor to A/D channels of the MC9S12DG256 microcontroller.

Table 6.1 C Function calls for the A/D converters

Function	Description
`void ad0_enable(void);`	Enable ATD0 for 10 bits
`int adOconv(char ch#);`	Return the average of 4 successive readings of channel *ch#*
`void ad1_enable(void);`	Enable ATD1 for 10 bits
`int ad1conv(char ch#);`	Return the average of 4 successive readings of channel *ch#*

Table 6.2 Pinouts for A/D Converter

ATD0			ATD1		
Channel No.	Pin Name	Pin No.	Channel No.	Pin Name	Pin No.
0	PADD0	67	0	PAD08	68
1	PADD1	69	1	PAD09	70
2	PADD2	71	2	PAD10	72
3	PADD3	73	3	PAD11	74
4	PADD4	75	4	PAD12	76
5	PADD5	77	5	PAD13	78
6	PADD6	79	6	PAD14	80
7	PADD7	81	7	PAD15	82

Example 17 – Reading the Potentiometer Value

Listing 6.1 shows a program that reads channel 7 of *ATD*0, divides the value by 2 (to reduce noise in the least-significant bit), and displays the result on the LCD display. The values should vary from 0 to 511 as you turn the pot with a small screwdriver. Try it.

On the DRAGON12-Plus-USB, if you change the channel number from 7 to 4 in Listing 6.1, the program will read the output of the on-board phototransistor. The resulting display on the LCD will increase as you shine more light on the phototransistor.

Listing 6.1 Example 17

```
// Example 17: A/D Converter -- Pot
#include <hidef.h>      /* common defines and macros */
#include <mc9s12dg256.h>     /* derivative information */
#pragma LINK_INFO DERIVATIVE "mc9s12dg256b"

#include "main_asm.h" /* interface to the assembly module */

int val;

void main(void) {
  PLL_init();                // set system clock frequency to 24 MHz
  ad0_enable();              // enable a/d converter 0
  lcd_init();                // enable lcd
  while(1) {
    val = ad0conv(7);        // read pot on channel 7
    val = val >> 1;          // shift 1 bit right (divide by 2)
    set_lcd_addr(0x40);      // display on 2nd row of LCD
    write_int_lcd(val);      // write value in field of 5
    ms_delay(100);           // delay 0.1 seconds
  }
}
```

Under the Hood

The subroutines in *main.asm* corresponding to the C functions shown in Table 6.1 are given in Listing 6.2. The first three subroutines apply to *ATD0*, and the last three subroutines apply to *ATD1*. The subroutine *ad0_enable* will enable *ATD0* for 10-bit resolution. The frequency of the A/D clock can be between 500 kHz and 2 MHz. It is set using the bits *PRS*[4:0] in the ATD Control Register 4 shown in Fig. 6.3 according to the formula

$$ATDclock = \frac{[BusClock]}{2(PRS+1)} \tag{6.1}$$

In the subroutine *ad0_enable* in Listing 6.2, we have stored the value $0B in the control register *ATD0CTL4*. This will select 10-bit resolution and use a value of *PRS* = 11 in Eq. (6.1), which will divide the bus clock frequency of 24 MHz by 24, giving an A/D clock frequency of 1 MHz. Storing a value of $C0 in the control register *ATD0CTL2* will turn on the A/D module and select the fast flag clear mode. This convenient feature will clear the A/D conversion complete flag when data are read from the corresponding result register.

Listing 6.2 A/D Assembly Language Subroutines from *main.asm*

```
; A/D converter PADD0-PADD7
;   ad0_enable();
ad0_enable:
      movb  #$0B, ATD0CTL4    ;10-bit resolution  /24 clock
      movb  #$C0, ATD0CTL2    ;set ADPU & AFFC
      rts

;   int adconv(char ch#)
ad0conv:
      andb  #$07              ;ch. 0 - 7
      orab  #$80              ;right just  SCAN=0  MULT=0
      stab  ATD0CTL5
ad01  brclr ATD0STAT0,#$80,ad01     ;wait for conv
      bsr   avg40
      rts

avg40:
      pshx                    ;save reg
      ldx   #ATD0DR0H
      ldd   2,x+              ;adr0
      addd  2,x+              ;+adr1
      addd  2,x+              ;+adr2
      addd  2,x+              ;+adr3
      lsrd
      lsrd                    ;divide by 4
      pulx                    ;restore reg
      rts

; A/D converter PAD8-PAD15
;   ad1_enable();
ad1_enable:
      movb  #$0B, ATD1CTL4    ;10-bit resolution  /24 clock
      movb  #$C0, ATD1CTL2    ;set ADPU & AFFC
      rts

;   int adconv(char ch#)
ad1conv:
      andb  #$07              ;ch. 0 - 7
      orab  #$80              ;right just  SCAN=0  MULT=0
      stab  ATD1CTL5
ad11  brclr ATD1STAT0,#$80,ad11     ;wait for conv
      bsr   avg41
      rts

avg41:
      pshx                    ;save reg
      ldx   #ATD1DR0H
      ldd   2,x+              ;adr0
      addd  2,x+              ;+adr1
      addd  2,x+              ;+adr2
      addd  2,x+              ;+adr3
      lsrd
      lsrd                    ;divide by 4
      pulx                    ;restore reg
      rts
```

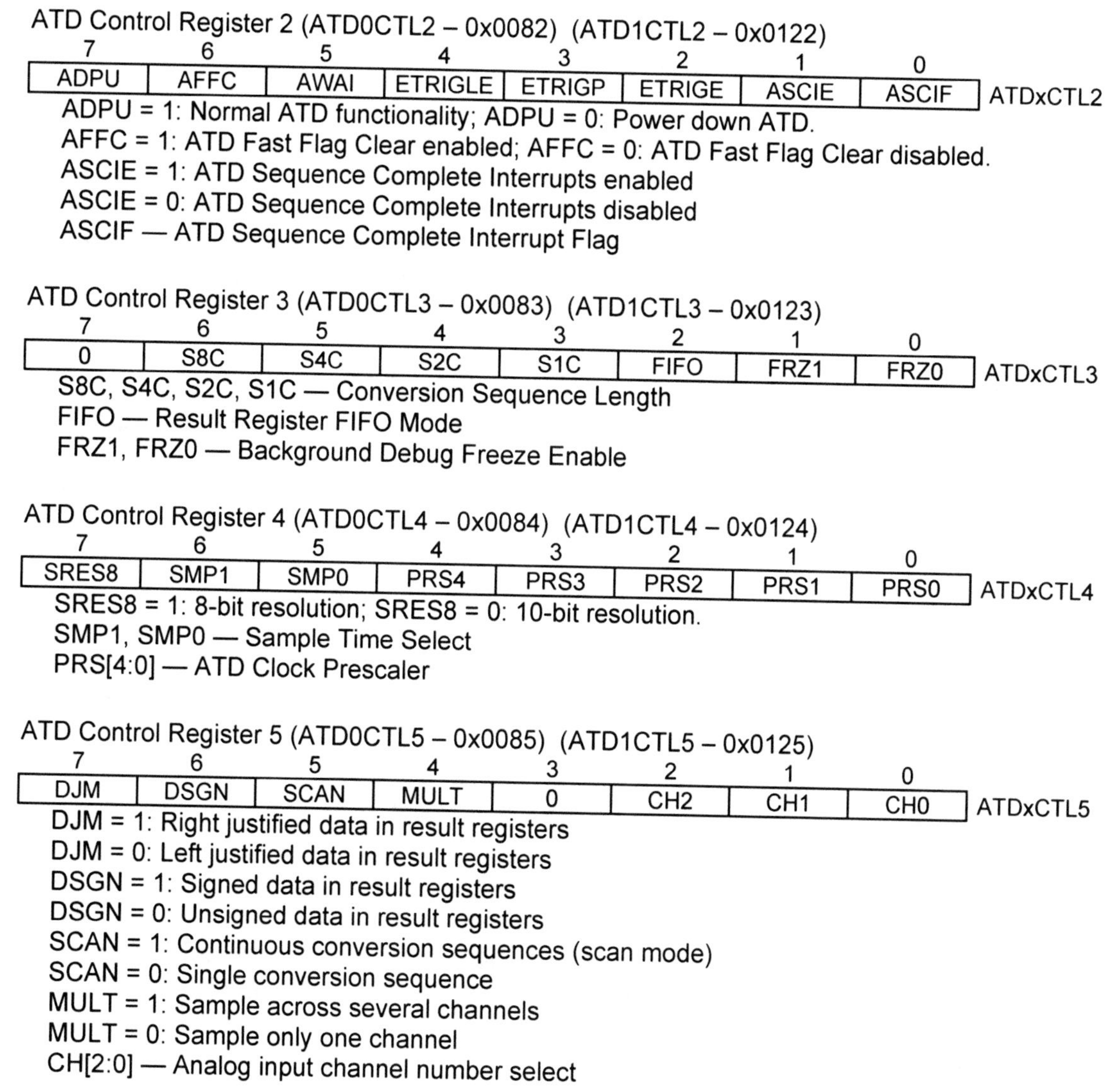

ATD Control Register 2 (ATD0CTL2 – 0x0082) (ATD1CTL2 – 0x0122)
7 6 5 4 3 2 1 0
ADPU AFFC AWAI ETRIGLE ETRIGP ETRIGE ASCIE ASCIF ATDxCTL2
ADPU = 1: Normal ATD functionality; ADPU = 0: Power down ATD.
AFFC = 1: ATD Fast Flag Clear enabled; AFFC = 0: ATD Fast Flag Clear disabled.
ASCIE = 1: ATD Sequence Complete Interrupts enabled
ASCIE = 0: ATD Sequence Complete Interrupts disabled
ASCIF — ATD Sequence Complete Interrupt Flag
ATD Control Register 3 (ATD0CTL3 – 0x0083) (ATD1CTL3 – 0x0123)
7 6 5 4 3 2 1 0
0 S8C S4C S2C S1C FIFO FRZ1 FRZ0 ATDxCTL3
S8C, S4C, S2C, S1C — Conversion Sequence Length
FIFO — Result Register FIFO Mode
FRZ1, FRZ0 — Background Debug Freeze Enable
ATD Control Register 4 (ATD0CTL4 – 0x0084) (ATD1CTL4 – 0x0124)
7 6 5 4 3 2 1 0
SRES8 SMP1 SMP0 PRS4 PRS3 PRS2 PRS1 PRS0 ATDxCTL4
SRES8 = 1: 8-bit resolution; SRES8 = 0: 10-bit resolution.
SMP1, SMP0 — Sample Time Select
PRS[4:0] — ATD Clock Prescaler
ATD Control Register 5 (ATD0CTL5 – 0x0085) (ATD1CTL5 – 0x0125)
7 6 5 4 3 2 1 0
DJM DSGN SCAN MULT 0 CH2 CH1 CH0 ATDxCTL5
DJM = 1: Right justified data in result registers
DJM = 0: Left justified data in result registers
DSGN = 1: Signed data in result registers
DSGN = 0: Unsigned data in result registers
SCAN = 1: Continuous conversion sequences (scan mode)
SCAN = 0: Single conversion sequence
MULT = 1: Sample across several channels
MULT = 0: Sample only one channel
CH[2:0] — Analog input channel number select

Figure 6.3 A/D Control Registers

Once the A/D converter module has been enabled, a conversion is started by writing to control register *ATD0CTL5*. Setting bit 7 (*DJM*) to 1 will right justify the data in the result registers. Storing a 0 in bit 5 (*SCAN*) and bit 4 (*MULT*) will cause a single conversion sequence of only one channel. The channel number is stored in bits 2 – 0. In the subroutine *ad0conv* in Listing 6.2, the channel number is passed as a parameter in accumulator *B*. After masking this number to the lower three bits, bit 7 is set to 1 to right justify the data in the result registers, and the resulting value is written to *ATD0CTL5*. At this point, the conversion begins. The number of conversions that take place is determined by the value of the conversion sequence length in ATD Control Register 3 shown in Fig. 6.3. On reset, the default value of this conversion sequence length is 4, which means, in our case, that four separate conversions of the analog signal on the selected channel are performed, and the results are stored in the first four words of the ATD Conversion Result Registers (*ATDDRHx*/*ATDDRLx*).

When the conversion is complete, bit 7 (*SCF*) of the ATD Status Register 0, shown in Fig. 6.4, is set to 1. The *branch on clear* statement

```
ad01  brclr ATD0STAT0,#$80,ad01
```

in the subroutine *ad0conv* in Listing 6.2 will branch on itself as long as the AND of *ATD0STAT0* with $80 is zero, i.e., as long as bit 7 of *ATD0STAT0* is 0. As soon as this *SCF* flag goes to 1, the branch will fail, and the next instruction, *bsr avg40*, will be executed.

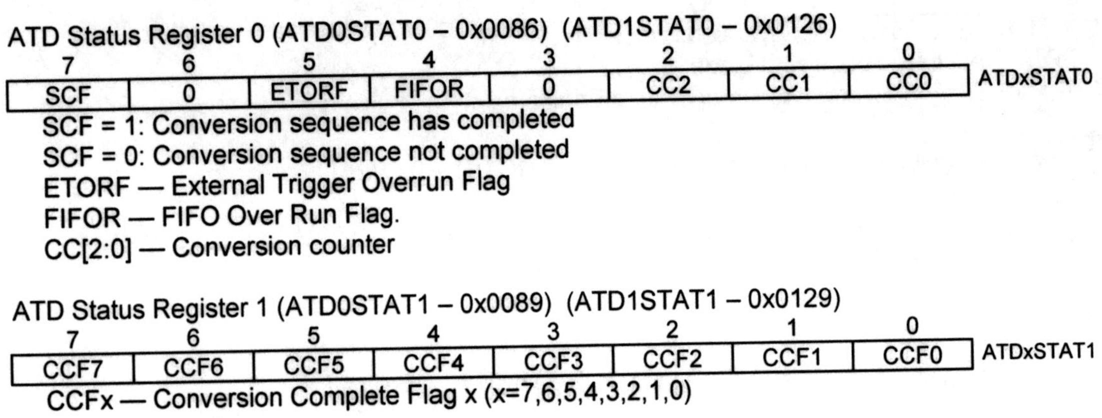

ATD Status Register 0 (ATD0STAT0 – 0x0086) (ATD1STAT0 – 0x0126)

7	6	5	4	3	2	1	0	
SCF	0	ETORF	FIFOR	0	CC2	CC1	CC0	ATDxSTAT0

SCF = 1: Conversion sequence has completed
SCF = 0: Conversion sequence not completed
ETORF — External Trigger Overrun Flag
FIFOR — FIFO Over Run Flag.
CC[2:0] — Conversion counter

ATD Status Register 1 (ATD0STAT1 – 0x0089) (ATD1STAT1 – 0x0129)

7	6	5	4	3	2	1	0	
CCF7	CCF6	CCF5	CCF4	CCF3	CCF2	CCF1	CCF0	ATDxSTAT1

CCFx — Conversion Complete Flag x (x=7,6,5,4,3,2,1,0)

Figure 6.4 A/D Status Registers

The subroutine, *avg40*, will average the four values that have been stored in the first four ATD Conversion Result Registers shown in Fig. 6.5. Note that the 10-bit conversion result is right justified in the two bytes *ATD0DRxH*/*ATD0DRxL*. In the subroutine, *avg40*, index register *X* points to *ATD0DR0H*. The first conversion result in *ATD0DR0H*/*ATD0DR0L* is loaded into accumulator *D*, and then each of the next three conversion results are added to this value. The result is then divided by 4 (by shifting 2 bits to the right) to produce the average value in *D*. This is the result that is returned in the C function int *adconv*(char *ch#*).

ATD Conversion Result Registers (ATD0DR0H – 0x0090) (ATD1DR0H – 0x0130)

7	6	5	4	3	2	1	0	
0	0	0	0	0	0	bit9	bit8	ATD0DR0H
bit 7	bit 6	bit 5	bit 4	bit 3	bit 2	bit 1	bit0	ATD0DR0L
0	0	0	0	0	0	bit9	bit8	ATD0DR1H
bit 7	bit 6	bit 5	bit 4	bit 3	bit 2	bit 1	bit0	ATD0DR1L
0	0	0	0	0	0	bit9	bit8	ATD0DR2H
bit 7	bit 6	bit 5	bit 4	bit 3	bit 2	bit 1	bit0	ATD0DR2L
0	0	0	0	0	0	bit9	bit8	ATD0DR3H
bit 7	bit 6	bit 5	bit 4	bit 3	bit 2	bit 1	bit0	ATD0DR3L

Figure 6.5 The first four (of eight) Conversion Result Registers

6.3 Measuring Acceleration

It is easy to measure all three components of acceleration using low-cost *x-y-z* acceleration modules based on MEMS technology. Wytec provides a tiny board that contains the Kionix KXPS5-3157 *x-y-z* accelerometer. The board comes with a 6 foot ribbon cable that plugs into header J36 on the DRAGON12-Plus-USB board. This connects the *x*-, *y*-, and *z*-components from the accelerometer module to channels 0 – 2 of *ATD*1 respectively.

Example 18 – Measuring the *x-y-z* Components of Acceleration

Listing 6.3 shows a program that will allow you to test the accelerometer module by continuously displaying the *x*-, *y*-, and *z*-components of acceleration on the first row of the LCD. As you tilt the accelerometer module these values will change because you are measuring the acceleration of gravity. When the module is horizontal the *z*-value will be maximum (corresponding to 1 g) and will become minimum if you turn the module over (corresponding to -1 g). When the module is horizontal the *x*- and *y*-values are reading an acceleration value corresponding to 0 g. These values will increase or decrease as you tilt the module in one direction or another.

You should run this program and tilt the accelerometer until you understand what it is measuring. Try shaking the module to see what maximum (and minimum) accelerations you can detect.

Listing 6.3 Example 18

```
// Example 18: Using accelerometer module: A/D Converter
#include <hidef.h>      /* common defines and macros */
#include <mc9s12dg256.h>     /* derivative information */
#pragma LINK_INFO DERIVATIVE "mc9s12dg256b"

#include "main_asm.h" /* interface to the assembly module */

int ax;
int ay;
int az;

void main(void) {
  PLL_init();          // set system clock frequency to 24 MHz
  ad1_enable();                  // enable a/d converter 1
  lcd_init();                    // enable lcd
  while(1) {
    set_lcd_addr(0x00);          // display on 1st row of LCD
    ax = ad1conv(0);             // read ax on channel 0
    write_int_lcd(ax);           // write value in field of 5
    ay = ad1conv(1);             // read ax on channel 1
    write_int_lcd(ay);           // write value in field of 5
    az = ad1conv(2);             // read ax on channel 2
    write_int_lcd(az);           // write value in field of 5
    ms_delay(100);               // delay 0.1 seconds
  }
}
```

Example 19 – Measuring the Coefficient of Static Friction

The accelerometer module can be used to measure the coefficient of static friction using the setup shown in Fig. 6.6. A small block is placed on a piece of poster board that is taped at one end to the table. The other end of the poster board is lifted up until the block just starts to slide down the inclined plane. If this occurs at an angle θ then the coefficient of static friction μ_s is given by

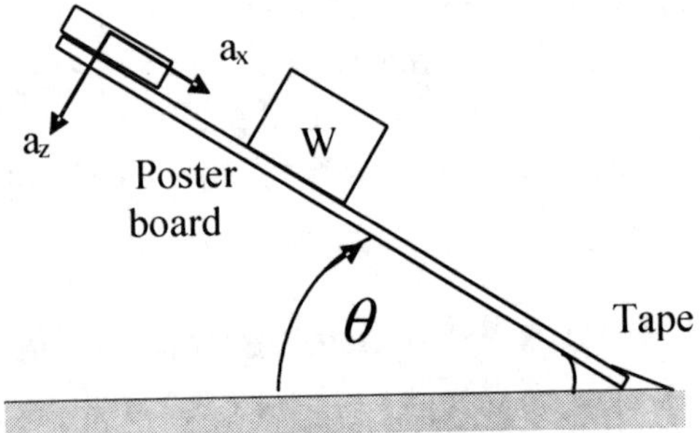

Figure 6.6 Measuring the coefficient of static friction

$$\mu_s = \tan\theta \qquad (6.2)$$

This result is easily derived by drawing a free-body diagram of the block.

The accelerometer is mounted on the poster board as shown in Fig. 6.6 where a_x and a_z measure the components of the acceleration of gravity, g. Thus,

$$a_x = g\sin\theta \qquad (6.3)$$

and

$$a_z = g\cos\theta \qquad (6.4)$$

From Eqs. (6.2) – (6.4) we see that

$$\mu_s = \tan\theta = \frac{a_x}{a_z} \qquad (6.5)$$

To calculate the values of a_x and a_z to use in Eq. (6.5) we must subtract the value corresponding to zero gravity from the measured accelerometer values. Let a_0 be the measured accelerometer reading corresponding to zero gravity. We will assume that this value is the same value for both a_x and a_z. That is, it is the a_x value when $\theta = 0$, and is the a_z value when $\theta = 90°$. We will measure a_0 by measuring a_x when $\theta = 0$. In order to deal only with integer values we multiply Eq. (6.5) by 1000 before doing the calculation. Thus, the integer that we compute will be calculated from

$$\mu_s = 1000\frac{a_x - a_0}{a_z - a_0} \qquad (6.6)$$

Listing 6.4 will perform this calculation. To make the measurement you would make sure that the poster board was horizontal and then press the reset button. This will start the program and calculate *a*0 by averaging eight readings of *ax*. Then lift the poster board slowly. The value of $\tan\theta$ times 1000 will continuously be displayed on the LCD. This displayed value when the block just starts to slide down the poster board will be 1000 times the coefficient of static friction.

Listing 6.4 Example 19

```
// Example 19: Calculating coefficient of static friction
#include <hidef.h>      /* common defines and macros */
#include <mc9s12dg256.h>     /* derivative information */
#pragma LINK_INFO DERIVATIVE "mc9s12dg256b"

#include "main_asm.h" /* interface to the assembly module */

int ax;
int az;
int a0;
int i;
long ax0;
long az0;
long tan_theta;

void main(void) {
  PLL_init();                 // set system clock frequency to 24 MHz
  ad1_enable();                  // enable a/d converter 1
  lcd_init();                    // enable lcd
  a0 = 0;                        // average 8 values of ax to get a0
  for(i = 0; i < 8; i++){
    a0 += ad1conv(0);            // add 8 values of ax
  }
  a0 >>= 3;                      // divide by 8
  while(1) {
    ax = 0;
    az = 0;                      // average 8 values of ax and az
    for(i = 0; i < 8; i++){
      ax += ad1conv(0);          // add 8 values of ax
      az += ad1conv(2);          // add 8 values of az
    }
    set_lcd_addr(0x00);               // display on 1st row of LCD
    ax >>= 3;                    // divide by 8
    az >>= 3;                    // divide by 8
    write_int_lcd(a0);       // write a0 in field of 5
    write_int_lcd(ax);       // write ax in field of 5
    write_int_lcd(az);       // write az in field of 5
   // calculate coeff of static friction
    ax0 = ax - a0;
    az0 = az - a0;
    tan_theta = 1000*ax0/az0;
    set_lcd_addr(0x40);             // display on 2nd row of LCD
    write_long_lcd(tan_theta);      // write value in field of 10
    ms_delay(100);                  // delay 0.1 seconds
  }
}
```

6.4 Measuring Temperature

The Microchip MCP9701A Linear Active Thermistor is a sensor that converts temperature to an analog voltage. The output voltage is given by

$$V_{out} = 400\text{ mV} + 19.5\frac{\text{mV}}{^{\circ}\text{C}}T_C \qquad (6.7)$$

where T_C is the temperature in degrees Centigrade. This sensor is mounted on the DRAGON12-Plus-USB board and the output analog voltage is connected to channel 5 of *ATD*0.

Example 20 – Displaying the Temperature on the LCD

We can measure the temperature by reading the analog signal on channel 5 of *ATD*0 on the DRAGON12-Plus-USB. A reading of 1024 will correspond to 5 volts. We can convert Eq. (6.7) to A/D value readings by noting that 400 mV corresponds to a reading of 82 and 19.5 corresponds to a reading of 4. Therefore, in terms of the A/D reading, *val*, Eq. (6.7) can be written as $val = 82 + 4T_C$, from which we can approximate the temperature in Centigrade as

$$T_C = \frac{val}{4} - 20 \tag{6.8}$$

Listing 6.5 uses this formula to compute and display the temperature on the LCD in both Centigrade and Fahrenheit.

Listing 6.5 Example 20

```
// Example 20: A/D Converter -- Temperature sensor
// Vout = 19.5 mV/C x Ta + 400 mV
// Ta = val/4 - 20 deg C
#include <hidef.h>      /* common defines and macros */
#include <mc9s12dg256.h>     /* derivative information */
#pragma LINK_INFO DERIVATIVE "mc9s12dg256b"
#include "main_asm.h" /* interface to the assembly module */

void main(void) {
int val, Tc, Tf;
  char* q1;
  char* q2;
  q1 = " deg C";
  q2 = " deg F";
  PLL_init();                   // set system clock frequency to 24 MHz
  ad0_enable();                 // enable a/d converter 0
  lcd_init();                   // enable lcd
  while(1) {
    val = ad0conv(5);           // read temp sensor on channel 5
    val = val >> 2;             // shift 2 bit right (divide by 4)
    Tc = val - 20;              // degrees C
    Tf = Tc*9/5 + 32;           // degrees F
    set_lcd_addr(0x00);         // display on 1st row of LCD
    write_int_lcd(Tc);          // write value in field of 5
    type_lcd(q1);               // write deg C
    set_lcd_addr(0x40);         // display on 2nd row of LCD
    write_int_lcd(Tf);          // write value in field of 5
    type_lcd(q2);               // write deg F
   ms_delay(100);               // delay 0.1 seconds
  }
}
```

Chapter 7

Pulse-Width Modulation (PWM): Motors and Servos

In this chapter we will show how to control the speed and direction of a DC motor and the position of a servo. The DRAGON12-Plus-USB board has convenient headers and terminals for connecting motors and servos.

7.1 Connecting a Motor to a Microcontroller

When connecting a motor or some other load that may draw significant current to a microcontroller, it is necessary to use some type of driver circuit. The DRAGON12-Plus-USB board contains an SN754410 quadruple half-H driver. This is a 16-pin chip with the connections shown in Fig. 7.1. Separate power supply connections are provided for the input stage and the output stage of the four tri-state buffers. Jumper J18 on the DRAGON12-Plus-USB will connect the 5 volts of V_{cc} to the input stage. Jumper J25 on the DRAGON12-Plus-USB determines the source of power for the output stage. When using motors it is desirable to use a separate external power supply V_{ext} to provide the current to the motors. Each driver in Fig. 7.1 can output up to 1 ampere of current. You connect the external voltage source to the *VMOT* lug on the terminal block T4 on the DRAGON12-Plus-USB. The SN754410 driver can handle voltages between 4.5 V and 36 V.

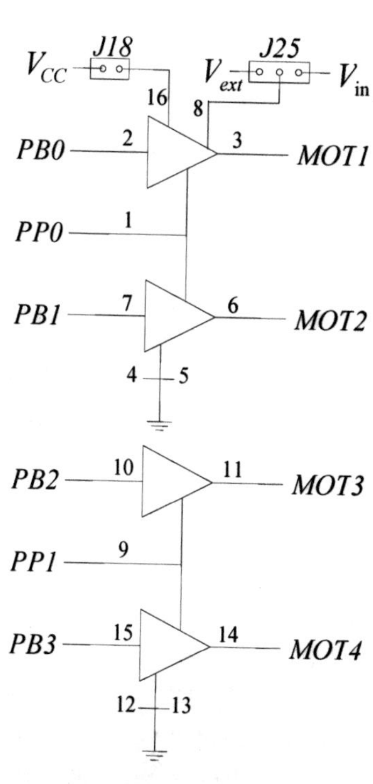

Figure 7.1
SN754410 quadruple half-H driver

The DC motor would be connected between pins *MOT1* and *MOT2* (or between *MOT3* and *MOT4*) in Fig. 7.1. These are labeled on terminal block T4. The two top drivers in Fig. 7.1 are enabled with *PP0*. When *PP0* is 1 the output *MOT1* is high when *PB0* is high and low when *PB0* is low. Similarly, the output *MOT2* is high when *PB0* is high and low when *PB0* is low. When *PP0* is low the outputs *MOT1* and *MOT2* are in the high impedance state. That is, it is the same as disconnecting the motor from the circuit. The lower two drivers in Fig. 7.1 are controlled by PP1 in a similar way.

If a motor is connected between pins *MOT1* and *MOT2* in Fig. 7.1, and if *PB0* is high and *PB1* is low and *PP0* is 1 then the motor will rotate in one direction. If *PB0* is low and *PB1* is high, then current will flow through the motor in the opposite direction and the motor will rotate in the opposite direction. When *PB0* and *PB1* are both high or both low then no current will flow through the motor and the motor will stop.

The speed of a DC motor depends on the voltage applied to the motor – the higher the voltage the faster the motor will turn. If you just want to turn on a motor at a constant speed, you can connect one side of the motor to *MOT1* in Fig. 7.1 and connect the other side of the motor to ground. In this way you could connect up to four motors to the SN754410 in Fig. 7.1. The polarity of the voltage connected to the motor will determine which way the motor turns. If it is turning the wrong way, just exchange the two connections to the motor.

Example 21 – Controlling the Speed of a DC Motor Using PWM

To control the speed of a DC motor using a microcontroller, one normally uses a pulse-width modulated signal of the type shown in Fig. 7.2. If this signal is connected to *PP0* in Fig. 7.1, then when the signal is high, current will flow through the motor assuming that *PB0* and *PB1* have different values. When the PWM signal (*PP0*) is low, then the motor is disconnected from the circuit, and no current flows through the motor.

The period of this pulse train remains constant and the width of the high time, called *duty* in Fig. 7.2, is varied. The *duty cycle* of a PWM signal is defined as the percent time that the signal is high. That is,

$$\text{duty cycle} = \frac{duty}{period} \times 100\%$$

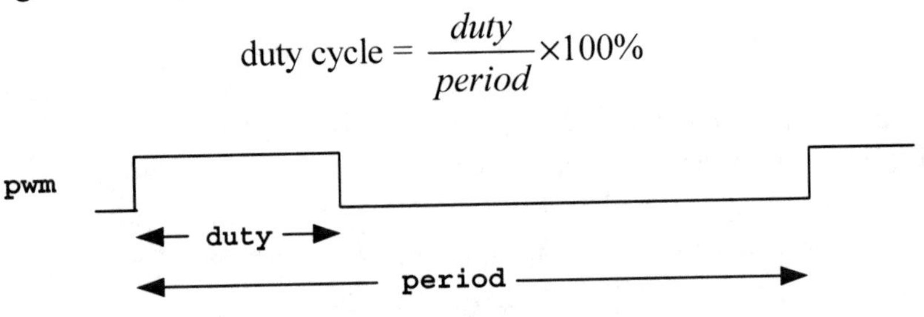

Figure 7.2 A pulse-width modulated signal

The average DC value of the *pwm* signal in Fig. 7.2 will be proportional to the duty cycle. A duty cycle of 100% will have a DC value equal to the maximum value of the *pwm* signal. A duty cycle of 50% will have a DC value equal to half of the maximum value of the *pwm* signal, and so forth. If the voltage across the motor is proportional to this *pwm* signal, then simply changing the pulse width *duty* and therefore the duty cycle changes the speed of the motor.

Port P of the MC9S12DG256 can be used to generate up to eight 8-bit PWM signals or four 16-bit PWM signals. An 8-bit PWM signal will have a resolution of 256 different values of the pulse width *duty*. A 16-bit PWM signal will have a resolution of 65,536 different values of the pulse width *duty*. For speed control of a DC motor an 8-bit PWM signal is usually more than adequate. We provide assembly language routines for generating up to eight different 8-bit PWM signals. For controlling a servo, a 16-bit PWM signal is sometimes needed, and we will provide two such routines in the next section.

The SN754410 quadruple half-H driver shown in Fig. 7.1 has internal diodes from the output to V_{ext} and to ground that will eliminate possible voltage spikes that would tend to show up when the current through the motor changes quickly.

The built-in C functions that can be used to control the speed of a DC motor are shown in Table 7.1.

Table 7.1 C function calls for controlling the speed of a DC motor

C Function Call	Meaning
`motor0_init();`	Initialize PWM0 with 10 ms period
`motor1_init();`	Initialize PWM1 with 10 ms period
`motor2_init();`	Initialize PWM2 with 10 ms period
`motor3_init();`	Initialize PWM3 with 10 ms period
`motor4_init();`	Initialize PWM4 with 10 ms period
`motor5_init();`	Initialize PWM5 with 10 ms period
`motor6_init();`	Initialize PWM6 with 10 ms period
`motor7_init();`	Initialize PWM7 with 10 ms period
`motor0(int speed);`	Set speed of motor0 (0 – 255)
`motor1(int speed);`	Set speed of motor1 (0 – 255)
`motor2(int speed);`	Set speed of motor2 (0 – 255)
`motor3(int speed);`	Set speed of motor3 (0 – 255)
`motor4(int speed);`	Set speed of motor4 (0 – 255)
`motor5(int speed);`	Set speed of motor5 (0 – 255)
`motor6(int speed);`	Set speed of motor6 (0 – 255)
`motor7(int speed);`	Set speed of motor7 (0 – 255)
`motor0_off();`	Disable PWM0
`motor1_off();`	Disable PWM1
`motor2_off();`	Disable PWM2
`motor3_off();`	Disable PWM3
`motor4_off();`	Disable PWM4
`motor5_off();`	Disable PWM5
`motor6_off();`	Disable PWM6
`motor7_off();`	Disable PWM7

A sample program for the DRAGON12-Plus-USB is shown in Listing 7.1. In this example the pot on the board controls the speed of a DC motor. The rightmost two slide switches *S*1 control the direction of motor rotation.

Under the Hood

The registers used for programming the PWM module are shown in Figs. 7.3a and 7.3b. Each of the eight outputs of Port P (*PTP*) can be enabled as a PWM output using the *PWME* register in Fig. 7.3a. The time at which the output goes high and low is controlled by the 8-bit counter, *PWMCNTx*, shown in Fig. 7.3b. The clock source for this counter can be clock *A*, *B*, *SA*, or *SB*, depending on the settings in register PWMCLK. For channels 0 and 1, which are used in the motor driver in Fig. 7.1, we have selected clock *SA* in the subroutines *motor0_init* and *motor1_init* in Listing 7.2. The clock frequency is determined by clock scaling and prescaling registers, *PWMSCLA*, *PWMSCLB*, and *PWMPRCLK* in Fig. 7.3b. In Listing 7.2, we have set the prescalar clock, *PWMPRCLK*, to hex $22, which means that the clock *A* rate is the bus clock (24 MHz) divided by 4, or 6 MHz. The scale *A* register is set to hex $75 = 117, which means that the *SA* clock rate is $6\text{ MHz}/(2\times117)=25.64\text{ kHz}$. If we set the period register, *PWMPER*, in Fig. 7.3b to 255, the period will be 255/25.64 kHz = 9.95 ms.

Listing 7.1 Example 21 – DRAGON12-Plus-USB

```
// Example 21: Motor speed and direction -- H-Bridge
#include <hidef.h>      /* common defines and macros */
#include <mc9s12dg256.h>     /* derivative information */
#pragma LINK_INFO DERIVATIVE "mc9s12dg256b"
#include "main_asm.h" /* interface to the assembly module */

int val;
int speed;

void main(void) {
  PLL_init();                 // set system clock frequency to 24 MHz
  ad0_enable();               // enable a/d converter 0
  seg7_disable();             // disable 7-segment displays
  led_enable();               // enable leds
  lcd_init();                 // enable lcd
  SW_enable();                // enable switches
  motor0_init();              // enable 8-bit pwm0 for motor
  while(1) {
    leds_on(SW1_dip());       // display dip switch settings on leds
    val = ad0conv(7);         // read pot on channel 7; 0 - 1023
    speed = val >> 2;         // shift 2 bit right; 0 - 255
    motor0(speed);            // set motor speed
    set_lcd_addr(0x40);       // display on 2nd row of LCD
    write_int_lcd(speed);     // write value in field of 5
    ms_delay(100);            // delay 0.1 seconds
  }
}
```

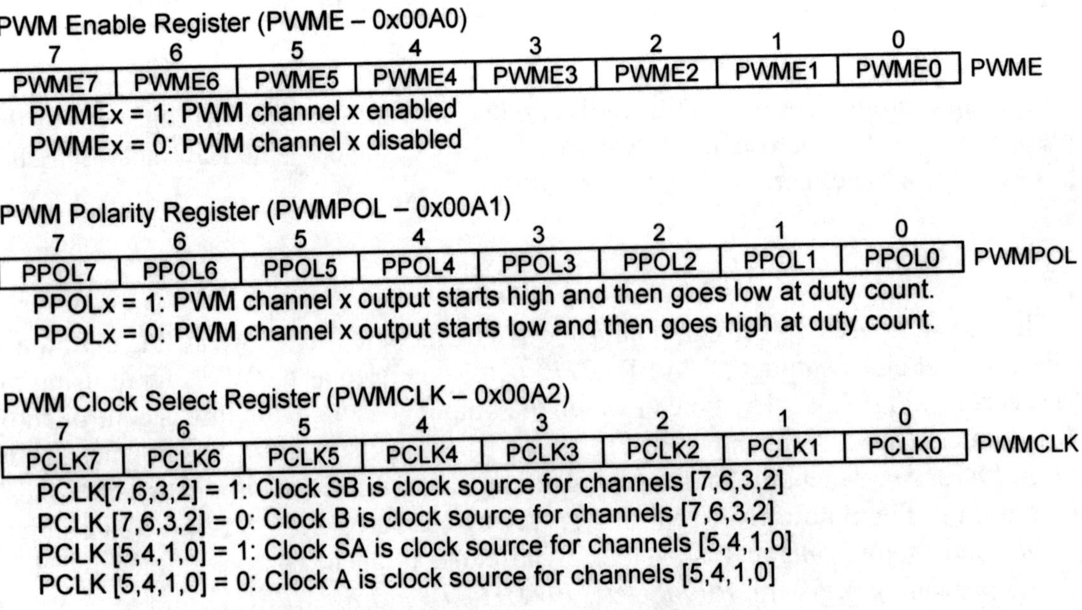

PWM Enable Register (PWME – 0x00A0)

7	6	5	4	3	2	1	0	
PWME7	PWME6	PWME5	PWME4	PWME3	PWME2	PWME1	PWME0	PWME

PWMEx = 1: PWM channel x enabled
PWMEx = 0: PWM channel x disabled

PWM Polarity Register (PWMPOL – 0x00A1)

7	6	5	4	3	2	1	0	
PPOL7	PPOL6	PPOL5	PPOL4	PPOL3	PPOL2	PPOL1	PPOL0	PWMPOL

PPOLx = 1: PWM channel x output starts high and then goes low at duty count.
PPOLx = 0: PWM channel x output starts low and then goes high at duty count.

PWM Clock Select Register (PWMCLK – 0x00A2)

7	6	5	4	3	2	1	0	
PCLK7	PCLK6	PCLK5	PCLK4	PCLK3	PCLK2	PCLK1	PCLK0	PWMCLK

PCLK[7,6,3,2] = 1: Clock SB is clock source for channels [7,6,3,2]
PCLK [7,6,3,2] = 0: Clock B is clock source for channels [7,6,3,2]
PCLK [5,4,1,0] = 1: Clock SA is clock source for channels [5,4,1,0]
PCLK [5,4,1,0] = 0: Clock A is clock source for channels [5,4,1,0]

Figure 7.3a PWM Registers

PWM Prescale Clock Select Register (PWMPRCLK – 0x00A3)

7	6	5	4	3	2	1	0	
0	PCKB2	PCKB1	PCKB0	0	PCKA2	PCKA1	PCKA0	PWMPRCLK

PCKB[2:0] – Prescalar select for clock B. Clock B rate = $\text{BusClock}/2^{\text{PCKB[2:0]}}$

PCKA[2:0] – Prescalar select for clock A. Clock A rate = $\text{BusClock}/2^{\text{PCKA[2:0]}}$

PWM Center Align Enable Register (PWMCAE – 0x00A4)

7	6	5	4	3	2	1	0	
CAE7	CAE6	CAE5	CAE4	CAE3	CAE2	CAE1	CAE0	PWMCAE

CAEx = 1: PWM channel x operates in Center Aligned Output Mode.
CAEx = 0: PWM channel x operates in Left Aligned Output Mode.

PWM Control Register (PWMCTL – 0x00A5)

7	6	5	4	3	2	1	0	
CON67	CON45	CON23	CON01	PSWAI	PFRZ	0	0	PWMCTL

CONxy = 1: Channels x and y are concatenated to form a 16-bit PWM.
Channel x is the high order byte and channel y is the low order byte.
Channel y pin is the output pin of the 16-bit PWM.
Channel y PCLK bit, PPOL bit, PWME bit, and CAE bit apply.
CONxy = 0: Channels x and y are separate 8-bit PWMs.

PWM Scale A Register (PWMSCLA – 0x00A8)

7	6	5	4	3	2	1	0	
bit7	bit 6	bit 5	bit 4	bit 3	bit 2	bit 1	bit 0	PWMSCLA

Clock SA = $\text{Clock A}/(2\times PWMSCLA)$

A value of $PWMSCLA = \$00$ corresponds to $PWMSCLA = 256$.

PWM Scale B Register (PWMSCLB – 0x00A9)

7	6	5	4	3	2	1	0	
bit7	bit 6	bit 5	bit 4	bit 3	bit 2	bit 1	bit 0	PWMSCLB

Clock SB = $\text{Clock B}/(2\times PWMSCLB)$

A value of $PWMSCLB = \$00$ corresponds to $PWMSCLB = 256$.

PWM Channel Counter Registers (PWMCNTx; x = 0 – 7: 0x00AC – 0x00B3)

7	6	5	4	3	2	1	0	
bit7	bit 6	bit 5	bit 4	bit 3	bit 2	bit 1	bit 0	PWMCNTx

8-bit up/down counter for each of the eight PWM channels

PWM Channel Period Registers (PWMPERx; x = 0 – 7: 0x00B4 – 0x00BB)

7	6	5	4	3	2	1	0	
bit7	bit 6	bit 5	bit 4	bit 3	bit 2	bit 1	bit 0	PWMPERx

Period register determines the period for each of the eight PWM channels

PWM Channel Duty Registers (PWMDTYx; x = 0 – 7: 0x00BC – 0x00C3)

7	6	5	4	3	2	1	0	
bit7	bit 6	bit 5	bit 4	bit 3	bit 2	bit 1	bit 0	PWMDTYx

Duty register determines the duty for each of the eight PWM channels

Figure 7.3b PWM Registers (cont.)

Listing 7.2 *motor* Assembly Language Subroutines from *main.asm*

```
; PWM -- motors   10 ms period   8-bit mode
;        inputs  0 - 255
;        motors input duty cycles between 0 - 100%

; motor0_init();       Initialize pwm 0 - pin PP0
motor0_init:
            bset  PWMPOL, #$01      ;start high
            bset  PWMCLK, #$01      ;use clock SA
            movb  #$22,   PWMPRCLK  ;/4  24/4 = 6 MHz
            movb  #$75,   PWMSCLA   ;SA = 6MHz/2*117 = 25.64KHz
            clr   PWMCAE            ;left align
            bclr  PWMCTL, #$10      ;8-bit channels 0 and 1
            movb  #255,   PWMPER0   ;period =~ 10ms
            movb  #128,   PWMDTY0   ;initial duty cycle = 50%
            bset  PWME,   #$01      ;enable PWM0
            rts

; motor1_init();       Initialize pwm 1 - pin PP1
motor1_init:
            bset  PWMPOL, #$02      ;start high
            bset  PWMCLK, #$02      ;use clock SA
            movb  #$22,   PWMPRCLK  ;/4  24/4 = 6 MHz
            movb  #$75,   PWMSCLA   ;SA = 6MHz/2*117 = 25.64KHz
            clr   PWMCAE            ;left align
            bclr  PWMCTL, #$10      ;8-bit channels 0 and 1
            movb  #255,   PWMPER1   ;period =~ 10ms
            movb  #128,   PWMDTY1   ;initial duty cycle = 50%
            bset  PWME,   #$02      ;enable PWM1
            rts

; MOTORS -- Input: duty cycle between 0 and 100%
; motor0(int duty);
motor0:
            stab    PWMDTY0      ;set new pulse width
            rts

; motor1(int duty);
motor1:
            stab    PWMDTY1      ;set new pulse width
            rts

; MOTORS -- turn motors off
; motor0_off();        Turn motor 0 off
motor0_off:
            bclr  PWME,   #$01      ;disable PWM0
            rts

; motor1_off();        Turn motor 1 off
motor1_off:
            bclr  PWME,   #$02      ;disable PWM1
            rts
```

The polarity register, *PWMPOL*, in Fig. 7.3a will determine if the PWM signal starts high and goes low, or starts low and goes high. In Listing 7.2, we set the channel bits to 1 in this register, so in our case, the PWM signal will start high. By clearing the center align enable register, *PWMCAE*, in Listing 7.2, the PWM signal will be left aligned. Two PWM channels can be concatenated to form a 16-bit PWM channel by setting the appropriate bits in the PWM control register, *PWMCTL*, in Fig. 7.3b. For the motors, we are using the two 8-bit channels 0 and 1, so we clear bit 4 in *PWMCTL* in Listing 7.2.

The value stored in the channel duty register, *PWMDTYx*, in Fig. 7.3b will determine when the PWM signal will go low. By storing a value of 128 in this register in Listing 7.2, the initial duty cycle will be 50%. The last *bset* instruction in the motor initialization subroutine will set the appropriate bit in the PWM enable register, *PWME*, in Fig. 7.3a. Once the PWM channel is enabled, the PWM signal will appear on the corresponding pin of Port P (*PTP*). The subroutines, *motor0_off* and *motor1_off*, in Listing 7.2 will stop the motors by disabling the PWM signal.

The speed of the motor is changed by changing the value in the channel duty register, *PWMDTYx*. The subroutines *motor0* and *motor1* in Listing 7.2 do this by writing the value passed in accumulator *B* to the channel duty register, *PWMDTYx*.

7.2 DC Servo Motors

A servo motor is a special type of device that contains a DC motor, some gears, a potentiometer, and electronic circuitry for position feedback control, all packaged in a single compact device. These servos are widely used in model airplanes and radio controlled cars and are therefore mass produced and very inexpensive. A typical servo of this type, the Futaba S3004, is shown in Fig. 7.4. This servo has three wires attached to it: the red wire goes to +5 volts, the black wire goes to ground, and the white wire goes to a PWM signal that controls the position of the motor shaft.

The motor shaft is prevented from moving more than about 90 degrees by limit stops. The PWM signal used to control the position of a servo is shown in Fig. 7.5. Note that the period is fixed at 20 ms and the pulse width varies from about 1.1 ms to 1.9 ms in order to move the shaft position through a total angle of about 90 degrees.

Figure 7.4
The Futaba S3004 servo

Inasmuch as the useful duty cycle of this PWM signal varies from only about 5 to 10 percent, we will use the 16-bit option with a 3 MHz PWM clock in order to provide a resolution of 60,000 over the 20 ms period. In this case, the value of *duty* in Fig. 7.2 would be about 4500 for the neutral position, 3300 for the +45 degree position, and 5700 for the –45 degree position.

The built-in C functions that can be used to control the position of a servo are shown in Table 7.2.

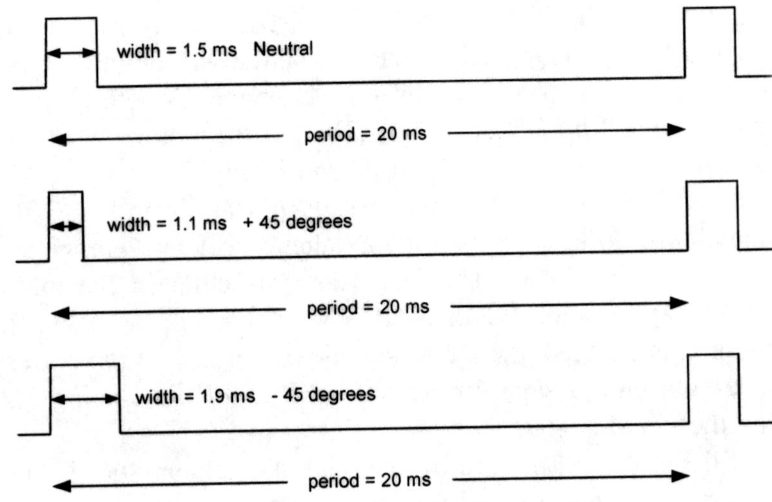

Figure 7.5 PWM signals for controlling the position of a servo

Table 7.2 C function calls for controlling the position of a servo

C Function Call	Meaning
`servo54_init();`	Initialize PWM5 with 20 ms period
`servo76_init();`	Initialize PWM7 with 20 ms period
`set_servo54(int width);`	Set position of servo5 (3300 – 5700)
`set_servo76(int width);`	Set position of servo7 (3300 – 5700)

Example 22 – Controlling the Position of a Servo Using PWM

A sample program that uses these functions is shown in Listing 7.3. In this example the pot on the board controls the position of a servo.

A second sample program that continually rotates the servo back and forth through an angle of about 90 degrees is shown in Listing 7.4. You can experiment with this program by changing the *for* loop values and the delay time.

Listing 7.3 Example 22a

```
// Example 22a: Servo demo with pot
#include <hidef.h>      /* common defines and macros */
#include <mc9s12dg256.h>     /* derivative information */
#pragma LINK_INFO DERIVATIVE "mc9s12dg256b"

#include "main_asm.h" /* interface to the assembly module */

void main(void) {
  int val;
  int width;

  PLL_init();        // set system clock frequency to 24 MHz
  ad0_enable();                 // enable a/d converter 0
  lcd_init();                   // enable lcd
  servo76_init();               // enable pwm1 for servo
  while(1) {
    val = ad0conv(7);           // 0 - 1023
    width = (val << 1) + 3477;  // width: 3477 - 5523
    set_lcd_addr(0x40);         // line 2 of lcd display
    write_int_lcd(width);       // display width on lcd
    set_servo76(width);         // move servo to pos width
  }
}
```

Listing 7.4 Example 22b

```
// Example 22b: Servo demo with for loop
#include <hidef.h>      /* common defines and macros */
#include <mc9s12dg256.h>     /* derivative information */
#pragma LINK_INFO DERIVATIVE "mc9s12dg256b"

#include "main_asm.h" /* interface to the assembly module */

void main(void) {
  int width;
  PLL_init();      // set system clock frequency to 24 MHz
  servo76_init();              // enable pwm1 for servo
  while(1) {
    for(width = 4500; width <= 6000; width = width + 5){
      set_servo76(width);      // move servo from 4500 to 6000
      ms_delay(5);
    }
    for(width = 6000; width >= 3000; width = width - 5){
      set_servo76(width);      // move servo from 6000 to 3000
      ms_delay(5);
    }
    for(width = 3000; width < 4500; width = width + 5){
      set_servo76(width);      // move servo from 3000 to 4500
      ms_delay(5);
    }
  }
}
```

Under the Hood

Listing 7.5 shows the assembly language routines corresponding to the four C function calls in Table 7.2. In the subroutine, *servo54_init*, we concatenate channels 4 and 5 by writing a 1 to bit 6 in the PWM control register, *PWMCTL*, in Fig. 7.3b. Note that the channel 5 pin will be used for the output, and the channel 5 bits are used in the *PWMPOL*, *PWMCLK*, *PWMCAE*, and *PWME* registers. We select clock *A* by clearing bit 5 in *PWMCLK*. By storing a hex $33 in *PWMPRCLK*, we set the clock frequency to 3 MHz by dividing the 24 MHz bus clock by 8. To make the period exactly 20 ms, we store a value of 60000 in *PWMPER4* (which is the concatenation of channels 4 and 5), which will give a period of 60000/3 MHz = 20.0 ms. Storing 4500 in PWMDTY4 will give an initial pulse width of 1.5 ms.

The subroutine *set_servo54* will store the value passed in accumulator *D* in register *PWMDTY4*, which will be the concatenation of *PWMDTY4* and *PWMDTY5*, with *PWMDTY4* being the high byte. To move the servo over its complete range, this value stored in *PWMDTY4* should range from about 3000 to 6000.

The subroutines *servo76_init* and *set_servo76* in Listing 7.5 behave in a similar manner to *servo54_init* and *set_servo54* except in this case channels 6 and 7 are being concatenated. The channel 7 pin is used for the output, and the channel 7 bits are used in the *PWMPOL*, *PWMCLK*, *PWMCAE*, and *PWME* registers. The 16-bit period and duty values are stored in *PWMPER6* and *PWMDTY6*, respectively.

Listing 7.5 ***servo*** **Assembly Language Subroutines from** ***main.asm***

```
; PWM -- servos  20 ms period   16-bit mode
;        pulse width 1.1 ms - 1.5 ms - 1.9 ms
;        for duty inputs  -3300    4500      +5700

; servo54_init();     Initialize pwm 5 - pin PP5
servo54_init:
            bset  PWMPOL,#$20     ;start high
            bclr  PWMCLK,#$20     ;use clock A
            movb  #$33,PWMPRCLK   ;/8  24/8 = 3 MHz
            clr   PWMCAE          ;left align
            bset  PWMCTL,#$40     ;concatenate 4 and 5
            movw  #60000,PWMPER4  ;period = 20ms
            movw  #4500,PWMDTY4   ;initial pulse width = 1.5ms
            bset  PWME,#$20       ;enable PWM5
            rts

; set duty cycle
; set_servo54(int width);
set_servo54:
            std   PWMDTY4         ;set new pulse width
            rts

; servo76_init();     Initialize pwm 7 - pin PP7
servo76_init:
            bset  PWMPOL,#$80     ;start high
            bclr  PWMCLK,#$80     ;use clock B
            movb  #$33,PWMPRCLK   ;/8  24/8 = 3 MHz
            clr   PWMCAE          ;left align
            bset  PWMCTL,#$80     ;concatenate 6 and 7
            movw  #60000,PWMPER6  ;period = 20ms
            movw  #4500,PWMDTY6   ;initial pulse width = 1.5ms
            bset  PWME,#$80       ;enable PWM7
            rts

; set duty cycle
; set_servo76(int width);
set_servo76:
            std   PWMDTY6         ;set new pulse width
            rts
```

Chapter 8

Serial Communication Interface (SCI)

In this chapter, we will show how to communicate from a serial port on your PC to an SCI port on the DRAGON12-Plus-USB board. We will provide new C function calls to make it easy to do this. The DRAGON12-Plus-USB has a USB port that connects directly to a USB port on your computer. However, it will be listed as a serial port under Ports in the Components section of the System Summary on your computer. You will need to determine from this Ports section what COM port number to use in CodeWarrior to connect to the DRAGON12-Plus-USB board. If you are using an older DRAGON12-Plus board that has a standard 9-pin serial connector, you will need to use a USB-to-serial converter cable to connect a USB port on your computer to the serial connector on the DRAGON12-Plus board.

8.1 Asynchronous Serial I/O

There are two basic types of serial communication: *synchronous* and *asynchronous*. In synchronous communication, the timing is controlled by a standard clock at both the transmitter and receiver ends, and data are normally sent in blocks that often contain error checking. On the other hand, the timing for asynchronous communication is handled one character at a time and while the clocks at the transmitter and receiver must be approximately the same, they are resynchronized with each character. Because each character requires these additional synchronizing bits, asynchronous communication is slower than synchronous communication. However, it is simpler to implement and is in widespread use.

Asynchronous serial communication uses a *start bit* to tell when a particular character is being sent. This is illustrated in Fig. 8.1, which shows the transmitted waveform when the character *"T"* (ASCII code = 0x54) is sent with odd parity. Before a character is sent, the line is in the high, or *mark* state. The line is then brought low (called a *space*) and held low for a time τ called the bit time. This first space is called the *start bit*. It is typically followed by seven or eight data bits. The least significant bit *D*0 is transmitted first. For example, in Fig. 8.1 the seven bits corresponding to the ASCII code 0x54 (the character *"T"*) are sent starting with *D*0. These seven bits are followed by a *parity bit*. This bit is set to a 1 or a 0 such that the sum of the number of 1's transmitted is either even or odd. We have used odd parity in Fig. 8.1. Since three 1's were sent (*D*2, *D*4, and *D*6) the parity bit is zero. Often a character is sent with no parity and 8 data bits. The parity bit is followed by one or two stop bits, which are always high (a *mark*). The next character will be indicated by the presence of the next start bit.

The reciprocal of the bit time is called the *baud rate*. Some common baud rates used in serial communication are given in Table 8.1. We will provide you with a C function call that allows you to set any baud rate when you initialize the SCI port.

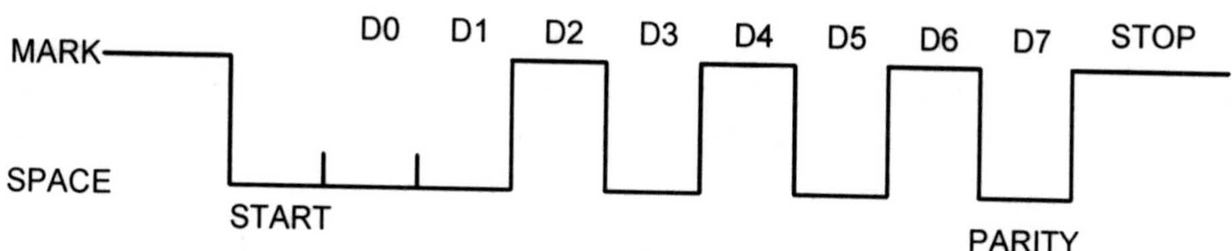

Figure 8.1 ASCII code 54H = 1010100 ("T") sent with odd parity

Table 8.1 Common Asynchronous Serial Baud Rates

Baud rate	Bit time (msec)	No. of STOP bits	Char. time (msec.)	Char./sec.
110	9.09	2	100.00	10
300	3.33	1	33.3 3	30
600	1.67	1	16.67	60
1200	0.833	1	8.33	120
2400	0.417	1	4.17	240
4800	0.208	1	2.08	480
9600	0.104	1	1.04	960
14400	0.069	1	0.69	1440
19200	0.052	1	0.52	1920
28800	0.035	1	0.35	2880
38400	0.026	1	0.26	3840
57600	0.017	1	0.17	5760

8.2 The 68HCS12 SCI Interface

The MC9S12DG256 has two separate SCI modules, SCI0 and SCI1. On the DRAGON12-Plus-USB board, jumper J42 is used to select whether SCI0 or SCI1 is connected to the USB connector that you use to connect to a USB port of your PC. SCI0 is normally selected. Both SCI0 and SCI1 have TTL header connectors on the DRAGON12-Plus-USB board.

A functional block diagram of the serial communication interface is shown in Fig. 8.2. The main function of the SCI is to transform parallel data from the HCS12 into serial data and send it out through the transmit data pin *TxD*, and to receive serial data through the receive data pin *RxD* and transform it to parallel data that can be read by the HCS12.

The signals *TxD* (pins *PS*1 or *PS*3) and *RxD* (pins *PS*0 or *PS*2) are generally connected to a 9-pin "D" connector through an EIA-232-D (formally RS-232C) driver/receiver chip. This driver/receiver transforms the logic 0 (0 volts) and logic 1 (5 volts) signals to +12 volts and –12 volts respectively. (Sometimes +5 volts and –5 volts are used.) This allows for more noise immunity when sending the signals over a long distance.

Pin 2 on the "D" connector is normally the "transmit" pin *TxD* on the microcontroller board and pin 3 is the "receive" pin *RxD*. But if a straight-through cable is connected from the serial port on a PC to your target HCS12 board, then the PC's "transmit" pin must be pin 3 so that it is connected to the *RxD* pin on the HCS12 board. Similarly, pin 2 on the PC will be the "receive" pin so that it is connected to the *TxD* pin on the HCS12 board.

If you want to communicate between two DRAGON12-Plus-USB boards using the SCI1 port, it is necessary to interchange the wires in the cable so that the transmit pin at one end is connected to the receive pin at the other end, and vice versa. We call this a *null modem*.

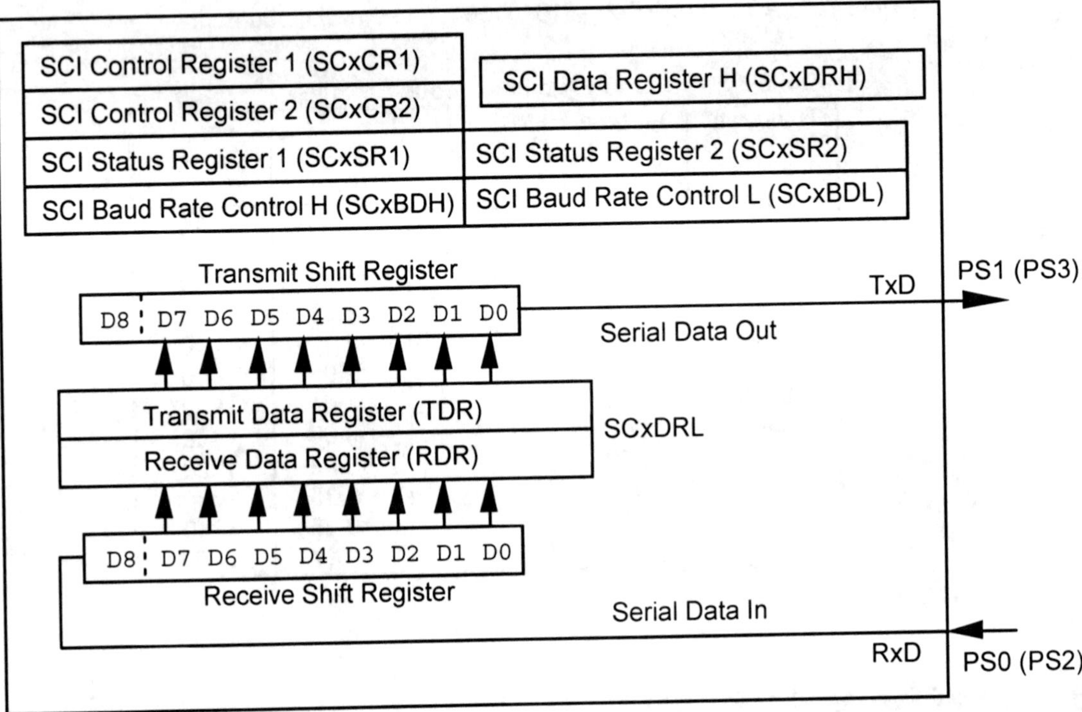

Figure 8.2 Functional diagram of the Serial Communications Interface (SCI)

To use the SCI ports on the HCS12 it is necessary to program a number of different registers, some of which are shown in Fig. 8.2. We have done this for you by providing the C function calls shown in Table 8.2. Additional SCI C function calls that are provided are described in Section 8.4

Table 8.2 C Function calls for the SCI port

Function	Description
`void SCI0_init(int b);`	Initialize SCI0 with baud rate *b*
`char inchar0(void);`	Wait for character in SCI0 and return char
`void outchar0(char c);`	Output character *c* out SCI0 TxD pin
`void SCI1_init(int b);`	Initialize SCI1 with baud rate *b*
`char inchar1(void);`	Wait for character in SCI1 and return char
`void outchar1(char c);`	Output character *c* out SCI1 TxD pin

Example 23 – SCI Echo with LCD Display

Listing 8.1 is a program that initializes the SCI0 port to 9600 baud, waits for a character to come in *RxD*, and then sends the same character back out *TxD*. To test this program download it to the DRAGON12-Plus-USB board in the usual way, execute the program, and then make sure that you close the Real-Time Debugger window. Then run any convenient terminal program, such as HyperTerminal, running at 9600 baud. You can find HyperTerminal on your PC by going to *Start* -> *Programs* -> *Accessories* -> *Communications* -> *HyperTerminal*. Make sure you set up HyperTerminal with no hardware handshaking. Pressing any key on the PC keyboard will send the ASCII code of the key out the serial port to the DRAGON12-Plus-USB, which will display the character on the LCD and then echo it back to the PC, where it will be displayed. Note that the terminal program does not display a character on the screen until it has made a round trip to the DRAGON12-Plus-USB board and back. Try it. Note that when you get to the end of the first line of the LCD display you must type 48 more characters before a character gets displayed on the second line. (Recall the LCD memory addresses in Fig. 4.3.)

Listing 8.1 Example 23

```
// Example 23: SCI Echo with LCD display
#include <hidef.h>      /* common defines and macros */
#include <mc9s12dg256.h>     /* derivative information */
#pragma LINK_INFO DERIVATIVE "mc9s12dg256b"
#include "main_asm.h" /* interface to the assembly module */

void main(void) {
   char c;
   PLL_init();         // set system clock frequency to 24 MHz
   lcd_init();         // enable lcd
   SCI0_init(9600);    // initialize SCI0 at 9600 baud
   while(1){
     c = inchar0();    // wait for character
     data8(c);         // write it to the LCD
     outchar0(c);      // echo it back
   }
}
```

Under the Hood

The registers used for programming the SCI module are shown in Fig. 8.3. Listing 8.2 shows the assembly language routines corresponding to the six C function calls in Table 8.2.

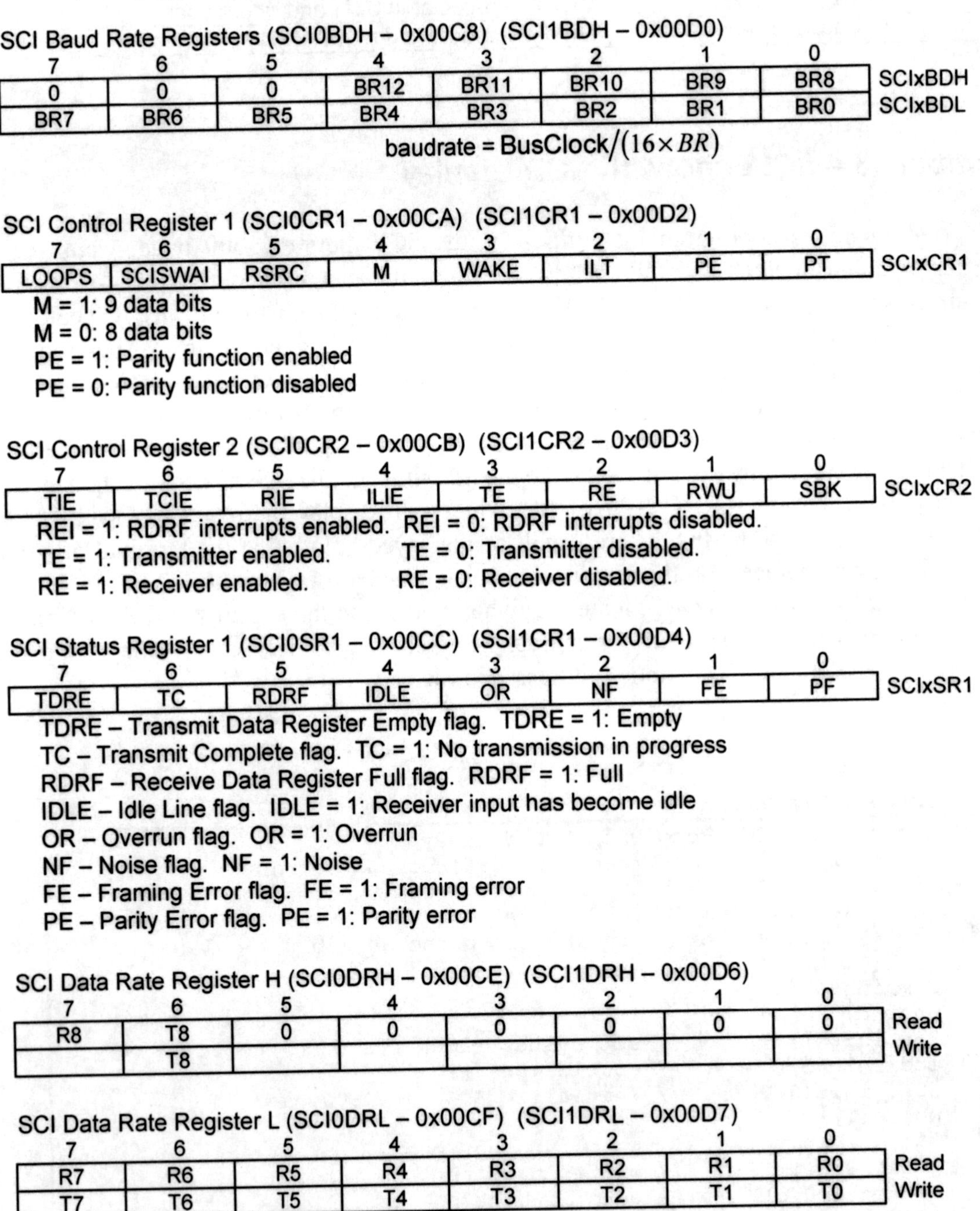

SCI Baud Rate Registers (SCI0BDH – 0x00C8) (SCI1BDH – 0x00D0)
7 6 5 4 3 2 1 0
0 0 0 BR12 BR11 BR10 BR9 BR8 SCIxBDH
BR7 BR6 BR5 BR4 BR3 BR2 BR1 BR0 SCIxBDL
baudrate = BusClock/(16×BR)
SCI Control Register 1 (SCI0CR1 – 0x00CA) (SCI1CR1 – 0x00D2)
7 6 5 4 3 2 1 0
LOOPS SCISWAI RSRC M WAKE ILT PE PT SCIxCR1
M = 1: 9 data bits
M = 0: 8 data bits
PE = 1: Parity function enabled
PE = 0: Parity function disabled
SCI Control Register 2 (SCI0CR2 – 0x00CB) (SCI1CR2 – 0x00D3)
7 6 5 4 3 2 1 0
TIE TCIE RIE ILIE TE RE RWU SBK SCIxCR2
REI = 1: RDRF interrupts enabled. REI = 0: RDRF interrupts disabled.
TE = 1: Transmitter enabled. TE = 0: Transmitter disabled.
RE = 1: Receiver enabled. RE = 0: Receiver disabled.
SCI Status Register 1 (SCI0SR1 – 0x00CC) (SSI1CR1 – 0x00D4)
7 6 5 4 3 2 1 0
TDRE TC RDRF IDLE OR NF FE PF SCIxSR1
TDRE – Transmit Data Register Empty flag. TDRE = 1: Empty
TC – Transmit Complete flag. TC = 1: No transmission in progress
RDRF – Receive Data Register Full flag. RDRF = 1: Full
IDLE – Idle Line flag. IDLE = 1: Receiver input has become idle
OR – Overrun flag. OR = 1: Overrun
NF – Noise flag. NF = 1: Noise
FE – Framing Error flag. FE = 1: Framing error
PE – Parity Error flag. PE = 1: Parity error
SCI Data Rate Register H (SCI0DRH – 0x00CE) (SCI1DRH – 0x00D6)
7 6 5 4 3 2 1 0
R8 T8 0 0 0 0 0 0 Read
T8 Write
SCI Data Rate Register L (SCI0DRL – 0x00CF) (SCI1DRL – 0x00D7)
7 6 5 4 3 2 1 0
R7 R6 R5 R4 R3 R2 R1 R0 Read
T7 T6 T5 T4 T3 T2 T1 T0 Write

Figure 8.3 SCI Registers

In the subroutine *SCI0_init*, all of the bits in control register, *SCI0CR1*, are cleared to zero. This will select 8 data bits and no parity as shown in Fig. 8.3. You can refer to the file *S12SCIV2.pdf*, available from Freescale, for a description of the other bits in this control register. We will always clear them to zero. The hex value $0C is stored in control register, *SCI0CR2*. This will enable the SCI transmitter and receiver, while disabling all interrupts. Finally, the subroutine *SCI0_init*, sets the baud rate. The *baudrate* is passed to the subroutine in accumulator *D*. The 13-bit value, *BR*, to store in the baud rate registers, *SCI0BDH:SCI0BDL*, is found using the formula

$$BR = \text{BusClock}/(16 \times \text{baudrate})$$

In our case, the BusClock is 24 MHz, and $24000000/16 = 1500000 = \$16E360$. Therefore, we need to calculate $BR = \$16E360/D$. The *ediv* instruction will divide (*Y:D*) by *X* and leave the quotient in *Y*. We must therefore first transfer *D* to *X* and then store $0016 in *Y* and $E360 in *D*. After calling *ediv*, the quotient, *Y*, will be the value of *BR* to be stored in *SCI0BDH*.

When receiving a character, you must first wait for the *RDRF* flag in status register 1 to go high. In the subroutine *inchar*0 in Listing 8.2, the statement

```
inchar0:    brclr   SCI0SR1,#$20,inchar0
```

will do this. Recall that this statement will branch on itself as long as the AND of *SCI0SR1* and $20 is zero, i.e. as long as bit 5 of *SCI0SR1* is zero. As soon as the *RDRF* flag goes to 1, a character has been received in *SCI0DRL*, and this value is loaded into accumulator *B*, which returns this value to the calling function in the C program.

When sending a character, you must first wait for the *TDRE* flag in status register 1 to go high, meaning that the transmit data register is empty. In the subroutine *outchar0* in Listing 8.2, the statement

```
outchar0:    brclr SCI0SR1,#$80,outchar0
```

will do this by waiting for bit 7 of *SCI0SR1* to go to 1. As soon as the *TDRE* flag goes to 1, the transmit data register is empty, and the value in accumulator *B*, passed from the calling function in the C program, is stored in *SCI0DRL*.

The three SCI1 subroutines in Listing 8.2 are the same as the SCI0 subroutines, except that they use the SCI1 registers.

Listing 8.2 ***SCI*** **Assembly Language Subroutines from** ***main.asm***

```
; SCI0 - Serial Communications Interface
; Initialize SCI0, input: D = baudrate
SCI0_init:
        CLR SCI0CR1            ;8-bit data, no parity
        MOVB #$0C, SCI0CR2 ;enable TE,RE. no interrupts
        TFR D,X                ;calculate baud rate
        LDY #$0016             ;baudrate = 24MHz/(16*BR)
        LDD #$E360             ;24Mhz/16 = $16E360
        EDIV                   ;Y = (Y:D)/X = $16E360/baudrate
        STY SCI0BDH            ;BR = (SCI0BDH:SCI0BDL)
        RTS

inchar0:
        brclr SCI0SR1,#$20,inchar0      ;wait for RDRF
        LDAB  SCI0DRL                   ;get char
        RTS

outchar0:
        brclr SCI0SR1,#$80,outchar0     ;wait for TDRE
        STAB  SCI0DRL                   ;write char
        RTS

; SCI1 - Serial Communications Interface
; Initialize SCI1, input: D = baudrate
SCI1_init:
        CLR SCI1CR1            ;8-bit data, no parity
        MOVB #$0C, SCI1CR2 ;enable TE,RE. no interrupts
        TFR D,X                ;calculate baud rate
        LDY #$0016             ;baudrate = 24MHz/(16*BR)
        LDD #$E360             ;24Mhz/16 = $16E360
        EDIV                   ;Y = (Y:D)/X = $16E360/baudrate
        STY SCI1BDH            ;BR = (SCI0BDH:SCI0BDL)
        RTS

inchar1:
        brclr SCI1SR1,#$20,inchar1      ;wait for RDRF
        LDAB  SCI1DRL                   ;get char
        RTS

outchar1:
        brclr SCI1SR1,#$80,outchar1     ;wait for TDRE
        STAB  SCI1DRL                   ;write char
        RTS
```

8.3 A Circular Queue Data Structure

A *circular queue* is a useful data structure to use when you need to store characters read in an interrupt service routine. The queue can then be read as necessary without missing any of the received characters. In Example 24, we will illustrate using a queue by storing values read from a keypad in a queue and then displaying them all on an LCD. In Example 25 we will use a queue to store characters received in the SCI port using interrupts.

A circular queue is shown in Fig. 8.4. Multiple values can be stored in this queue before they are removed (in the same order they were stored). Therefore, characters will not be lost if they are received faster than they are removed. Of course, if the queue is full and another character is received, it will be lost. We will implement this queue by writing four C functions whose prototypes are shown in Listing 8.3. The C programs for these four functions are in the separate C file called *queue.c* that is shown in Listing 8.4.

The queue is defined to be an array called *qbuff* containing *QMAX* bytes. The index of the first byte in the queue (0) is stored in the variable *min* and the index of the last byte in the queue (*QMAX*-1) is stored in the variable *max*. The index values *front* and *rear* are initialized to 0 in the C function *initq*( ) in Listing 8.4 and serve as pointers to the front and rear of the queue. To store a value in the queue, the index *rear* is incremented and the value is stored at *qbuff*[*rear*]. However, when *rear* exceeds *max* it must wrap around to *min*. If *rear* ever runs into *front*, then the queue is full and we will back up *rear* and not store the new value. The complete algorithm for storing a value in the queue is implemented by the C function *qstore*(char *c*) in Listing 8.4 which stores the character *c* in the queue.

To read a value from the queue the index *front* is incremented, and the value at *qbuff*[*front*] is read. This will guarantee that the first value stored in the queue will be the first one read from the queue. The queue will be empty any time that *front* = *rear*. The C function int *qempty*(void) shown in Listing 8.4 will return a 1 (true) if the queue is empty and return a 0 (false) if the queue is not empty.

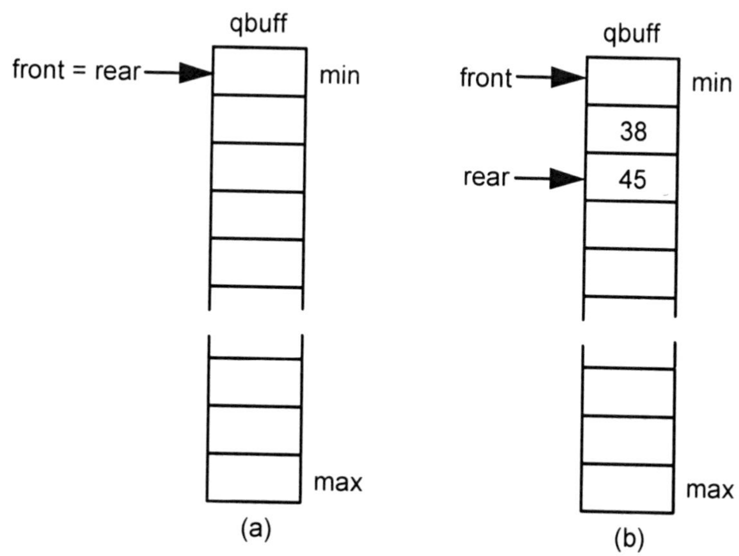

Figure 8.4 A circular queue:
(a) empty; (b) containing two values

The variables in Listing 8.4 are defined to be *static* so they will not be visible to your main program *main.c*. When you create a project using the stationery file

LBE_DRAGON12-Plus-USB, the files *queue.c* (Listing 8.4) and *queue.h* shown in Listing 8.3, will be in the source folder of your CodeWarrior project. These will be available for you to use by including the statement *#include "queue.h"* in your main program as shown in Examples 24 and 25 below.

Note that the default value of QMAX (the size of the queue) is 16. This is too small for many real applications, so you may want to increase it for your particular application.

Listing 8.3 Function prototypes (queue.h)

```
// queue.h  A character queue
void  initq(void);          // initialize the queue
void  qstore(char);         // store character in queue
int   qempty(void);         // return 0 if queue is not empty
char  getq(void);           // read character from queue
```

Listing 8.4 A character queue (queue.c)

```
// queue.c  A character queue
#include   "queue.h"      // prototype definitions
#define    QMAX 16        // size of queue

static char qbuff[QMAX];  // the queue
static int  front;
static int  rear;         // queue pointers
static int  min = 0;      // start of queue
static int  max = QMAX-1; // end of queue

void initq(void){
       min = 0;
       front = 0;
       rear = 0;
       max = QMAX-1;
}

void  qstore(char c){
  rear++;                       // inc rear
  if(rear > max)
    rear = min;
  if(rear == front){
    rear--;                     // queue is full
    if(rear < min)              //  rewind rear
      rear = max;
  }else
    qbuff[rear] = c;            // store c at rear
}
```

Listing 8.4 (cont.) A character queue (queue.c)

```
int qempty(void){
  int flag;
    if(front == rear)
      flag = 1;
    else
      flag = 0;
  return (flag);
}

char  getq(void){
  front++;                        // inc front
  if(front > max)
    front = 0;
  return qbuff[front];            // return value at front
}
```

Example 24 – Keypad Input to LCD Using a Queue

As an example of using the queue described in Listing 8.4, the program shown in Listing 8.5 will display the characters (0 – 9) that you type on the keypad on the first line of the LCD and store each character in the queue. When you press the the * key ("E"), the program will read (and remove) each character stored in the queue, in turn, and display the result on the second line of the LCD. The first line will be cleared, waiting to enter more characters into the queue. Pressing the # key ("F") will clear the display.

Listing 8.5 Example 24

```
// Example 24: Example of using a queue
#include <hidef.h>              /* common defines and macros */
#include <mc9s12dg256.h>        /* derivative information */
#pragma LINK_INFO DERIVATIVE "mc9s12dg256b"

#include "queue.h"
#include "main_asm.h" /* interface to the assembly module */

void main(void) {
  char* blanks;
  char  c, a;
  blanks = "                ";
  PLL_init();                     // set system clock frequency to 24 MHz
  lcd_init();                     // enable lcd
  initq();                  // initialize the queue
  keypad_enable();                // enable keypad
  set_lcd_addr(0x00);       // display on 1st line
```

Listing 8.5 (cont.) Example 24

```
  while(1) {
     c = getkey();              // read keypad
     a = hex2asc(c);            // convert to ascii
     qstore(a);                 //   and store in queue
     data8(a);                  //   display on LCD
     wait_keyup();              //   wait to release key
     switch(c){
        case 0xE:               // if enter (*) key
           set_lcd_addr(0x40); // display on 2nd line
           while(qempty() != 1){     // empty the queue
              data8(getq());    //  and display on lcd
           }
           set_lcd_addr(0x00); // clear 1st line
           type_lcd(blanks);
           wait_keyup();             // wait to release key
           set_lcd_addr(0x00); // display on 1st line
           break;
        case 0xF:               // if clear (#) key
           clear_lcd();         // clear lcd display
           wait_keyup();             // wait to release key
           break;
        default:
           break;
     }
  }
}
```

8.4 SCI Interface Using Interrupts

In Example 23 we used the SCI port to receive characters typed on the PC keyboard and displayed the characters on the LCD. The problem with that example is that it takes some time to display a character on the LCD. If many characters are coming in the SCI port one after the other, then some of the characters may be lost. This will happen if, during the time it takes to write to the LCD and echo back the character, one or more characters have overrun each other before they can be read using *inchar*0( ). The solution to this problem is to enable receiver interrupts so that an SCI interrupt is generated each time a character is received. The interrupt service routine can then read the received byte and store the value in a queue using the function *qstore*(char *c*) as described in Section 8.3.

The built-in assembly language routines that can be used for SCI receive interrupts can be called using the C functions shown in Table 8.3. The functions for using the queue described in Section 8.3 are shown in Table 8.4.

Table 8.3 C Function calls for the SCI port with interrupts

Function	Description
`void SCI0_int_init(int b);`	Initialize SCI0 with interrupts and baud rate *b*
`char read_SCI0_Rx(void);`	Read character received in SCI0 Rx port
`void outchar0(char c);`	Output character *c* out SCI0 TxD pin
`void SCI1_int_init(int b);`	Initialize SCI1 with interrupts and baud rate *b*
`char read_SCI1_Rx(void);`	Read character received in SCI1 Rx port
`void outchar1(char c);`	Output character *c* out SCI1 TxD pin

Table 8.4 C Function calls for using the character queue in queue.c

Function	Description
`void initq(void);`	initialize the queue
`void qstore(char);`	store character in queue
`int qempty(void);`	return 0 if queue is not empty
`char getq(void);`	read character from queue

Example 25 – Display SCI Input on LCD Using Receive Interrupts

An example of using an SCI interrupt with a queue is given in Listing 8.6. Interrupt number 20 is the SCI0 interrupts and the function *SCI0_int_init(9600)* will enable receive interrupts and initialize the SCI0 port to 9600 baud. Every time a character is received, the interrupt service routine *handler*( ) shown in Listing 8.6 will execute. This routine simply reads the received character using *read_SCI0_Rx*( ) and stores this value in the queue.

The main program continually monitors the queue, and if there is a character in the queue, it will read it (which removes it from the queue), write it to the LCD, and echo it back to the PC. Note that as long as the queue does not become full you will not miss any characters.

Test this program by downloading it to the DRAGON12-Plus-USB board and executing the program. Then close the download window so as to disconnect from the serial port. Run the program *host.exe* and download some text file that contains between 16 and 32 characters by pressing function key F6 and typing in the filename. Experiment by changing the size of the queue in *queue.c* so that you can display all 32 characters on the LCD.

Listing 8.6 Example 25

```
// Example 25: SCI using receive interrupts
#include <hidef.h>              /* common defines and macros */
#include <mc9s12dp256.h>        /* derivative information */
#include "queue.h"

#include "main_asm.h" /* interface to the assembly module */

#pragma LINK_INFO DERIVATIVE "mc9s12dp256b"

// SCI0 receive Interrupt Service Routine
void interrupt 20 handler(){
      qstore(read_SCI0_Rx());
}

void main(void) {
char c;
   PLL_init();           // set system clock frequency to 24 MHz
   lcd_init();            // enable lcd
   initq();               // initialize the queue
   SCI0_int_init(9600);   // initialize SCI0 at with interrupts
   while(1){
     while(qempty() != 1){       // empty the queue
        c = getq();              //  and display on lcd
        data8(c);                // write it to the LCD
        outchar0(c);             // echo it back
     }
   }
}
```

Under the Hood

Listing 8.7 gives the assembly language subroutines associated with the new C function calls shown in Table 8.3. The only differences between the subroutines *SCI0_init* in Listing 8.2 and *SCI0_int_init* in Listing 8.7 is that in the latter case we store the hex value $2C in *SCI0CR2*, which will enable receive interrupts by writing a 1 to bit 5 (*REI*) in control register 2 in Fig. 8.3. We also need to enable hardware interrupts by including the instruction *CLI* at the end of the *SCI0_int_init* subroutine.

The subroutine *read_SCI0_Rx* in Listing 8.7 will just read the byte that has been shifted in *Rx* and loaded into *SCI0DRL*. A dummy read of *SCI0SR1* is required, because the *RDRF* flag is cleared by a read of *SCI0SR1* followed by a read of *SCI0DRL*. Note how C function *read_SCI0_Rx*( ) is used in the interrupt service routine in Listing 8.6 to read the value received in the SCI port and storing it in the queue.

Listing 8.7 *SCI_INT* Assembly Language Subroutines from *main.asm*

```
;   SCI0 receive interrupt setup 9600 baud
;   void SCI0_int_init(int)
SCI0_int_init:
        SEI                         ;disable interrupts
        CLR  SCI0CR1                ;8-bit data, no parity
        MOVB #$2C, SCI0CR2          ;enable TE,RE. RX int
        TFR  D,X                    ;calculate baud rate
        LDY  #$0016                 ;baudrate = 24MHz/(16*BR)
        LDD  #$E360                 ;24Mhz/16 = $16E360
        EDIV                        ;Y = (Y:D)/X = $16E360/baudrate
        STY  SCI0BDH                ;BR = (SCI0BDH:SCI0BDL)
        CLI                         ;enable interrupts
        RTS

;   Read Rx byte
;   char read_SCI0_Rx()
read_SCI0_Rx:
        LDAA SCI0SR1                ; clears RDRF flag
        LDAB SCI0DRL                ; return data
        RTS

;   SCI1 receive interrupt setup 9600 baud
;   void SCI1_int_init(int)
SCI1_int_init:
        SEI                         ;disable interrupts
        CLR  SCI1CR1                ;8-bit data, no parity
        MOVB #$2C, SCI1CR2          ;enable TE,RE. RX int
        TFR  D,X                    ;calculate baud rate
        LDY  #$0016                 ;baudrate = 24MHz/(16*BR)
        LDD  #$E360                 ;24Mhz/16 = $16E360
        EDIV                        ;Y = (Y:D)/X = $16E360/baudrate
        STY  SCI1BDH                ;BR = (SCI1BDH:SCI1BDL)
        CLI                         ;enable interrupts
        RTS

;   Read Rx byte
;   char read_SCI1_Rx()
read_SCI1_Rx:
        LDAA  SCI1SR1               ; clears RDRF flag
        LDAB  SCI1DRL               ; return data
        RTS
```

Example 26 – Sending Periodic Acceleration Measurements to Matlab

It is often useful to measure the acceleration at fixed time intervals (say every 10 ms) and send this data to a Matlab program for further analysis. Listing 8.8 shows a program that will do this.

The real-time interrupt service routine (see Chapter 5) will read the *x*-, *y*-, and *z*-acceleration values every 10.24 ms if the variable *reading* is set to 1 and the arrays defined for *ax*[*count*], *ay*[*count*], and *az*[*count*] are not full. The maximum buffer size is defined to be 1024 (about 10 seconds of data) at the beginning of the program. Note that the main program will collect acceleration data as long as you are holding down switch SW5 on the DRAGON12-Plus-USB board.

Listing 8.8 Example 26 – DRAGON12-Plus-USB

```
// Example 26: Read all three acceleration channels every 10 ms
// and send the data to MATLAB
#include <hidef.h>      /* common defines and macros */
#include <mc9s12dg256.h>     /* derivative information */
#pragma LINK_INFO DERIVATIVE "mc9s12dg256b"

#include "main_asm.h" /* interface to the assembly module */
#define BufMax 1024      // size of buffer arrays (~10s/10.24ms)


int ax[BufMax];
int ay[BufMax];
int az[BufMax];
int count;
int reading;

void interrupt 7 handler(){  // RTI service routine
  if (count<BufMax && reading==1) {
    ax[count]=ad1conv(0);  // ax: channel 0
    ay[count]=ad1conv(1);  // ay: channel 1
    az[count]=ad1conv(2);  // az: channel 2
    count++;
  }
  clear_RTI_flag();
}

void main(void) {
  int i;
  char* message;
  int lsb,msb,al,ah;

  PLL_init();              // set system clock frequency to 24 MHz
  ad1_enable();         // enable a/d converter 1
  lcd_init();           // enable lcd
  SCI0_init(9600);       // initialize SCI0 at 9600 baud
  SW_enable();          // enable switches
  RTI_init();           // enable RTI
  count=0;              // initialize count
  reading=0;            // read flag: false

  message="SW5: get data";
  set_lcd_addr(0x00);
  type_lcd(message);

  message="SW2: send data";
  set_lcd_addr(0x40);
  type_lcd(message);
```

Listing 8.8 (cont.) Example 26 – DRAGON12-Plus-USB

```
  while(1) {
    if(SW5_down()){
      //  collecting the acceleration data
      message = " Collecting data";
      set_lcd_addr(0x00);
      type_lcd(message);
      reading=1;                  // set read flag true
      while(SW5_down()){          // wait to release SW5
      }
      reading=0;                  // stop reading data
      set_lcd_addr(0x00);
      write_int_lcd(count);
      message=" values    ";
      type_lcd(message);
    }
    if(SW2_down()){
      // sending the acceleration data to MATLAB
      if (count>0){
        message=" Sending data...";
        set_lcd_addr(0x40);
        type_lcd(message);
        count--;              // make sure buffer has data
        lsb = count & 0x00FF;
        msb = count >>8;
        outchar0(lsb);        // send LSB of count
        outchar0(msb);        // send MSB of count
        for(i=0;i<count;i++){
          al = ax[i] & 0x00FF;
          ah = ax[i] >> 8;
          outchar0(al);           // send ax lo
          outchar0(ah);           // send ax hi
          al = ay[i] & 0x00FF;
          ah = ay[i] >> 8;
          outchar0(al);           // send ay lo
          outchar0(ah);           // send ay hi
          al = az[i] & 0x00FF;
          ah = az[i] >> 8;
          outchar0(al);           // send az lo
          outchar0(ah);           // send az hi
        }
        message="                ";
        set_lcd_addr(0x40);
        type_lcd(message);
        while(SW2_down()){        // wait to release SW2
        }
      }
      else {
        message="No data to send";
        set_lcd_addr(0x40);
        type_lcd(message);
        while(SW2_down()){        // wait to release SW2
        }
        message="                ";
        set_lcd_addr(0x40);
        type_lcd(message);
      }
    }
  }
}
```

Once you have collected the acceleration data, you must make sure that the CodeWarrior Debug window is closed, and then run the Matlab function *dragon2matlab( )* shown in Listing 8.9. Press switch SW2 to send the data out the serial port to Matlab. This Matlab function will collect the acceleration data and plot it on a graph. An example in which the accelerometer was bounced three times is shown in Fig. 8.5.

Listing 8.9 Matlab program to collect acceleration data

```
function dragon2matlab()
% 1.  Complile and flash the program in Example 26
% 2.  Run the program and close the CodeWarrior Debug window
% 3.  Press and hold pushbutton S1 to collect acceleration data
% 4.  Run the MATLAB function dragon2matlab()
% 5.  Press pushbutton S2 to send collected data
% dragon2matlab()

s = serial('COM1','BaudRate',9600,'DataBits',8);
fopen(s);  %opens the serial port
count = fread(s,1,'int16')        %get 16-bit integer
for i = 1:count                   %get acceleration data
    ax(i)=fread(s,1,'int16');
    ay(i)=fread(s,1,'int16');
    az(i)=fread(s,1,'int16');
end
fclose(s);
dt=0.01024;                       %data collected every 10.24 ms
for i=1:count
    t(i)=(i-1)*dt;
end
plot(t,ax,'-r', t, ay, '-g', t, az, '-b')
```

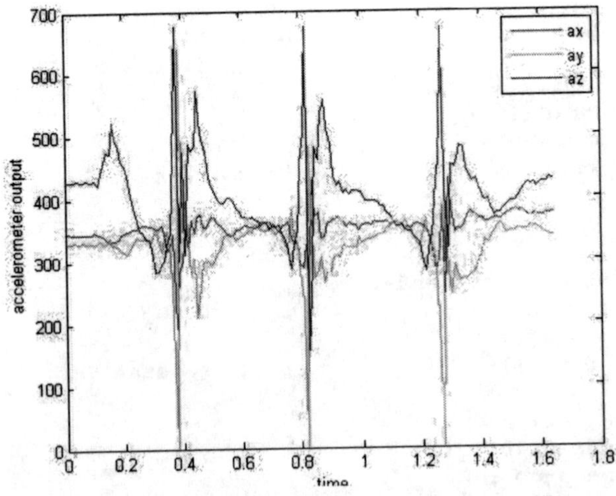

Figure 8.5 Matlab plot resulting from three bounces of the accelerometer

PROBLEMS

8.1 Modify Listing 8.1 to type your name on the PC keyboard and display it on the second row of the LCD display as you type it.

8.2 Write a program that uses the hex keypad described in Section 3.2. As you type characters on the keyboard, convert the hex value to ASCII and send the character out the SCI0 port. Test the program by running a terminal program on the PC that should display the characters that you type on the keypad.

8.3 Write a program that will collect light data from the light sensor on the DRAGON12-Plus-USB board every 100 ms for a period of 10 seconds when key 1 on the hex keypad is pressed. When key A on the hex keypad is pressed, the 100 samples of light data will be sent out the serial port to a Matlab program that will plot the data as a function of time.

Chapter 9

The Serial Peripheral Interface (SPI)

In this chapter we will show how the serial peripheral interface (SPI) can be interfaced to the LTC1661 dual 10-bit D/A converter (DAC) on the DRAGON12-Plus-USB board and used to read up to 16 switches on a hex keypad.

9.1 Operation of the SPI

There are two different methods of serial communications on HCS12 microcontrollers. We have already seen the use of the serial communications interface (SCI) in Chapter 8, which uses start and stop bits to synchronize each transmitted character. The second method of serial communications is the serial peripheral interface (SPI), which is a synchronous serial interface in which a clock signal is sent along with the data signal.

The SPI is a synchronous serial interface in which data in an 8-bit byte can be shifted in and/or out one bit at a time. It can be used to communicate with a serial peripheral device or with another microcontroller with an SPI interface. The MC9S12DG256 has three SPI modules that behave the same. Each module contains four signals as shown in Table 9.1. The pin numbers in parentheses in Table 9.1 are the MC9S12DG256 pin numbers. The system can operate in either a master or slave mode. When communicating with a peripheral device the MC9S12DG256 SPI will operate as the master. When one MC9S12DG256 (the master) is connected to a second MC9S12DG256 (the slave) the four SPI signals will be connected as shown in Fig. 9.1.

Table 9.1 MC9S12DP256 SPI Signals

Pin	SPI signal	Name
SPI0		
PS4 (93)	MISO0	Master-In-Slave-Out
PS5 (94)	MOSI0	Master-Out-Slave-In
PS6 (95)	SCK0	Serial Clock
PS7 (96)	SS0	Slave Select
SPI1		
PP0 (4)	MISO1	Master-In-Slave-Out
PP1 (3)	MOSI1	Master-Out-Slave-In
PP2 (2)	SCK1	Serial Clock
PP3 (1)	SS1	Slave Select
SPI2		
PP4 (112)	MISO2	Master-In-Slave-Out
PP5 (111)	MOSI2	Master-Out-Slave-In
PP7 (109)	SCK2	Serial Clock
PP6 (110)	SS2	Slave Select

In the master, the bits are sent out the *MOSI* (master out - slave in) pin and received in the *MISO* (master in - slave out) pin. In the slave, the bits are received in the *MOSI* (master out - slave in) pin and sent out the *MISO* (master in - slave out) pin. The bits to be shifted out are stored in the SPI data register, *SP0DR*, and by default are sent out most-significant bit (bit 7) first as shown in Figure 9.1. By programming a bit in one of the control registers, the bits can be sent out least significant bit first. At the same time that bit 7 is being shifted out the *MOSI* pin in the master, a bit from bit 7 of the slave is being shifted into bit 0 of the master via the *MISO* pin. This bit will eventually end up in bit 7 of the master after eight clock pulses or shifts. The clock which controls how fast the bits are shifted out of and into *SP0DR* is the signal *SCK*. The frequency of this clock can be controlled by the SPI baud rate register. The *SS* (slave-select) pin must be low to select a slave. This signal can come from any pin on the master, including its *SS* pin when it is configured as an output.

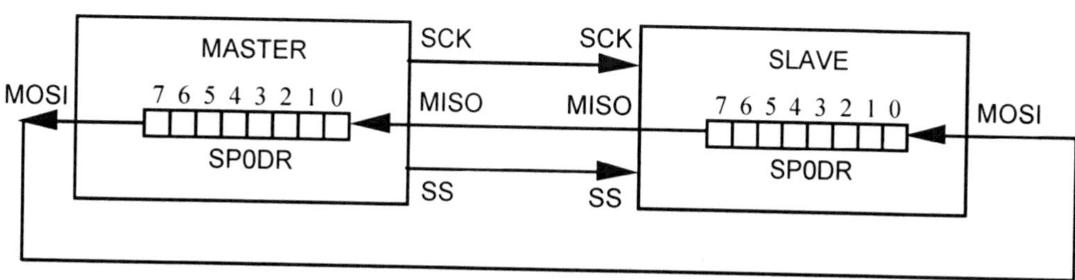

Figure 9.1 Two SPI modules connected in a master-slave configuration

9.2 Programming the SPI in C and Assembly Language

To make it easy to use the SPI ports, we have written assembly language routines that can be called using the C functions shown in Table 9.2. There are four functions associated with each of the three SPI modules (x = 0, 1, 2). The function *SPIx_init*( ) will initialize the SPI port as a master and set the clock rate to 250 kHz.

The function char *send_SPIx*(char *c*) will send a byte out the *MOSI* pin, wait for the transfer to be complete, and then return the value of the byte shifted into the data register. Finally, the functions *SSx_HI*( ) and *SSx_LO*( ) set the corresponding *SS* pin high and low.

To send a byte of data out the *SPI*0 *MOSI* pin you just need to put the byte in a character *c* and call the function *send_SPI*0(*c*). Note that when you do this a new byte will come into the SPI data register, *SPI0DR*, from the *MISO* pin. This may or may not be meaningful data, depending on whether that pin is connected to some peripheral. Similarly, the byte you send out the *MOSI* pin may or may not be meaningful, depending on whether that pin is connected to some peripheral. In Example 27, we will illustrate the use of the SPI port by interfacing it with the LTC1661 dual 10-bit D/A converter.

Table 9.2 C Function calls for the SPI ports

Function	Description
`void SPI0_init(void);`	Initialize SPI0 with baud rate of 250 kHz
`char send_SPI0(char c);`	Send character *c* out SCI0; returns character shifted in
`void SS0_HI(void);`	Set SS0 (PS7, pin 95) HI
`void SS0_LO(void);`	Set SS0 (PS7, pin 95) LO
`void SPI1_init();`	Initialize SPI1 with baud rate of 250 kHz
`char send_SPI1(char c);`	Send character *c* out SCI1; returns character shifted in
`void SS1_HI(void);`	Set SS1 (PP3, pin 1) HI
`void SS1_LO(void);`	Set SS1 (PP3, pin 1) LO
`void SPI2_init();`	Initialize SPI2 with baud rate of 250 kHz
`char send_SPI2(char c);`	Send character *c* out SCI2; returns character shifted in
`void SS2_HI(void);`	Set SS2 (PP6, pin 110) HI
`void SS2_LO(void);`	Set SS2 (PP6, pin 110) LO

Example 27 – Interfacing with the LTC1661 10-Bit DAC

The DRAGON12-Plus-USB includes a LTC1661 dual 10-bit D/A converter (DAC) on the board, which is interfaced to the MC9S12DG256 microcontroller through the *SPI0* port. A schematic of this chip is shown in Fig. 9.2. To produce an analog output on either output pins *OUTA* or *OUTB* or both the 16-bit word shown in Fig. 9.3 is shifted in the *DIN* pin from the *MOSI*0 pin (*PS5*) of the MC9S12DG256 microcontroller.

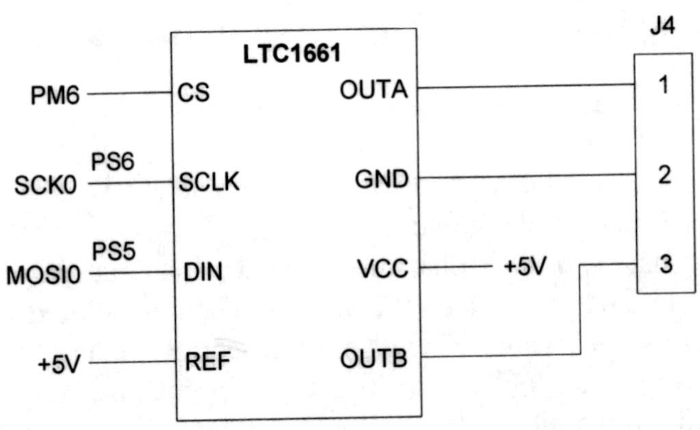

Figure 9.2 Connections of the LTC1661 on the DRAGON12-Plus-USB board

15	14	13	12	11	10	9	8	7	6	5	4	3	2	1	0
A3	A2	A1	A0	D9	D8	D7	D6	D5	D4	D3	D2	D1	D0	X1	X0

Figure 9.3 Input word to the LTC1661

The upper 4 bits in Fig. 9.3 are a 4-bit control code, whose functions are shown in Table 9.3. Bits 11 – 2 in Fig. 9.3 are the 10 bits of the binary number whose analog output is desired. The lower two bits in Fig. 9.3 are don't cares.

Table 9.3 DAC Control Functions

A0 A2 A1 A0	Operation
0 0 0 0	No change
0 0 0 1	Load Input Register A with Data. DAC outputs unchanged.
0 0 1 0	Load Input Register A with Data. DAC outputs unchanged.
0 0 1 1	Reserved
0 1 0 0	Reserved
0 1 0 1	Reserved
0 1 1 0	Reserved
0 1 1 1	Reserved
1 0 0 0	Load Both DAC Regs with Existing Contents of Input Regs. Outputs update.
1 0 0 1	Load Input Reg A. Outputs update.
1 0 1 0	Load Input Reg B. Outputs update.
1 0 1 1	Reserved
1 1 0 0	Reserved
1 1 0 1	No change in input or DAC registers.
1 1 1 0	No change in input or DAC registers.
1 1 1 1	Load both input registers A and B with same 10-bit code. Outputs update.

To begin a conversion the *CS* pin in Fig. 9.2 is brought low. This pin is connected to *PM*6 on the MC9S12DG256 microcontroller and can be brought low using the C statement

```
PTM &= 0xBF;
```

which is equivalent to

```
PTM = PTM & 0xBF;
```

and will force bit 6 of *PTM* to become 0 by ANDing *PTM* with 10111111.

After sending out the high byte of Fig. 9.3 and then the low byte using the C function call *send_SPI0(char)* from Table 9.2, the *CS* pin in Fig. 9.2 is brought high using the C statement

```
PTM |= 0x40;
```

which will force bit 6 of *PTM* to become 1 by ORing *PTM* with 01000000.

The *SCLK* pin in Fig. 9.2 is connected to the *SCK*0 pin (*PS*6) on the MC9S12DG256 microcontroller. The C function call *SPI0_init*( ) from Table 9.2 will initialize the *SPI*0 port with a baud rate of 250 kHz and shift the data into the DAC on the rising edge of the clock.

Listing 9.1 shows a C program that will read the DIP switches as an 8-bit binary number, store this data in bits 9:2 of Fig. 9.3, add the control code 1111 to load both *A* and *B*

DAC registers, send this 16-bit word to the LTC1661 DAC, read channel 1 of the ADC1 A/D converter, and display this value on the LCD. To test this program you must connect a wire between *OUTA* from the DAC (pin 1 of header *J4*) and channel 1 of ADC1 (pin *PAD*09 of header *H6*).

Listing 9.1 Example 27

```
// Example 27: SPI-Driven DAC
#include <hidef.h>          /* common defines and macros */
#include <mc9s12dg256.h>      /* derivative information */
#pragma LINK_INFO DERIVATIVE "mc9s12dg256b"

#include "main_asm.h" /* interface to the assembly module */

int val;
int w0;
char c;

void main(void) {
  PLL_init();         // set system clock frequency to 24 MHz
  ad1_enable();             // enable a/d converter 1
  lcd_init();               // enable lcd
  SPI0_init();              // enable SPI0 mode 0
  SW_enable();              // enable DIP switch
  DDRM = 0xFF;              // port M outputs
  while(1) {
    val = SW1_dip();        // read dip switch
    val = val << 2;         // shift 2 bits left
    val = val & 0x03FF;     // 8-bit input data
    val = val | 0xF000;     // add control code; load DACs A&B
    w0 = val >> 8;          // get high byte
    PTM &= 0xBF;            // bring PM6 low
    c = send_SPI0(w0);      // send high byte
    c = send_SPI0(val);     // send low byte
    PTM |= 0x40;            // bring PM6 high
    val = ad1conv(1);       // read channel 1 of ADC1
    set_lcd_addr(0x40);     // display on 2nd row of LCD
    write_int_lcd(val);     // write value in field of 5
    ms_delay(100);          // delay 0.1 seconds
  }
}
```

Note that the statement

```
val = val << 2;
```

will shift the 8-bit DIP switch reading that has been stored in the 16-bit variable *val* two bits to the left. When doing this, it performs a *sign-extend* operation. This means that a DIP switch reading of 10000000, when shifted 2 bits to the left, will be stored in *val* as 1111111000000000. Thus, bits *D*9 and *D*8 in Fig. 9.3 become 1 when they should be 0. We therefore use the instruction

```
val = val & 0x03FF;
```

to force the upper six bits in Fig. 9.3 to be zero before adding the control code with the instruction

```
val = val | 0xF000;
```

Under the Hood

The SPI registers are shown in Fig. 9.4. There are two control registers, a baud rate register, a status register, and a data register.

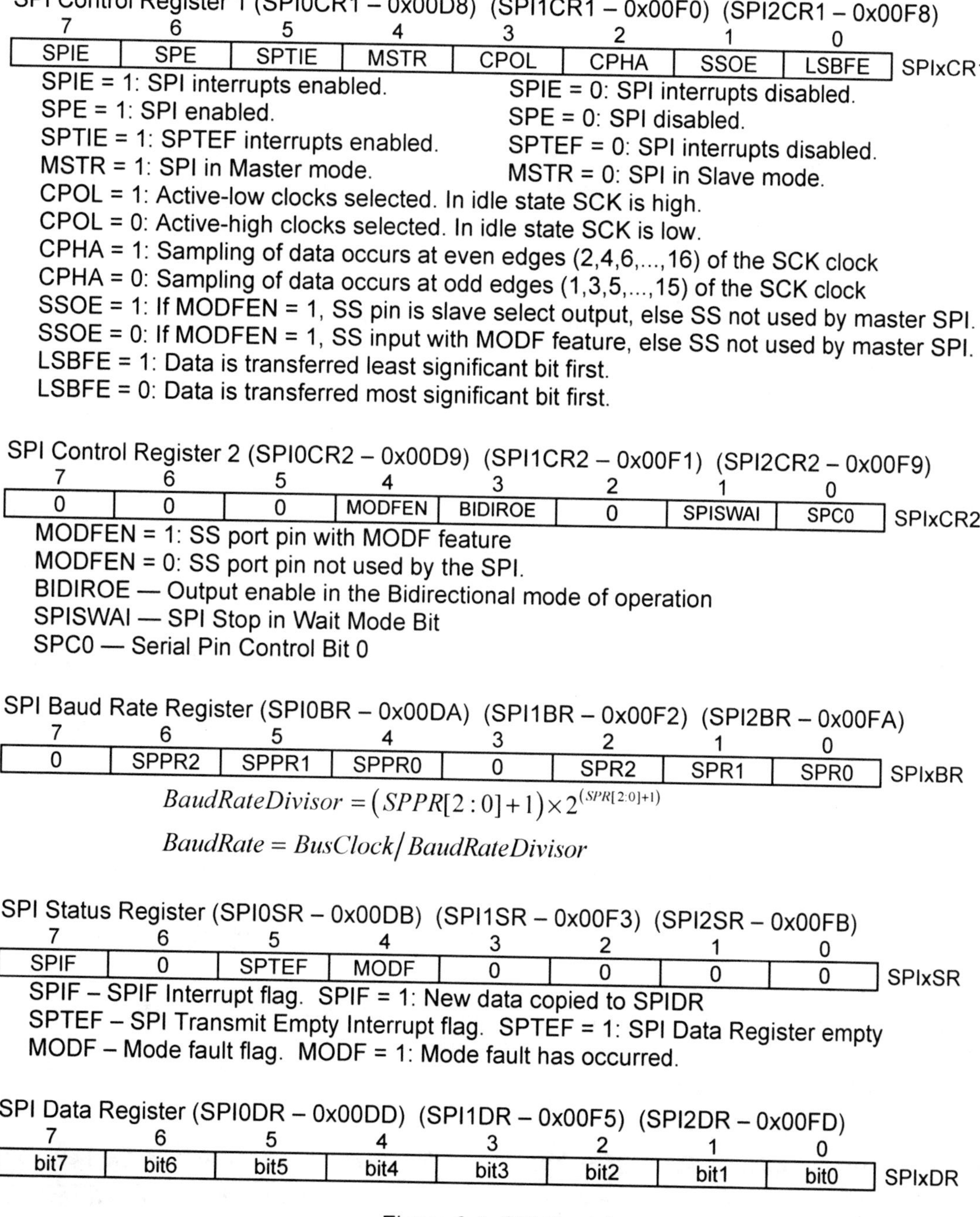

SPI Control Register 1 (SPI0CR1 – 0x00D8) (SPI1CR1 – 0x00F0) (SPI2CR1 – 0x00F8)

7	6	5	4	3	2	1	0	
SPIE	SPE	SPTIE	MSTR	CPOL	CPHA	SSOE	LSBFE	SPIxCR1

SPIE = 1: SPI interrupts enabled. SPIE = 0: SPI interrupts disabled.
SPE = 1: SPI enabled. SPE = 0: SPI disabled.
SPTIE = 1: SPTEF interrupts enabled. SPTEF = 0: SPI interrupts disabled.
MSTR = 1: SPI in Master mode. MSTR = 0: SPI in Slave mode.
CPOL = 1: Active-low clocks selected. In idle state SCK is high.
CPOL = 0: Active-high clocks selected. In idle state SCK is low.
CPHA = 1: Sampling of data occurs at even edges (2,4,6,...,16) of the SCK clock
CPHA = 0: Sampling of data occurs at odd edges (1,3,5,...,15) of the SCK clock
SSOE = 1: If MODFEN = 1, SS pin is slave select output, else SS not used by master SPI.
SSOE = 0: If MODFEN = 1, SS input with MODF feature, else SS not used by master SPI.
LSBFE = 1: Data is transferred least significant bit first.
LSBFE = 0: Data is transferred most significant bit first.

SPI Control Register 2 (SPI0CR2 – 0x00D9) (SPI1CR2 – 0x00F1) (SPI2CR2 – 0x00F9)

7	6	5	4	3	2	1	0	
0	0	0	MODFEN	BIDIROE	0	SPISWAI	SPC0	SPIxCR2

MODFEN = 1: SS port pin with MODF feature
MODFEN = 0: SS port pin not used by the SPI.
BIDIROE — Output enable in the Bidirectional mode of operation
SPISWAI — SPI Stop in Wait Mode Bit
SPC0 — Serial Pin Control Bit 0

SPI Baud Rate Register (SPI0BR – 0x00DA) (SPI1BR – 0x00F2) (SPI2BR – 0x00FA)

7	6	5	4	3	2	1	0	
0	SPPR2	SPPR1	SPPR0	0	SPR2	SPR1	SPR0	SPIxBR

$$BaudRateDivisor = \left(SPPR[2:0]+1\right)\times 2^{(SPR[2:0]+1)}$$

$$BaudRate = BusClock / BaudRateDivisor$$

SPI Status Register (SPI0SR – 0x00DB) (SPI1SR – 0x00F3) (SPI2SR – 0x00FB)

7	6	5	4	3	2	1	0	
SPIF	0	SPTEF	MODF	0	0	0	0	SPIxSR

SPIF – SPIF Interrupt flag. SPIF = 1: New data copied to SPIDR
SPTEF – SPI Transmit Empty Interrupt flag. SPTEF = 1: SPI Data Register empty
MODF – Mode fault flag. MODF = 1: Mode fault has occurred.

SPI Data Register (SPI0DR – 0x00DD) (SPI1DR – 0x00F5) (SPI2DR – 0x00FD)

7	6	5	4	3	2	1	0	
bit7	bit6	bit5	bit4	bit3	bit2	bit1	bit0	SPIxDR

Figure 9.4 SPI Registers

The master initiates a transfer by storing a byte in the SPI data register. By default, the bits are shifted out of *SPIxDR* most-significant bit (bit 7) first and received in the least-significant bit (bit 0) as shown in Figure 9.1. If the *LSBFE* bit in the SPI control register 1, *SPIxCR1*, is set to 1, then data is transferred least-significant bit first rather than the more normal most-significant bit first.

The clock which controls how fast the bits are shifted out of and into *SPIxDR* is the serial clock *SCK*. The frequency of this clock can be controlled by the SPI baud rate register, *SPIxBR*, shown in Figure 9.4. The SPI baud rate is determined by dividing the bus clock (24 MHz) by the baud rate divisor given by

$$BaudRateDivisor = (SPPR[2:0]+1)\times 2^{(SPR[2:0]+1)}$$

The SPI control register 1, *SPIxCR1*, is shown in Figure 9.4. The two bits *CPOL* and *CPHA* control the polarity and phase of the clock. If *CPOL* = 0, the clock idles low and data are shifted in and out on the rising edge of the clock if *CPHA* = 0, and on the falling edge of the clock if *CPHA* = 1. If *CPOL* = 1, the clock idles high and data are shifted in and out on the falling edge of the clock if *CPHA* = 0, and on the rising edge of the clock if *CPHA* = 1. If *CPHA* = 1, the *SS* slave select line can remain low during successive transfers. On the other hand, if *CPHA* = 0, the *SS* line must be deasserted and reasserted between each successive byte of data transferred.

To use the SPI, the *SPE* bit in the control register *SPIxCR1* must be set to 1, and to use the SPI as the master the *MSTR* bit must be set to 1. Setting the SPIE bit will enable interrupts which will cause a hardware interrupt to occur when a byte data transfer has been completed.

When the eight bits have been completely shifted out of (and/or into) the *SPIxDR* the *SPIF* flag (bit 7) in the SPI status register, *SPIxSR*, shown in Figure 9.4 is set to 1. This bit is cleared by reading the status register, *SPIxSR*, followed by accessing the data register, *SPIxDR*.

The *SSOE* bit in *SPIxCR1* can enable an *SS* output mode in a master (if *MODFEN* in *SPIxCR2* is set to 1) in which the *SS* output automatically goes low during each SPI transmission and then goes high during each idling state so that external devices are deselected.

In the bidirectional mode, a single pin (*MOSI* for a master and *MISO* for a slave) can be used for both input and output. The bidirectional mode is enabled by setting bit SPC0 in the SPI control register 2, *SPIxCR2*, shown in Figure 9.4. When in the bidirectional mode, bit *BIDIROE* in *SPIxCR2* is the output enable bit. When $BIDIROE = 1$, the output drives the *MOSI* pin. When $BIDIROE = 0$, the output buffer is in the high-impedance state, and an input from the *MOSI* pin can be read.

Listing 9.2 shows the assembly language routines corresponding to the twelve C function calls in Table 9.2. In the subroutine *SPI0_init*, the hex value $53 is stored in *SPI0BR*, which sets the BaudRateDivisor to

$$BaudRateDivisor = (5+1)\times 2^{(3+1)} = 6\times 16 = 96$$

The SPI baud rate is then 24 MHz/96 = 250 kHz. The next statement moves the hex value $50 into *SPI0CR1*. This enables the SPI as a master by setting the *SPE* and *MSTR* bits, and clears both *CPOL* and *CPHA* bits to zero. This means that the clock idles low and data are shifted in and out on the rising edge of the clock. Clearing all bits in *SPI0CR2* disables the *MODF* feature. Finally, the SS0 pin is configured as an output by setting bit 7 of the data direction register, DDRS. The output of this SS0 pin is then cleared to zero. Similar subroutines are used to initialize SPI1 and SPI2.

Listing 9.2 ***SPI*** **Assembly Language Subroutines from** ***main.asm***

```
; SPI ports
; Initialize SPI with baud rate of 250 KHz
; void SPI0_init();
SPI0_init:
            movb  #$53, SPI0BR      ;divide 24 MHz clock by 96
            movb  #$50, SPI0CR1     ;master, CPHA=0, CPOL=0
            clr   SPI0CR2           ;disable MODF
            bset  DDRS, #$80        ;SS0 an output port
            bclr  PTS,  #$80        ;SS0 = 0
            rts

; void SPI1_init();
SPI1_init:
            movb  #$53, SPI1BR      ;divide 24 MHz clock by 96
            movb  #$50, SPI1CR1     ;master, CPHA=0, CPOL=0
            clr   SPI1CR2           ;disable MODF
            bset  DDRP, #$08        ;SS1 an output port
            bclr  PTP,  #$08        ;SS1 = 0
            rts

; void SPI2_init();
SPI2_init:
            movb  #$53, SPI2BR      ;divide 24 MHz clock by 96
            movb  #$50, SPI2CR1     ;master, CPHA=0, CPOL=0
            clr   SPI2CR2           ;disable MODF
            bset  DDRP, #$40        ;SS2 an output port
            bclr  PTP,  #$40        ;SS2 = 0
            rts

; send byte out SPI port and receive byte in
; char send_SPI0(char);
send_SPI0:
snd0        brclr SPI0SR,#$20,snd0   ;wait for SPTEF=1
            stab  SPI0DR             ;start sending byte
snd01       brclr SPI0SR,#$80,snd01  ;wait until sent
            ldab  SPI0DR             ;get received byte
            rts

; char send_SPI1(char);
send_SPI1:
snd1        brclr SPI1SR,#$20,snd1   ;wait for SPTEF=1
            stab  SPI1DR             ;start sending byte
snd11       brclr SPI1SR,#$80,snd11  ;wait until sent
            ldab  SPI1DR             ;get received byte
            rts

; char send_SPI2(char);
send_SPI2:
snd2        brclr SPI2SR,#$20,snd2   ;wait for SPTEF=1
            stab  SPI2DR             ;start sending byte
snd21       brclr SPI2SR,#$80,snd21  ;wait until sent
            ldab  SPI2DR             ;get received byte
            rts
```

Listing 9.2 (cont.) *SPI* Assembly Language Subroutines from *main.asm*

```
; set SS high
; SS0_HI();
SS0_HI:
            bset   PTS, #$80          ;set bit 7 of port S
            rts

; SS1_HI();
SS1_HI:
            bset   PTP, #$08          ;set bit 3 of port P
            rts

; SS2_HI();
SS2_HI:
            bset   PTP, #$40          ;set bit 6 of port P
            rts

; set SS low
; SS0_LO();
SS0_LO:
            bclr   PTS, #$80          ;clear bit 7 of port S
            rts

; SS1_LO();
SS1_LO:
            bclr   PTP, #$08          ;clear bit 3 of port P
            rts

; SS2_LO();
SS2_LO:
            bclr   PTP, #$40          ;clear bit 6 of port P
            rts
```

The subroutine *send_SPI0* must first wait for the *SPTEF* bit in the status register, *SPI0SR*, to go to 1, indicating that the SPI data register is empty. The character passed to the subroutine in accumulator *B* from the C program is then stored in the SPI data register, *SPI0DR*. The subroutine then waits for the *SPTEF* bit in the status register, *SPI0SR*, to go to 1, indicating that the character has been sent. Finally, the byte received in the data register is loaded into accumulator *B*, which is returned to the C program. Similar subroutines are used to send and receive data in SPI1 and SPI2.

The subroutine *SS0_HI* will set pin *SS0* (bit 7 of port S) to 1 and the subroutine *SS0_LO* will clear *SS0* to 0. The subroutine *SS1_HI* will set pin *SS1* (bit 3 of port P) to 1 and the subroutine *SS1_LO* will clear *SS1* to 0. Finally, the *SS2_HI* will set pin *SS2* (bit 6 of port P) to 1 and the subroutine *SS2_LO* will clear *SS2* to 0.

9.3 Keypad Interfacing with 74165 Shift Registers

Keypad interfacing was described in Section 3.2 of Chapter 3. In that section the keypad was in the form of a 4 x 4 matrix. Some keypads have an alternate form in which one side of each key is connected to a common ground. In this section, we will show how the SPI port can be used to read this type of 16×1 hex keypad by using 74165 shift registers.

A 16×1 hex keypad (or any collection of 16 switches) can be connected to two 74165 shift registers as shown in Fig. 9.5. In this case, one side of each switch is connected to ground. The 74165 is an 8-bit parallel in/serial out shift register. The other side of each switch is connected to one of the parallel inputs (*A–H*) of the shift register. If pin 1 (*SH/~LD*) of the 74165 is brought low, the values on the eight parallel inputs are latched into the shift register. When the *SH/~LD* pin is high and the *CLK INH* pin is low, then on the rising edge of the *CLK* input the eight bits in the shift register are shifted one bit to the right. Bit *A* is shifted to *B*, *B* to *C*, etc. Bit *G* is shifted to *H* which shows up on the serial output pin, Q_H. In Fig. 9.5 the output Q_H of the lower 74165 is connected to the serial input pin, *SER*, of the upper 74165. The output Q_H of the upper 74165 is connected to the *MISO* pin of one of the SPI ports in the MC9S12DG256.

In Fig. 9.5, the SPI signal *SCK* is connected to each *CLK* pin of the two 74165 chips and the SPI signal *SS* is connected to each *SH/~LD* pin of the two 74165 chips. Note that the *MOSI* pin of the SPI port is not connected to anything. We are only interested in receiving bytes in the *MISO* pin. To do this, of course, we must write a dummy value (say zero) to the SPI data register, *SPI0DR*, (by calling our C function *send_SPI0*(0)) and it will be shifted out the unconnected *MOSI* pin at the same time that the desired byte is being shifted in the *MISO* pin.

Notice in Fig. 9.5 that pin *H* of the upper 74165 (key 3) will be the first bit shifted out. This will end up in the most-significant bit of the first byte transferred. After transferring one byte, the register contents of the lower 74165 will have been shifted into the upper 74165 shift register. The value associated with key 7 will now be at the output Q_H of the upper 74165. After a second byte is transferred, this key 7 value will be at the most-significant bit location of this second byte. If the first byte transferred becomes the most-significant byte of a 16-bit word then the bits of this 16-bit integer will be associated with the 16 hex key values as indicated in Fig. 9.6.

Example 28 – Reading Data from Shift Registers Using SPI

The C function *read_16shift*( ) shown in Listing 9.3 will return the 16-bit value shown in Fig. 9.6. It does this by shifting in two 8-bit bytes through the SPI port. Note that the high byte is read first, shifted 8 bits to the left, and then ORed with the low byte.

Note from Fig. 9.5 that if no key is being pressed, then all of the parallel inputs to the shift registers are pulled high. This means that all of the bits in Fig. 9.6 will be set to 1. Thus, the value of this 16-bit value will be 0xFFFF. If any key was being pressed when the function *read_16shift*( ) is executed then the bit associated with that key will be zero. The function *get_key*( ) shown in Listing 9.4 will search for the bit in Fig. 9.6 that is cleared to zero. It does this by ANDing *data* with a mask with only a single bit set and checking to see if that bit was zero. The mask starts with the most-significant bit set (0x8000) which corresponds to bit number 0 in Fig. 9.6 and then shifts the bit right each time through the *while* loop by using the statement

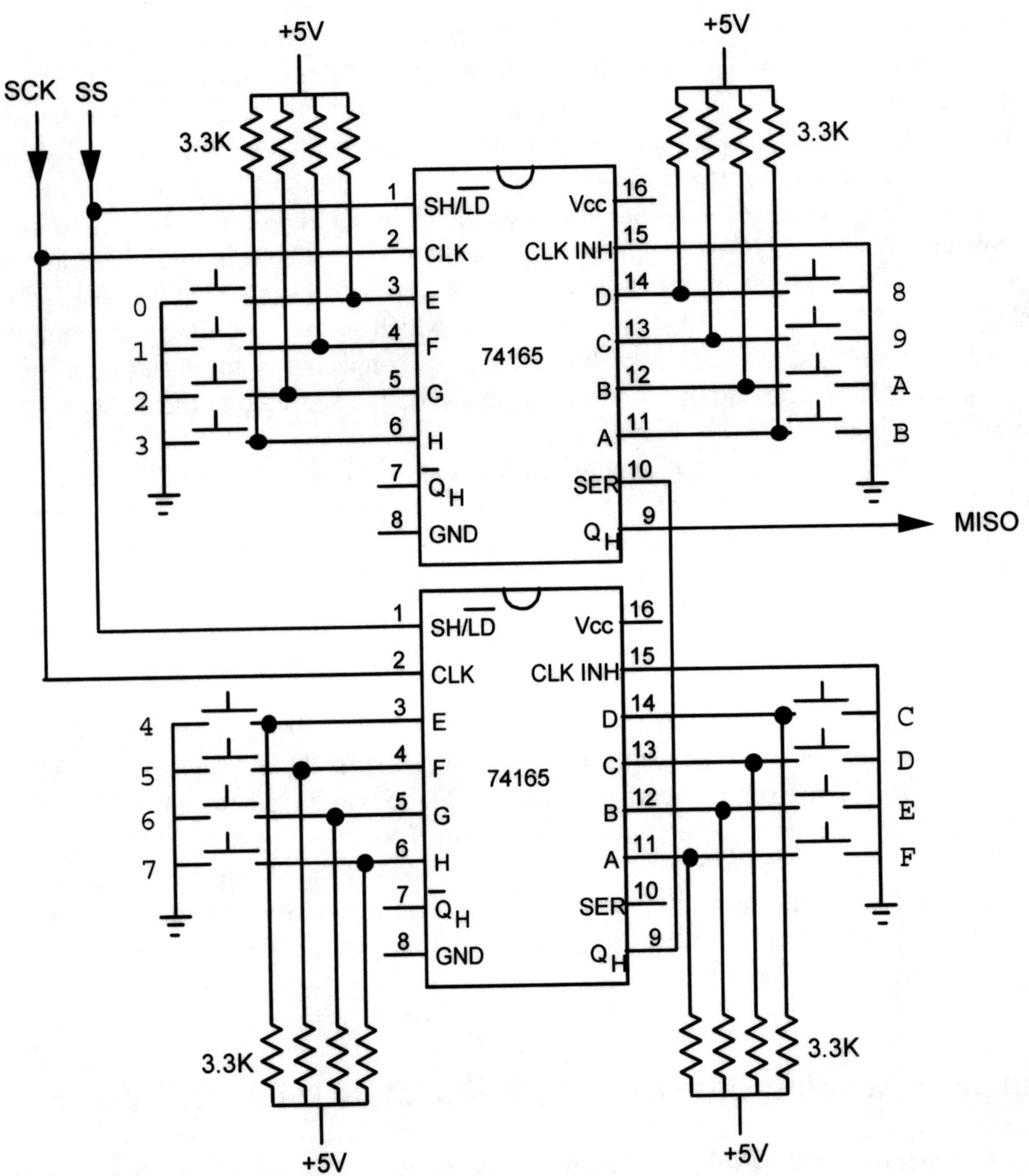

Figure 9.5 Connecting a 16 x 1 hex keypad to two 74165 shift registers

0	1	2	3	4	5	6	7	8	9	10	11	12	12	14	15
3	2	1	0	8	9	A	B	7	6	5	4	C	D	E	F

Figure 9.6 Keypad hex values after transferring 16 bits in Figure 9.5

Listing 9.3 read_16shift() function

```
int read_16shift(void){
  int   data;
  char  c;
     SSO_LO();                   // latch data
     SSO_HI();
     c = send_SPI0(0);        // get 1st byte by sending dummy data
     data = c;
     data = data << 8;
     c = send_SPI0(0);        // get 2nd byte by sending dummy data
     data = data | c;
     return data;
}
```

```
mask >>= 1;
```

which is equivalent to

```
mask = mask >> 1;
```

We label the most-significant bit in Fig. 9.6 as 0 rather than 15 so that this bit number will correspond to the index value in the table *keytbl*[ ] shown in Listing 9.4. When a zero bit value is found, the value of *keytbl*[*i*] will be the hex value of the key being pressed and this value is returned as the value of the function *get_key*( ). Note that if no key is being pressed the value of *get_key*( ) is 16.

Listing 9.5 shows a main program that will use the two functions given in Listings 9.3 and 9.4. This program will wait for you to press a key and then display the key value on the LCD.

Listing 9.4 get_key() function

```
char get_key(){
  const char keytbl[] = {
    0x3, 0x2, 0x1, 0x0,
    0x8, 0x9, 0xA, 0xB,
    0x7, 0x6, 0x5, 0x4,
    0xC, 0xD, 0xE, 0xF
  };
  int i, mask, data;
  char found;
  char key;
      data = read_16shift();
      mask = 0x8000;
      found = 0;
      i = 0;
      key = 16;          // not found if key = 16
      while((i < 16) && (found == 0)){
        if((data & mask) == 0){
          found = 1;
          key = keytbl[i];
        }
        else {
          mask >>= 1;
          i++;
        }
      }
      return key;
}
```

Listing 9.5 Example 28

```
// Example 28: SPI Keypad Interfacing with 74165 Shift Registers
#include <hidef.h>      /* common defines and macros */
#include <mc9s12dp256.h>     /* derivative information */
#include "main_asm.h" /* interface to the assembly module */
#pragma LINK_INFO DERIVATIVE "mc9s12dp256b"
int read_16shift(void);
char get_key(void);

void main(void) {
  char key;
  PLL_init();          // set system clock frequency to 24 MHz
  lcd_init();             // enable lcd
  SPI0_init();            // enable SPI0
  set_lcd_addr(0x40);
  while(1) {
    key = get_key();
    if(key < 16){
      key = hex2asc(key); // convert to ascii
      data8(key);         // display on lcd
    }
  }
}
```

PROBLEMS

9.1 The Analog Devices AD7376 is a ±15 V Operation Digital Potentiometer. A simplified block diagram is shown below.

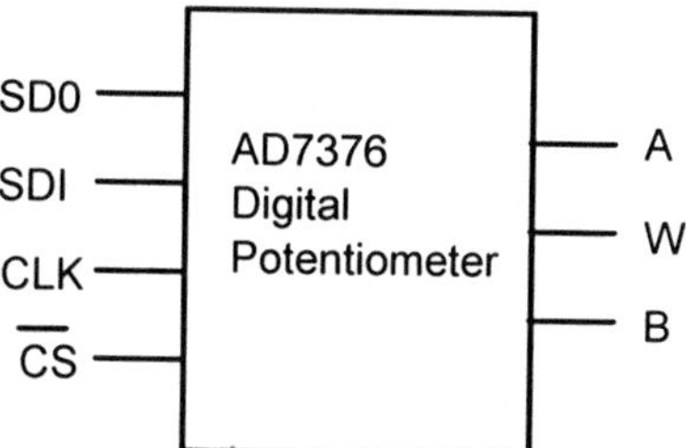

You can go to http://www.analog.com/en/prod/0,,761_797_AD7376%2C00.html to download the full data sheet. The fixed resistance between *A* and *B*, R_{AB}, can be 10 kΩ, 50 kΩ, 100 kΩ, or 1 MΩ. The output *W* is the "wiper" that causes the resistance between W and B to be given by the equation

$$R_{WB}(D) = (D/128) \times R_{AB} + R_W$$

where *D* is 7-bit data that has been shifted into *SDI* and R_W is the wiper contact resistance equal to 120 Ω.

You can interface the AD7376 to an SPI port by connecting the SPI *SS* signal to the *CS* pin, the *SCK* signal to the *CLK* pin, the *MOSI* signal to the *SDI* pin, and the *MISO* signal to the *SD0* pin. When *CS* is low 8-bit data is shifted into *SDI*, MSB first. Each bit is latched on the rising edge of the clock that idles low. The *SD0* pin can be connected to the *SDI* pin of a second AD7376 to daisy-chain multiple variable resistors.

Write a C function called *R(*int *n)* that will cause the resistance between *W* and *B* to be *n* ohms. Assume that R_{AB} = 10 kΩ, so that *n* should be between 0 and 10,000.

Chapter 10

Timer

Timers are an important part of microcontroller interfacing. They can be used to produce delays, measure time intervals such as pulse widths, create various output waveforms such as pulse-width modulated signals, count the number of events, and other similar activities. We have already used the pulse-width modulation (PWM) module in Chapter 7 and the real-time interrupt in Section 5.2. The HCS12 family of microcontrollers has a fairly sophisticated enhanced timer capture module associated with port T that can perform all of the above functions. All timer functions are based around a single, free-running 16-bit up counter called *TCNT*.

The two most basic functions that the timer can perform are output compares and input captures. In Section 10.1 we will use the output compare function to generate a pulse train using interrupts. We include an example that will play musical notes on the speaker that is built into the DRAGON12-Plus-USB board. In Section 10.2 we will use the input capture function to measure pulse widths and periods of input signals. The Pulse Accumulator feature of the timer module will be discussed in Section 10.3.

10.1 Output Compare

Each of the eight pins of port T can be programmed to output pulse trains using the output compare function. The way it works is that each pin has a 16-bit output compare register associated with it, into which you can write a 16-bit value. When the free-running up counter, *TCNT*, reaches the value in the output compare register, you can make any number of things happen. For example, you could have the pin go high, or go low, or toggle. You could cause an interrupt to occur on an output compare match at which time you could update the output compare register for the next event you want to happen.

It turns out that pin 7 of port T (*PTT7*) is special because it can be used in conjunction with any other pin to produce some useful effects. For example, suppose we want to produce the pulse train shown in Fig. 10.1. We can set it up such that on a *TC7* match (i.e. when the value of the free-running counter, *TCNT*, is equal to the contents of the output compare register, *TC7*) the signal on pin *PTT6* will go high. We can also set it up such that on a *TC6* match (i.e. when the value of the free-running counter, *TCNT*, is equal to the contents of the output compare register, *TC6*) the signal on pin *PTT6* will go low. If the value in *TC6* is *pwidth* greater than the value in *TC7* then the first pulse in Fig. 10.1 will occur when *TCNT* passes these two values. But how do we get it to produce the second pulse one period later? The answer is that we cause an interrupt to occur on the falling edge of the pulse train (i.e. on a *TC6* match), and in this interrupt service routine we will update the values of *TC6* and *TC7* based on the values of *pwidth* and *period*. The new value of *TC7* will be the old *TC7* plus *period* and the new value of *TC6* will be the new value of *TC7* plus *pwidth*. Note that it doesn't matter if these sums exceed 0xFFFF because the sum will simply wrap around as will the counter *TCNT*.

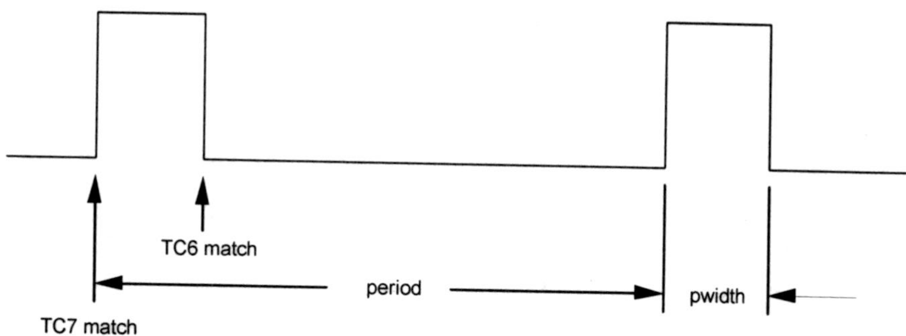

Figure 10.1 Pulse train

To make it easy, we have written assembly language routines that can be called from the C functions shown in Table 10.1. The first two functions in Table 10.1 can be used to produce the pulse train in Fig. 10.1. These functions will be used in Example 29. The last four functions in Table 10.1 will be used in Example 30 to play musical notes on the built-in speaker when keys on the keypad are pressed.

Table 10.1 C Function calls for generating a pulse train

Function	Description
`void ptrain6_init(void);`	initialize pulse train interrupts on PT6 timer clock = 1.5 MHz
`void ptrain6(int period, int pwidth);`	update TC6 and TC7 in timer 6 interrupt routine
`void sound_init(void);`	initialize pulse train interrupts on PT5 (speaker) timer clock = 1.5 MHz
`void sound_on(void);`	Turn sound on by enabling timer and interrupts
`void sound_off(void);`	Turn sound off by disabling timer and interrupts
`void tone(int pitch);`	Set pitch value of sound by updating TC5 and TC7 in timer 5 interrupt routine

Example 29 – Interrupt-Driven Pulse Train

The C program in Listing 10.1 uses the first two function calls in Table 10.1 to generate the pulse train shown in Fig. 10.1 on *PT6*. Note that the timer clock is set to 1.5 MHz so that the largest possible period is 65,535/1.5 MHz = 43.7 ms. To change this limitation, you will need to write your own assembly language subroutines using the information in the following *Under the Hood* section.

Listing 10.1 Example 29

```
// Example 29: Interrupt-Driven Pulse Train
#include <hidef.h>      /* common defines and macros */
#include <mc9s12dg256.h>     /* derivative information */
#pragma LINK_INFO DERIVATIVE "mc9s12dg256b"

#include "main_asm.h" /* interface to the assembly module */

int period;                  // period of pulse train
int pwidth;                  // high pulse width of pulse train

//  Timer channel 6 interrupt service routine
void interrupt 14 handler(){
    ptrain6(period, pwidth);
}

void main(void) {
  PLL_init();            // set system clock frequency to 24 MHz
  ptrain6_init();
  period = 5734;
  pwidth = 2867;
  while(1) {             // do nothing while generating pulse train
  }
}
```

Under the Hood

The registers associated with the timer are shown in Table 10.2. All timer functions are based around a single, free-running 16-bit up counter, *TCNT*, shown in Fig. 10.2. The address of *TCNT* ($0044) is the address of the high byte of *TCNT*. The contents of *TCNT* should be accessed as a word so as to read the real 16-bit value stored in *TCNT*.

Table 10.2 Timer Registers in the HCS12

Name	Register Addr	Description
TIOS	0040	Timer Input Capture/Output Compare Select
CFORC	0041	Timer Compare Force Register
OC7M	0042	Output Compare 7 Mask Register
OC7D	0043	Output Compare 7 Data Register
TCNT	0044	Timer Count Register
TSCR1	0046	Timer System Control Register 1
TTOV	0047	Timer Toggle Overflow Register
TCTL1	0048	Timer Control Register 1
TCTL2	0049	Timer Control Register 2
TCTL3	004A	Timer Control Register 3
TCTL4	004B	Timer Control Register 4
TIE	004C	Timer Interrupt Enable Register
TSCR2	004D	Timer System Control Register 2
TFLG1	004E	Main Timer Interrupt Flag 1
TFLG2	004F	Main Timer Interrupt Flag 2
TCn(0-7)	0050-005F	Timer Input Capture /Output Compare Register n

Timer Count Register (TCNT – 0x0044 – 0x0045)

7	6	5	4	3	2	1	0	
tcnt15	tcnt14	tcnt13	tcnt12	tcnt11	tcnt10	tcnt9	tcnt8	TCNTHi
tcnt7	tcnt6	tcnt5	tcnt4	tcnt3	tcnt2	tcnt1	tcnt0	TCNTLo

Free-running 16-bit up counter

Figure 10.2 Timer Counter

You must first enable the timer by setting bit 7 of the timer system control register 1, *TSCR1*, shown in Fig. 10.3. Thus, the assembly language instruction

```
movb   #$80,TSCR1
```

will enable the timer, and any time you access TCNT you will obtain a new counter value.

Timer System Control Register 1 (TSCR1 – 0x0046)

7	6	5	4	3	2	1	0	
TEN	TSWAI	TSFRZ	TFFCA	0	0	0	0	TSCR1

TEN = 1: Timer enabled. TEN = 0: Timer disabled.
TSWAI — Timer Module Stops While in Wait
TSFRZ — Timer and Modulus Counter Stop While in Freeze Mode
TFFCA — Timer Fast Flag Clear All

Figure 10.3 Timer System Control Register 1

The value of *TCNT* is incremented at a rate that depends on the three bits, *PR2: PR0*, in the timer system control register 2, *TSCR2*, shown in Fig. 10.4 according to the formula

$$\text{Timer clock rate} = \text{BusClock}/2^{PR[2:0]}$$

The default values of *PR*[2:0] are 000, so if the bus clock rate is 24 MHz, then the timer clock rate will be 24 MHz and *TCNT* will increment once about every 41.6 ns. This means that the counter will overflow (go from $FFFF to $0000) about every 2.73 ms. By changing these three bits in *TSCR2* you can divide the clock rate by 2, 4, 8, 16, 32, 64, or 128. These bits may be changed at any time; however, the change will not take effect until the next time that all prescaled counter stages are zero. For a 24 MHz bus clock, the slowest timer clock rate would be $24\ \text{MHz}/2^7 = 187.5\ \text{kHz}$, at which rate the timer would overflow about every 350 ms.

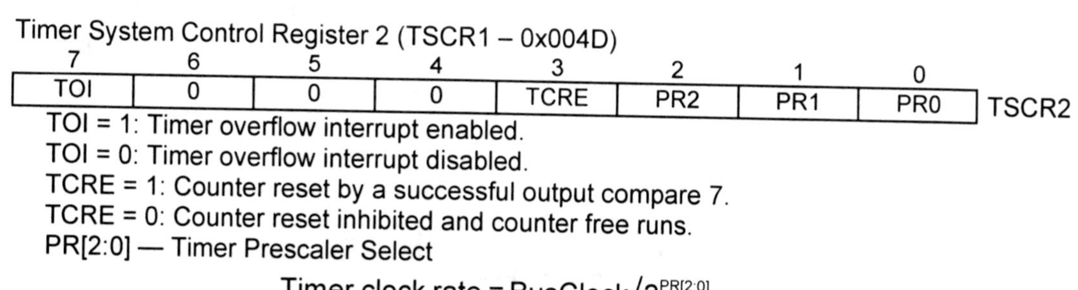

Timer System Control Register 2 (TSCR1 – 0x004D)

7	6	5	4	3	2	1	0	
TOI	0	0	0	TCRE	PR2	PR1	PR0	TSCR2

TOI = 1: Timer overflow interrupt enabled.
TOI = 0: Timer overflow interrupt disabled.
TCRE = 1: Counter reset by a successful output compare 7.
TCRE = 0: Counter reset inhibited and counter free runs.
PR[2:0] — Timer Prescaler Select

$$\text{Timer clock rate} = \text{BusClock}/2^{PR[2:0]}$$

Figure 10.4 Timer System Control Register 2

When the timer overflows the *TOF* bit of *TFLG2* (main timer interrupt flag 2) is set to 1 as shown in Fig. 10.5. This flag is cleared by writing a 1 to bit 7 (*TOF*) of *TFLG2*. Although this may seem strange, it is the standard way of clearing flags in the HCS12.

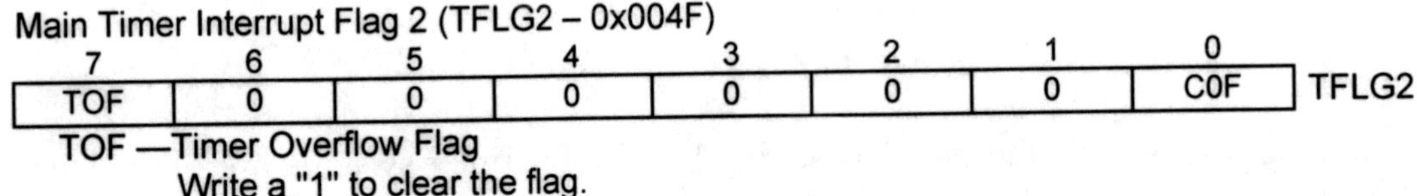

Main Timer Interrupt Flag 2 (TFLG2 – 0x004F)
7 6 5 4 3 2 1 0
TOF 0 0 0 0 0 0 C0F
TFLG2
TOF —Timer Overflow Flag
Write a "1" to clear the flag.

Figure 10.5 Main Timer Interrupt Flag 2 register

Each pin of Port T can be selected to act as either an input capture or an output compare. This selection is done by setting the bits in the timer input capture/output compare select register, *TIOS*, shown in Fig. 10.6.

Timer Input Capture/Output Compare Select Register (TIOS – 0x0040)

7	6	5	4	3	2	1	0	
IOS7	IOS6	IOS5	IOS4	IOS3	IOS2	IOS1	IOS0	TIOS

IOS[7:0] = 0: Channel acts as input capture
IOS[7:0] = 1: Channel acts as output compare

Figure 10.6 Timer System Control Register 2

The HCS12 has eight 16-bit timer input capture/output compare registers, *TCn*, as shown in Figure 10.7. Note, for example, that the address of *TC2* is \$0054-\$0055 and the address of *TC7* is \$005E-\$005F.

Timer Input Capture/Output Compare Registers 0 – 7 (TCn – 0x5(2n) [0x0050 – 0x005E])

7	6	5	4	3	2	1	0	
TCn15	TCn14	TCn13	TCn12	TCn11	TCn10	TCn9	TCn8	TCn
TCn7	TCn6	TCn5	TCn4	TCn3	TCn2	TCn1	TCn0	

Figure 10.7 Timer Input Capture/Output Compare Registers

When the value of the free-running counter, *TCNT*, is equal to the value stored in one of the output compare registers, the corresponding output compare channel flag, *CxF*, in the main timer interrupt flag 1 register, *TFLG1*, is set as shown in Figure 10.8. Note that this flag is cleared by writing a 1 to the corresponding bit position.

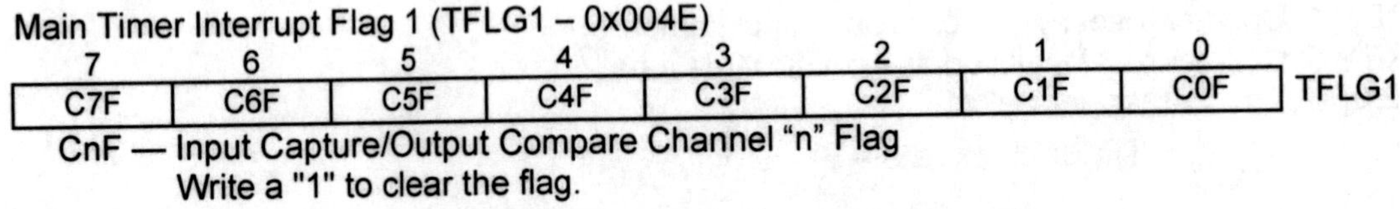

Figure 10.8 Main Timer Interrupt Flag 1 register

The eight output compares, *OC0–OC7*, are associated with pins *PTT0–PTT7* of Port T. As described above when the free-running counter, *TCNT*, matches the value in one of the output compare registers, *TCn*, shown in Fig. 10.7, the corresponding output compare flag, *CxF*, in *TFLG1* is set as shown in Fig. 10.8. When this occurs, it is possible to cause the output of *PTT0–PTT7* to change. In this way we can produce output waveforms on pins 0–7 of Port T.

In addition to the registers shown in Figs. 10.7 and 10.8, the registers shown in Figure 10.9 also are used for output compares. Output compare 7 can control the outputs of any of the pins *PTT0–PTT7*. On the other hand, output compares 0–6 can control only their own output pins. The output compare 7 mask register, *OC7M*, and the output compare 7 data register, *OC7D*, are used by output compare 7 to control the outputs on pins *PTT0–PTT7*. Setting an output compare mask, *OC7Mx*, in *OC7M* will enable the corresponding output pin *x*. If this mask bit is set, then the contents of the corresponding bit, *OC7Dx*, in *OC7D* will determine whether pin *x* of Port T will go high or low on a successful match of output compare 1. For example, if *OC7M6* is set to 1, and *OC7D6* is cleared to 0, then on a successful match of output compare 7 (*TC7*) the value on *PTT6* will go low.

It is possible to have output compare 7 (*TC7*) and output compare 6 (*TC6*) both control the output of pin *PTT6* at the same time. The way that *TC6* controls pin *PTT6* is determined by the two bits, *OM6* and *OL6*, in register *TCTL1* as shown in Figure 10.9. For example, if *OM6* = 1 and *OL6* = 1, then pin *PTT6* will be set to 1 on a successful match of output compare 6.

Output Compare 7 Mask Register (OC7M – 0x0042)

7	6	5	4	3	2	1	0	
OC7M7	OC7M6	OC7M5	OC7M4	OC7M3	OC7M2	OC7M1	OC7M0	OC7M

If OC7Mn = 1, [n = 6:0], the corresponding OC7Dn bit in the OC7D register is output on channel n on a TC7 match.

Output Compare 7 Data Register (OC7D – 0x0043)

7	6	5	4	3	2	1	0	
OC7D7	OC7D6	OC7D5	OC7D4	OC7D3	OC7D2	OC7D1	OC7D0	OC7D

OC7Dn [n = 6:0], is output on channel n on a TC7 match if OC7Mn = 1, [n = 6:0] in the OC7M register

Timer Control Register 1/ Timer Control Register 2 (TCTL1 – 0x0048) (TCTL2 – 0x0049)

7	6	5	4	3	2	1	0	
OM7	OL7	OM6	OL6	OM5	OL5	OM4	OL4	TCTL1
OM3	OL3	OM2	OL2	OM1	OL1	OM0	OL0	TCTL2

OMn — Output Mode OLn — Output Level

OMn	OLn	Action
0	0	Timer disconnected from output pins
0	1	Toggle OCn output line
1	0	Clear OCn output line to 0
1	1	Set OCn output line to 1

Figure 10.9 Additional registers used for output compare

You can cause an interrupt to occur on an output compare match by setting the corresponding bit in the timer interrupt enable register shown in Fig. 10.10. The timer overflow interrupt enable bit, *TOI*, is bit 7 of the timer system control register 2, *TSCR2*, shown in Fig. 10.4.

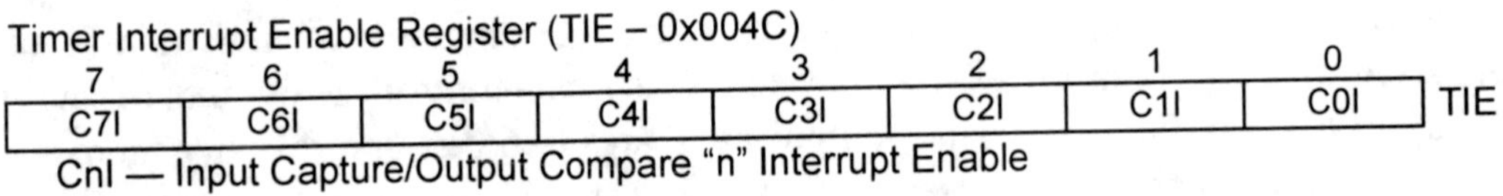

Figure 10.10 Timer Interrupt Enable Register

Sometimes you may want to force an output compare event to occur before *TCNT* reaches the value stored in the output compare register *TCn*. You can do this by writing a 1 to the corresponding bit, *FOCx*, in the timer compare force register, *CFORC*, shown in Fig. 10.11. When you do this the output compare flag, *CxF*, in *TFLG1* is not set and no interrupt will occur. Only the output compare event, such as toggling the Port T pin will occur.

Timer Compare Force Register (CFORC – 0x0041)

7	6	5	4	3	2	1	0	
FOC7	FOC6	FOC5	FOC4	FOC3	FOC2	FOC1	FOC0	CFORC

FOC[7:0] = 1: Force output compare action on channels 7 – 0. Interrupt flags not affected.
FOC[7:0] = 0: Normal operation. No action taken.

Figure 10.11 Timer Compare Force Register

Listing 10.2 shows the assembly language routines corresponding to the first two C function calls in Table 10.1. In the subroutine *ptrain6_init*, the hex value $C0 is stored in the Timer Input Capture/Output Compare Select Register, *TIOS*, (see Fig. 10.6) which will make bits 6 and 7 of Port T output compares.

The second instruction in the subroutine *ptrain6_init* in Listing 10.2 stores the hex value $04 in TSCR2 (See Fig. 10.4), which will set the timer clock rate to $24\text{ MHz}/2^4 = 1.5\text{ MHz}$. The timer is then enabled by setting the *TEN* bit (bit 7) in the timer system control register 1, *TSCR1* (see Fig. 10.3). The current value of *TCNT* is then stored in output compare registers, *TC6* and *TC7*.

Bits 6 of registers *OC7M* and *OC7D* (see Fig. 10.9) are set to 1, which will make pin *PTT6* go high on a *TC7* match. To make pin *PTT6* go low on a *TC6* match, *OM6* (bit 5) in *TCTL1* (see Fig. 10.9) is set to 1 and *OL6* (bit 4) in *TCTL1* is cleared to 0. To enable *TC6* interrupts, we set bit 6 of the timer interrupt enable register shown in Fig. 10.10. Finally, we must enable all hardware interrupts by clearing the interrupt mask bit (I) in the condition code register using the instruction *cli*.

The subroutine *ptrain6* shown in Listing 10.2 is called by the output compare interrupt service routine in Listing 10.1. The value of *pwidth* is passed to the subroutine in accumulator *D* and the value of *period* is pushed on the stack and located at *sp* + 2. After saving the value of *pwidth* by pushing *D* on the stack, the value of period (which is now at *sp*

+ 4) is loaded into *D* and added to the current value in *TC7*, with the result stored back in *TC7*. The next match of *TC7* will cause the output on pin *PTT6* to go high as shown in Fig. 10.1. The value of *pwidth*, now on the top of the stack, is added to this new value in *TC7* and stored in *TC6*. The next match of *TC6* will cause the output on pin *PTT6* to go low as shown in Fig. 10.1. The value of *pwidth*, which is still on top of the stack, must be pulled from the stack so that the return address will be back on top of the stack. Before returning from the subroutine *ptrain6*, both the *C7F* and *C6F* flags must be cleared by writing the value $C0 to *TFLG1* (see Fig. 10.8).

Listing 10.2 *Pulse Train* Assembly Language Subroutines from *main.asm*

```
;  ptrain6_init()
ptrain6_init:
            movb  #$C0,TIOS     ;select output compares 6 & 7
            movb  #$04,TSCR2    ;div by 16: 24MHz/16 = 1.5 MHz
            movb  #$80,TSCR1    ;enable timer
            ldd   TCNT
            std   TC6
            std   TC7                   ;init cnt in TC6 & TC7
            bset  OC7M,#$40     ;pulse train out PT6
            bset  OC7D,#$40     ;PT6 goes high on TC7 match
            bset  TCTL1,#$20    ;PT6 low on TC6  match
            bclr  TCTL1,#$10
            bset  TIE,#$40      ;enable TC6 interrupts
            cli                 ;enable interrupts
            rts

; void ptrain(int period, int pwidth);
; pwidth is in D
; period is at 2,sp
; return address is at 0,sp
ptrain6:
            pshd                ;save pwidth
            ldd   4,sp          ;D = period
            addd  TC7
            std   TC7           ;TC7new =TC7old + period
            addd  0,sp          ;add pwidth
            std   TC6           ;TC6new =TC7new + pwidth
            puld                ;restore D
            movb  #$C0,TFLG1    ;clear both C7F and C6F
            rts
```

Example 30 – Playing Musical Notes with the Keypad

The DRAGON12-Plus-USB speaker is connected to *PTT5*. We can produce sound by generating a square wave on *PTT5* as shown in Fig. 10.12. We'll use the same interrupt scheme described above for producing the pulse train on *PTT6* shown in Fig. 10.1. The C function *sound_init*( ) given in Table 10.1 will initialize pulse train interrupts on *PTT5* using a timer clock of 1.5 MHz. The C function *tone*(*pitch*) in Table 10.1 performs the same function as *ptrain(period, width)* by updating *TC5* and *TC7* in a timer 5 interrupt routine.

The C functions *sound_on*( ) and *sound_off*( ) in Table 10.1 turn the sound on and off by enabling and disabling the timer and interrupts.

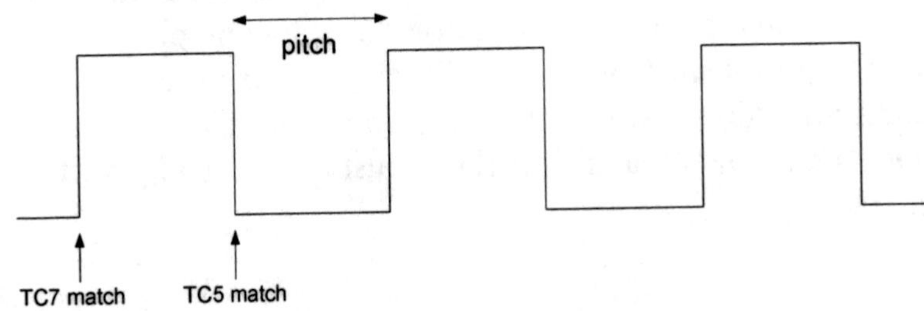

Figure 10.12 Square wave used to generate sound

The pitch values for different notes in the musical scale are shown in Table 10.3. Listing 10.3 is a C program that will play two octaves of the musical scale when you press keys on the keypad starting on the lower left of the keypad.

Table 10.3 Pitch values of musical scale

Note	Freq (Hz)	Period (ms)	Pitch
Middle C	261.63	3.822	2867
C# D^b	277.18	3.608	2706
D	293.66	3.405	2554
D# E^b	311.13	3.214	2411
E	329.63	3.034	2276
F	349.23	2.863	2148
F# G^b	369.99	2.703	2028
G	392.00	2.551	1914
G# A^b	415.30	2.408	1806
A	440.00	2.273	1705
A# B^b	466.16	2.145	1609
B	493.88	2.025	1519
C	523.25	1.911	1434
C# D^b	554.37	1.804	1353
D	587.33	1.703	1277
D# E^b	622.25	1.607	1206
E	659.26	1.517	1138
F	698.46	1.432	1074
F# G^b	739.99	1.351	1014
G	783.99	1.276	957
G# A^b	830.61	1.204	903
A	880.00	1.136	853
A# B^b	932.33	1.073	805
B	987.77	1.012	760
C	1046.50	0.956	717

Listing 10.3 Example 30

```
// Example 30: Sound Example - play notes with keypad
#include <hidef.h>      /* common defines and macros */
#include <mc9s12dg256.h>     /* derivative information */
#pragma LINK_INFO DERIVATIVE "mc9s12dg256b"
#include "main_asm.h" /* interface to the assembly module */
// Define note, pitch, &  frequency.
#define  c     2867     // 261.63 Hz
#define  d     2554     // 293.66 Hz
#define  e     2276     // 329.63 Hz
#define  f     2148     // 349.23 Hz
#define  g     1914     // 392.00 Hz
#define  a     1705     // 440.00 Hz
#define  b     1519     // 493.88 Hz
#define  C     1434     // 523.25 Hz
#define  D     1277     // 587.33 Hz
#define  E     1138     // 659.26 Hz
#define  F     1074     // 698.46 Hz
#define  G     957      // 783.99 Hz
#define  A     853      // 880.00 Hz
#define  B     760      // 987.77 Hz
#define  CC    717      // 1046.50 Hz
#define  DD    639      // 1174.66 Hz

char k;
int pitch;
int pitchval[16] = {
  d, A, B, CC, D, E, F, g, a, b, DD, G, C, f, c, e
};
char * pitchdisp[16] = {
  "d", "A", "B", "CC", "D", "E", "F", "g",
  "a", "b", "DD", "G", "C", "f", "c", "e"
};
// Timer channel 5 interrupt service routine
void interrupt 13 handler(){
  tone(pitch);
  }

void main(void) {
  PLL_init();            // set system clock frequency to 24 MHz
  keypad_enable();       // enable the keypad
  lcd_init();            // initialize LCD
  while(1){
      set_lcd_addr(0x00);      //set cursor to first line
      k = getkey();            //get keypad button pressed
      type_lcd(pitchdisp[k]); //display note on lcd
      pitch = pitchval[k];     //pitch value of button pressed
      sound_init();
      sound_on();              // start playing the note
      wait_keyup();            //wait for button to be released
      sound_off();             // stop playing the note
      clear_lcd();
  }
}
```

Under the Hood

Listing 10.4 shows the assembly language routines corresponding to the last four C function calls in Table 10.1. The subroutine *sound_init* is almost the same as the subroutine *ptrain6_init* in Listing 10.2 except that channel 5 replaces channel 6 and no interrupts are enabled. The subroutine *sound_on* in Listing 10.4 turns the sound on by enabling the timer and enabling hardware and *TC5* interrupts. The subroutine *sound_off* in Listing 10.4 turns the sound off by disabling the timer and disabling hardware and *TC5* interrupts.

The subroutine *tone* shown in Listing 10.4 is called by the output compare interrupt service routine in Listing 10.3. The value of *pitch* is passed to the subroutine in accumulator *D*. After saving the value of *pitch* by pushing *D* on the stack, this pitch value is added to the current value in *TC5*, with the result stored back in *TC7*. The next match of *TC7* will cause the output on pin *PTT5* to go high as shown in Fig. 10.12.

The value of *pitch* is pulled from the stack, added to this new value in *TC7*, and stored in *TC5*. The next match of *TC5* will cause the output on pin *PTT5* to go low as shown in Fig. 10.11. Before returning from the subroutine *tone*, both the *C7F* and *C5F* flags must be cleared by writing the value $A0 to *TFLG1* (see Fig. 10.8).

Listing 10.4 ***Sound*** **Assembly Language Subroutines from** ***main.asm***

```
;  sound_init()
sound_init:
            movb   #$A0,TIOS    ;select output compares 5 & 7
            movb   #$04,TSCR2   ;div by 16: 24MHz/16 = 1.5 MHz
            movb   #$80,TSCR1   ;enable timer
            ldd    TCNT
            std    TC5
            std    TC7          ;init cnt in TC5 & TC7
            bset   OC7M,#$20    ;pulse train out PT5
            bset   OC7D,#$20    ;PT5 goes high on TC7 match
            bset   TCTL1,#$08   ;PT5 low on TC5  match
            bclr   TCTL1,#$04
            rts

;  sound_on()
sound_on:
            movb   #$80,TSCR1   ;enable timer
            bset   TIE,#$20     ;enable TC5 interrupts
            cli                 ;enable interrupts
            rts

;  sound_off()
sound_off:
            sei                 ;disable interrupts
            clr    TSCR1        ;disable timer
            bclr   TIE,#$20     ;disable TC5 interrupts
            rts
```

Listing 10.4 (cont.) *Sound* Assembly Language Subroutines from *main.asm*

```
; void tone(int pitch);
; pitch is in D
; interrupt on falling edge of TC5
tone:
        pshd                    ;save pitch
        addd    TC5
        std     TC7             ;TC7new =TC5old + pitch
        puld                    ;get pitch
        addd    TC7             ;add pitch
        std     TC5             ;TC5new =TC7new + pitch
        movb    #$A0,TFLG1      ;clear both C7F and C5F
        rts
```

10.2 Input Capture

In Example 29 we generated a pulse train using the output compare feature of the timer module. The *input capture* feature of the timer module allows you to capture the value of the free-running counter, *TCNT*, into the input capture register, *TCx*, when a rising or falling edge (or both) occurs on the associated input pin *PTTx*.

The C function calls in Table 10.4 are assembly language routines that will allow you to measure both the high and low times of an input pulse train on pin *PTT1*. The function *HILO1_init*( ) will enable *TC1* interrupts on both edges of the pulse train. The timer clock is set to 1.5 MHz so that the maximum high or low pulse width that can be measured is 65,535/1.5 MHz = 43.7 ms.

The function *HILOtimes1*( ) is called in your interrupt service routine. It remembers the value of *TC1* that was read at the last interrupt and subtracts this value from the current reading of *TC1* to get the pulse width. It reads pin *PTT1* to see if the interrupt occurred on a rising edge (in which case the measured pulse width is low) or on a falling edge (in which case the measured pulse width is high). This function saves the most recent readings in two assembly language variables. You can get these values from your C program by calling the two functions *get_HItime1*( ) and *get_LOtime1*( ).

Table 10.4 C Function calls for measuring pulse widths on Channel 1

Function	Description
`void HILO1_init(void);`	initialize input capture interrupts on both edges of channel 1 timer clock = 1.5 MHz
`void HILOtimes1(void);`	update HI – LO times in input capture interrupt routine
`int get_HItime1(void);`	return latest HI time of input pulse train
`int get_LOtime1(void);`	return latest LO time of input pulse train

Example 31 – Measuring Input Pulse Widths

In this example we will show how to measure the high time and low time (and therefore the period) of an input pulse train using an input capture interrupt on timer channel 1. Listing 10.5 shows an example of reading the high and low pulse widths of an input pulse train, and displaying these values together with the period on the LCD display. Note that the values displayed will be multiples of 1/1.5 MHz = 0.667 μsec.

Listing 10.5 Example 31

```
// Example 31: Measuring Input Pulse Widths on Channel 1
#include <hidef.h>        /* common defines and macros */
#include <mc9s12dg256.h>      /* derivative information */
#pragma LINK_INFO DERIVATIVE "mc9s12dg256b"
#include "main_asm.h" /* interface to the assembly module */

//  Timer channel 1 interrupt service routine
void interrupt 9 handler1(){
    HILOtimes1();     // update HI-LO times on Ch 1
}

void main(void) {
  int period1;  // period of input pulse train on Ch 1
  int HI_time1; // measured HI time of pulse train on Ch 1
  int LO_time1; // measured LO time of pulse train on Ch 1

  PLL_init();          // set system clock frequency to 24 MHz
  lcd_init();
  HILO1_init();
  while(1) {
       HI_time1 = get_HI_time1();  // read new HItime1
       LO_time1 = get_LO_time1();  // read new LOtime1
       set_lcd_addr(0x00);
       write_int_lcd(HI_time1);     // write HItime on row 1 of lcd
       write_int_lcd(LO_time1);     // write LOtime on row 1 of lcd
       period1 = HI_time1 + LO_time1;
       set_lcd_addr(0x40);
       write_int_lcd(period1);      // write period on row 2 of lcd
       ms_delay(100);
  }
}
```

Under the Hood

The eight pins of Port T can be selected as input capture lines by clearing the appropriate bits in the *TIOS* register as shown in Figure 10.6. When configured for an input capture the corresponding input capture/output compare register, *TCx*, shown in Figure 10.7 are used to capture the current counter value, *TCNT*, when a rising or falling edge (or both) occurs on the associated pin *PTTx*. When this occurs, the corresponding input capture channel flag, *CxF*, in the main timer flag 1 register, *TFLG1*, is set as shown in Figure 10.8. Note that this flag is cleared by writing a 1 to the corresponding bit position. The two bits *EDGxB* and *EDGxA* in timer control registers, *TCTL3* and *TCTL4*, are used to select the capture edge as shown in Figure 10.13.

Timer Control Register 3/ Timer Control Register 4 (TCTL3 – 0x004A) (TCTL4 – 0x004B)

7	6	5	4	3	2	1	0	
EDG7B	EDG7A	EDG6B	EDG6A	EDG5B	EDG5A	EDG4B	EDG4A	TCTL3
EDG3B	EDG3A	EDG2B	EDG2A	EDG1B	EDG1A	EDG0B	EDG0A	TCTL4

EDGnB, EDGnA — Input Capture Edge Control

EDGnB	EDGnA	Configuration
0	0	Capture disabled
0	1	Capture on rising edges only
1	0	Capture on falling edges only
1	1	Capture on both rising and falling edges

Figure 10.13 Timer control registers 3 and 4

Listing 10.6 shows the assembly language routines corresponding to the last four C function calls in Table 10.1. The subroutine *HILO1_init* in Listing 10.6 first configures channel 1 to be an input capture port by clearing bit 1 of *TIOS*. It then sets the timer rate to 1.5 MHz by writing $04 to *TSCR2* (see Fig. 10.4) and enables the timer by setting bit 7 of *TSCR1* (see Fig. 10.3). After loading the current value of *TCNT* into *TC1*, it configures *TCTL4* (see Fig. 10.13) to capture (and interrupt) on both rising and falling edges of the input signal. Writing a 1 to bit 1 in *TFLG1* (see Fig. 10.8) will clear any old flag. Finally, *TC1* interrupts are enabled by setting bit 1 of *TIE* (see Fig. 10.10), and hardware interrupts are enabled with the *cli* instruction.

The subroutine *HILOtimes1* shown in Listing 10.6 is called by the input capture interrupt service routine in Listing 10.5. The first instruction loads *D* with the contents of *TC1*, which will be the value to *TCNT* captured when the interrupt occurred. This value is saved by pushing it on the stack. The value captured at the last interrupt, stored in *TC1old*, is then subtracted from the current value in *D*. Bit 1 of *PTT* is then tested to see if the interrupt occurred because of a rising or falling edge of the input signal. If the interrupt occurred because of a rising edge of the input signal, the branch will not occur and the value of *D* (the time since the last interrupt) is stored in the variable *LO_time1*. Otherwise, the branch will occur and the value of *D* is stored in the variable *HI_time1*. In either case, the instruction *puld* will get the saved value of *TC1*, which was captured by the interrupt, and store this value in *TC1old* – ready for the next interrupt. Before returning from the subroutine, the *C1F* flag is cleared by writing a 1 to bit 1 of *TFLG1* (see Fig. 10.8).

The subroutine *get_HI_time1* in Listing 10.6 simply load *D* with the value in *HI_time1* (which is continually being updated in the interrupt service routine) and returns this value to the C function int *get_HI_time1*( ). Similarly, the subroutine *get_LO_time1* in Listing 10.6 will load *D* with the value in *LO_time1* and return this value to the C function int *get_LO_time1*( ).

Listing 10.6 ***Sound*** **Assembly Language Subroutines from** ***main.asm***

```
; calc HI-LO times of pulse train on Ch 1
;   and store results in HI_time1 and LO_time1
; void HILO1_init(void);
HILO1_init:
        bclr  TIOS,#$02    ;select input capture 1
        movb  #$04,TSCR2   ;div by 16: 24MHz/16 = 1.5 MHz
        movb  #$80,TSCR1   ;enable timer
        ldd   TCNT
        std   TC1          ;init cnt in TC1
        bset  TCTL4,#$0C   ;interrupt on both edges of Ch 1
        movb  #$02,TFLG1   ;clear any old flag on Ch 1
        bset  TIE,#$02     ;enable TC1 interrupts
        cli                ;enable interrupts
        rts

; calc HI-LO times of pulse train on Ch 1
;   and store results in HI_time1 and LO_time1
; void getHILOtimes1(void);
HILOtimes1:
        ldd   TC1
        pshd               ;save TC1
        subd  TC1old       ;LO_time'
        brclr PTT,$02,HL1  ;if PTT1 is hi, rising edge
        std   LO_time1;    ;store LO_time1
        bra   HL2
HL1:    std   HI_time1;    ;save HI_time1
HL2:    puld               ;get TC1
        std   TC1old;      ;TC1old = TC1
        bset  TFLG1, #$02  ;clear int flag
        rts

; int get_HI_time1(void);
get_HI_time1:
        ldd   HI_time1
        rts

; int get_LO_time1(void);
get_LO_time1:
        ldd   LO_time1
        rts
```

Chapter 11

Fuzzy Control

In this example we will show how to use the DRAGON12-Plus-USB board as a fuzzy controller. Before reading this example you should read Appendix E.

11.1 Design of a Fuzzy Controller

In Appendix E we show that the design of a fuzzy controller consists of the three parts shown in Fig. 11.1. The crisp inputs are first mapped to fuzzy sets using *get_inputs( )*; the fuzzy rules are then applied to the input fuzzy sets using *fire_rules( )*; and then a defuzzification operation is performed on the output fuzzy sets to produce a crisp output using *find_output( )*.

In this example we will design a fuzzy controller that will keep a ping-pong ball floating at the center of a vertical, Plexiglas cylinder. The position of the ball could be measured using an ultrasonic transducer at the bottom of the cylinder. Two consecutive position readings can be used to determine the instantaneous velocity of the ball. The output of the fuzzy controller will be a signal that will control the speed of a muffin fan at the bottom of the cylinder that blows air up the cylinder to keep the ping-pong ball at the desired height. A second ultrasonic transducer outside the cylinder could measure the height of your hand above the floor, and the fuzzy controller could make the ping-pong ball follow your hand!

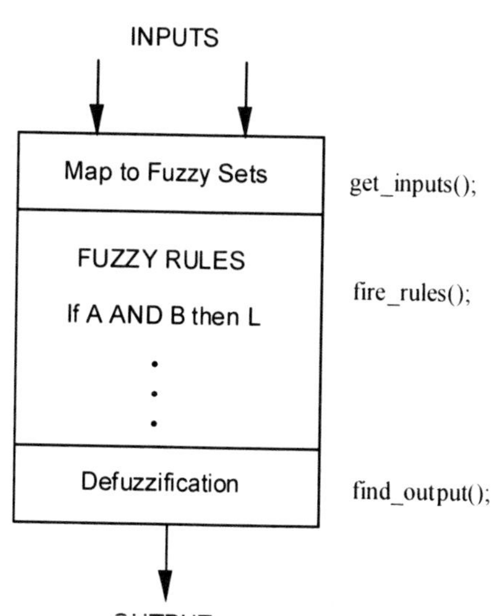

Figure 11.1 A fuzzy controller

The first step in the design is to define the membership functions for the inputs. The two inputs to the controller will be the *ball_position* and *ball_speed* and we will use the two sets of membership functions shown in Fig. 11.2. To use the built-in HCS12 fuzzy control assembly language instructions the values of *ball_position* and *ball_speed* must be an 8-bit number between 0 and 255.

The second step is to define the output motor power. The output membership functions are defined as singletons and are shown in Fig. 11.3. Again the value of *motor_power* must be between 0 and 255.

The third step is to determine the fuzzy rules. These will be common sense rules based on the two inputs, *ball_position* and *ball_speed*, and the output, *motor_power*. It is convenient to represent these rules in the form of a 5 x 5 fuzzy K-map of the form shown in

Fig. 11.4. The entries in this fuzzy K-map are the membership functions of the output, *motor_power*.

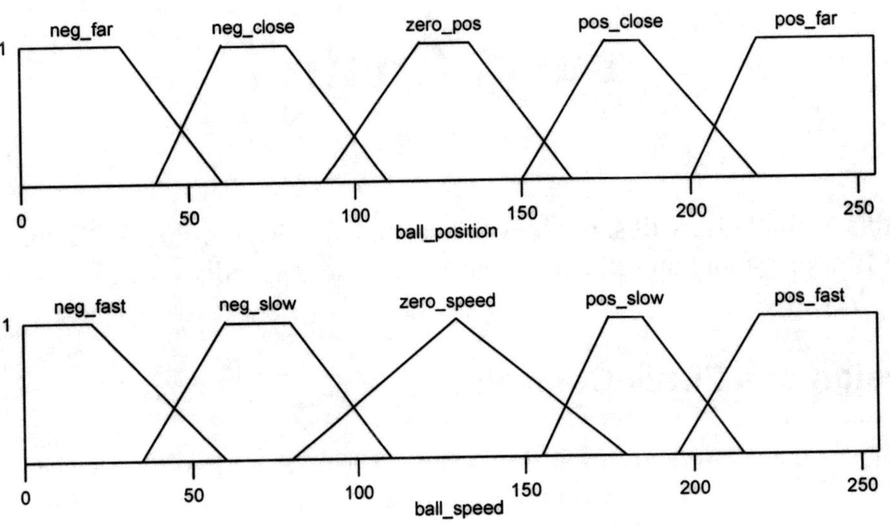

Figure 11.2 Input membership functions for floating ping-pong ball

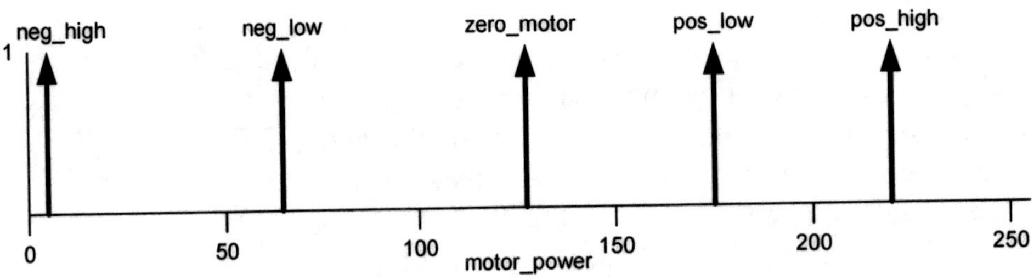

Figure 11.3 Output membership functions for floating ping-pong ball

For example, if the ball_position is *zero_p* (at its desired location) and the *ball_speed* is *zero_s* (it is not moving), then the change in *motor_power* should be *zero_m* (no change). This is the center entry in Fig. 11.4.

If the *ball_speed* is *zero_s* (the center row in Fig. 11.4) and the *ball_position* is *neg_close* (a little below the desired location) then we should increase the fan speed a little by setting *motor_power* to *pos_low*. If the *ball_position* is *neg_far* (a lot below the desired location) then we should increase the fan speed a lot by setting *motor_power* to *pos_high*. Similar arguments will hold if the *ball_position* is *pos_close* or *pos_far* leading to values of *motor_power* of *neg_low* (decrease fan speed a little) and *neg_high* (decrease fan speed a lot) respectively.

If the *ball_position* is *zero_p* (the center column in Fig. 11.4) and the *ball_speed* is *neg_slow* (ball is falling slowly through the desired location) then we should increase the fan speed a little by setting *motor_power* to *pos_low*. If the *ball_speed* is *neg_fast* (ball is falling rapidly through the desired location) then we should increase the fan speed a lot by setting *motor_power* to *pos_high*. Similar arguments will hold if the *ball_speed* is *pos_slow* or *pos_fast* leading to values of *motor_power* of *neg_low* (decrease fan speed a little) and *neg_high* (decrease fan speed a lot) respectively.

		ball_position				
		neg_far	neg_close	zero_p	pos_close	pos_far
	pos_fast	zero_m	neg_low	neg_high	neg_high	neg_high
	pos_slow	pos_low	zero_m	neg_low	neg_high	neg_high
ball_speed	zero_s	pos_high	pos_low	zero_m	neg_low	neg_high
	neg_slow	pos_high	pos_high	pos_low	zero_m	neg_low
	neg_fast	pos_high	pos_high	pos_high	pos_low	zero_m

Figure 11.4 Fuzzy K-map for floating ping-pong ball

Similar arguments can be made for the four entries in each of the four corners of the fuzzy K-map in Fig. 11.4. Note that the same fuzzy output membership function tends to occur on diagonal lines going from the upper-left to bottom-right of the diagram in Fig. 11.4. This is typical of many fuzzy controller rules.

The HCS12 assembly language contains three sets of instructions that are useful for implementing a fuzzy controller. The *MEM* instruction will fill a *weights* array given an input and a set of membership functions. We will describe a C function call that uses this instruction in Section 11.2. The *REV* instruction is used to fire the rules. We will describe a C function call that uses this instruction in Section 11.3. The *WAV* instruction is used to calculate the output defuzzification centroid. We will describe a C function call that uses this instruction in Section 11.4.

11.2 Fuzzification of Inputs – MEM and *fill_weights*(...)

The first step in designing a fuzzy controller is to define the membership functions for all inputs and the output. Each membership function can be defined by the four parameters *u1*, *u2*, *u3*, and *u4* shown in Fig. 11.5. The *MEM* instruction requires that the values *u1* and *u4* be 8-bit values between \$00 and \$FF. The weight values also range from \$00 to \$FF where \$FF represents a weight value of 1.0 in Fig. 11.5.

The *MEM* instruction does not use the parameters *u1*, *u2*, *u3*, and *u4* shown in Fig. 11.5 to define the membership function. Rather it uses *u1* (called *point_1*) and *u4* (called *point_2*) together with the values of the two slopes, *slope_1* and *slope_2*, shown in Fig. 11.5.

The value of *slope_1* is \$FF/(*u2* - *u1*) and the value of *slope_2* is \$FF/(*u4* - *u3*). These values can range from \$01 to \$FF. If u1 = u2 or u3 = u4 then the slope is really infinite. In this case the values of *slope_1* and/or *slope_2* are taken to be \$00 inasmuch as this value is not used otherwise. A special case is a singleton, or "crisp" membership function. This can be defined by setting *u1* = *u4* and *slope_1* = *slope_2* = \$00.

In the example program shown in Listing 11.1 we have allowed you to enter the membership functions for *ball_position* and *ball_speed* using the parameters *u1*, *u2*, *u3*, and *u4* from Fig. 11.5 in the arrays *ball_position*[ ] and *ball_speed*[ ]. The function *get_slopes*(const unsigned char *ball*[ ], unsigned char *memb*[ ] ,int *maxsize*) in Listing 11.1 will then fill the arrays *memb_pos*[20] and *memb_speed*[20] with the *point_1*, *point_2*, *slope_1*, and *slope_2* format used by the *MEM* instruction.

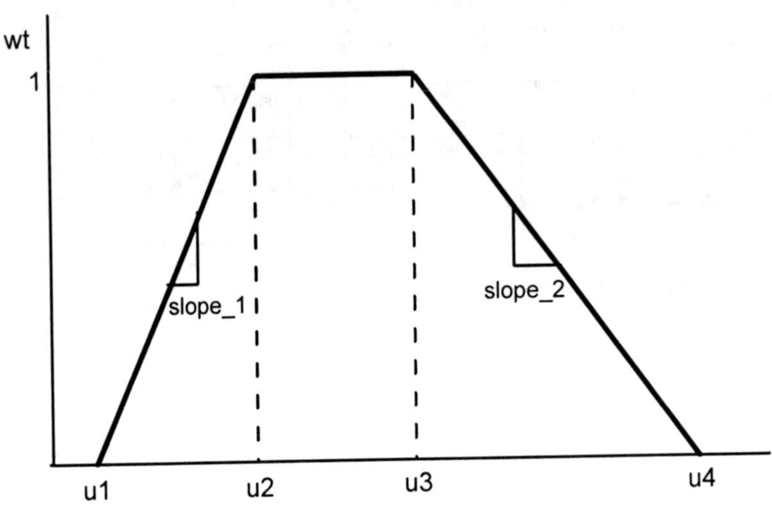

Figure 11.5 A membership function is defined in terms of u1, u2, u3, and u4

The *MEM* instruction requires accumulator *A* to contain the input value x_i and index register *X* to point to a data structure containing the two points and slopes that define the membership function as shown in Fig. 11.6. Index register *Y* points to the element of the array *weight*(*j*) corresponding to membership function *j*.

The *MEM* instruction will compute the weight value at the input value x_i based on the membership function whose parameters are pointed to by *X*. The computed weight value ($00-$FF) is stored in the byte pointed to by *Y*. After the *MEM* instruction is executed *X* will have been incremented by 4 and *Y* will have been incremented by 1. If the four parameters of all membership functions for a single input are stored in adjacent bytes of memory, then *X* will be pointing to the parameters of the next membership function. Similarly, *Y* will be pointing to the next element in the array *weight*(*j*).

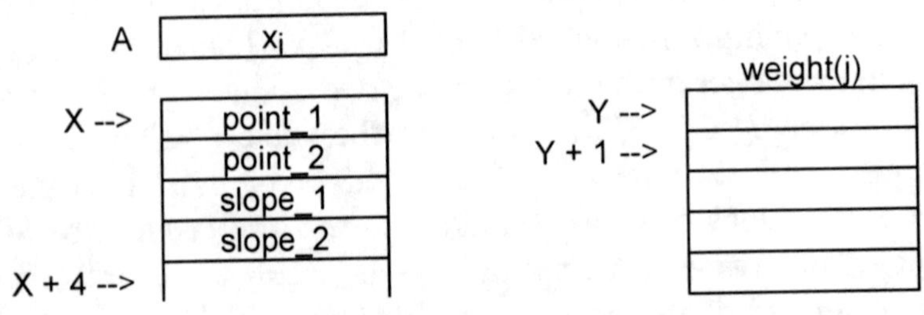

Figure 11.6 Data structure used by the HCS12 MEM instruction

Listing 11.1a Example 32

```
// Example 32:  Fuzzy Control -- ping-pong ball
#include <hidef.h>      /* common defines and macros */
#include <mc9s12dg256.h>     /* derivative information */
#pragma LINK_INFO DERIVATIVE "mc9s12dg256b"

#include "main_asm.h" /* interface to the assembly module */

#define NUM_MEMB = 5;

void get_slopes(const unsigned char ball[],unsigned char memb[],int num_memb);

/* global variables definitions */
static  int num_memb_pos = 5;
static  int num_memb_speed = 5;
static  int maxsize = 20;
static  int num_memb_motor = 5;
static  int num_rules = 25;

void main(void) {
  // input membership functions
  const unsigned char ball_position[] = {
      0,  0, 30, 60,              // neg_far
     40, 60, 80,110,              // neg_close
     90,120,135,165,              // zero_pos
    150,175,185,220,              // pos_close
    200,220,255,255        // pos_far
  };
  const unsigned char ball_speed[] = {
      0,  0, 20, 60,              // neg_fast
     35, 60, 80,110,              // neg_slow
     80,130,130,180,              // zero_speed
    155,175,185,215,              // pos_slow
    195,220,255,255        // pos_fast
  };
  unsigned char memb_pos[20];
  unsigned char memb_speed[20]
  ;
  // output membership functions
  unsigned char cent[] = {
    5,65,128,175,220
  };
  unsigned char inout_array[] = {
    0,  // weight_pos[]    0 neg_far
    0,  //                 1 neg_close
    0,  //                 2 zero_pos
    0,  //                 3 pos_close
    0,  //                 4 pos_far
    0,  // weight_speed[]  5 neg_fast
    0,  //                 6 neg_slow
    0,  //                 7 zero_speed
    0,  //                 8 pos_slow
    0,  //                 9 pos_fast
    0,  // out[]          10 neg_high
    0,  //                11 neg_low
    0,  //                12 zero_motor
    0,  //                13 pos_low
    0,  //                14 pos_high
  };
```

Listing 11.1b Example 21 (cont.)

```
unsigned char rules[] = {
    0,5,0xFE,14,0xFE,    // if x1 is neg_far && x2 is neg_fast then y is pos_high
    0,6,0xFE,14,0xFE,
    0,7,0xFE,14,0xFE,
    0,8,0xFE,13,0xFE,
    0,9,0xFE,12,0xFE,
    1,5,0xFE,14,0xFE,    // if x1 is neg_close && x2 is neg_fast then y is pos_high
    1,6,0xFE,14,0xFE,
    1,7,0xFE,13,0xFE,
    1,8,0xFE,12,0xFE,
    1,9,0xFE,11,0xFE,
    2,5,0xFE,14,0xFE,    // if x1 is zero_pos && x2 is neg_fast then y is pos_high
    2,6,0xFE,13,0xFE,
    2,7,0xFE,12,0xFE,
    2,8,0xFE,11,0xFE,
    2,9,0xFE,10,0xFE,
    3,5,0xFE,13,0xFE,    // if x1 is pos_close && x2 is neg_fast then y is pos_low
    3,6,0xFE,12,0xFE,
    3,7,0xFE,11,0xFE,
    3,8,0xFE,10,0xFE,
    3,9,0xFE,10,0xFE,
    4,5,0xFE,12,0xFE,    // if x1 is pos_far && x2 is neg_fast then y is zero_motor
    4,6,0xFE,11,0xFE,
    4,7,0xFE,10,0xFE,
    4,8,0xFE,10,0xFE,
    4,9,0xFE,10,0xFF
  };

  unsigned char* ptr_memb_pos;
  unsigned char* ptr_memb_speed;
  unsigned char* ptr_weight_pos;
  unsigned char* ptr_weight_speed;
  unsigned char* ptr_inout_array;
  unsigned char* ptr_out;
  unsigned char* ptr_rules;
  unsigned char* ptr_cent;
  unsigned char x1;                                   // input x1
  unsigned char x2;                                   // input x2
  unsigned char y;                                    // output y

  ptr_memb_pos = memb_pos;
  ptr_memb_speed = memb_speed;
  ptr_weight_pos = inout_array;
  ptr_weight_speed = inout_array+num_memb_pos;
  ptr_inout_array = inout_array;
  ptr_out = inout_array+num_memb_pos+num_memb_speed;
  ptr_rules = rules;
  ptr_cent = cent;

  PLL_init();        // set system clock frequency to 24 MHz
  get_slopes(ball_position,memb_pos,maxsize);
  get_slopes(ball_speed,memb_speed,maxsize);
```

Listing 11.1c Example 21 (cont.)

```
  // The fuzzy controller
  while(1) {
  //   x1 = get_position();      // (user defined)
       x1 = 100;                       // test case -- remove
       fill_weights(ptr_weight_pos,ptr_memb_pos,num_memb_pos,x1);
  //   x2 = get_speed();         // (user defined)
       x2 = 150;                       // test case -- remove
       fill_weights(ptr_weight_speed,ptr_memb_speed,num_memb_speed,x2);
       fire_rules(ptr_inout_array,ptr_rules,ptr_out,num_memb_motor);
       y = calc_output(ptr_out,ptr_cent,num_memb_motor);
  //   adjust_motor(y):          // (user defined)
  }
}


void get_slopes(const unsigned char ball[],unsigned char memb[],int maxsize) {
  int j;
  unsigned char diff;
  for(j = 0; j < maxsize; j=j+4){
    memb[j] = ball[j];                         // point_1
    memb[j+1] = ball[j+3];                     // point_2
    diff = (ball[j+1] - ball[j]);
    if(diff == 0)
        memb[j+2] = 0;
    else
        memb[j+2] = 255/diff;                  // slope_1
    diff = (ball[j+3] - ball[j+2]);
    if(diff == 0)
        memb[j+3] = 0;
    else
        memb[j+3] = 255/diff;                  // slope_2
  }
}
```

In Listing 11.1a we have included the three arrays *weight_pos*[ ], *weight_speed*[ ], and *out*[ ] in a single array called *inout_array*[ ]. The reason for doing this is that the *MEM* instruction requires that *weight_pos*[ ] and *weight_speed*[ ] be in consecutive memory locations and the definition of the fuzzy rules (described in the next section) requires the *out*[ ] array to follow the *weight_pos*[ ] and *weight_speed*[ ] arrays.

We have written an assembly language routine that is called by the C function *void* ***fill_weights***(*unsigned char* weight, unsigned char* membx, int num_mem_fncs, char x*) that will call the *MEM* function *num_mem_fncs* times. This function will fuzzify the crisp input *x* by filling the weight array pointed to by *weight* with the appropriate weights based on the set of membership functions pointed to by *membx*.

11.3 Processing the Rules – REV and *fire_rules(...)*

We will use the MIN-MAX rule described in Appendix E to find the contribution of each rule to the output. The outputs are assumed to be represented by k singleton membership functions L^k. These membership functions are defined by the singleton centroids, $cent^k$. An output array, *out*(k), will contain the maximum over all the rules of the minimum weights from all inputs. The purpose of the function *void* ***fire_rules***(*unsigned char* inout_array, unsigned char* rules, unsigned char* out, int numout*) is to fill the elements of the output weight vector, *out*(k). A fuzzy rule with two inputs can be represented by the triplet (A^1_j, A^2_j; L_j) where the subscript j refers to the jth fuzzy rule. Let the value A^1_j be the address (pointer) of the kth element of the weight vector $weight_1(k)$ for input 1. A^1_j will therefore correspond to one of the membership functions (and therefore one of the fuzzy sets) of input 1. Similarly, A^2_j will be the address of the kth element of the weight vector $weight_2(k)$ for input 2. In general, A^i_j will be the address of the kth element of the weight vector $weight_i(k)$ for input i. The pseudocode for the function *fire_rules*( ) is given in Fig. 11.7. We will next see how this pseudocode can be implemented using the HCS12 *REV* instruction.

```
fire_rules()
clear out array;
for j = 1, num_rules
   {
   min_wt = 1;
   for i = 1, num_inputs
      {
      wt = weighti[Aij]
      if wt < min_wt
         min_wt = wt;
      }
      out[Lj] = MAX(Out[Lj], min_wt);
   }
```

Figure 11.7 Pseudocode for *fire_rules*( )

The HCS12 REV Instruction

The setup required for the 68HC12 *REV* instruction is shown in Fig. 11.8. Index register *Y* points to an *inout_array* that contains the input *weight*(j) arrays and ends with the *out(k)* array described above. The elements of the *weight*(j) and *out*(k) arrays are assigned offsets (0 - 14) which represent the various membership functions such as *neg_far* and *pos_high* as shown in Fig. 11.8 and Listing 11.1a.

The array labeled *rules* in Fig. 11.8 contains a series of bytes, pointed to by index register *X*, that contains an encoding of all the rules. Each rule is of the form

if *x1* is *neg_far* and *x2* is *neg_fast* then *y* is *pos_high*

The offsets in the *inout_array* corresponding to *neg_far* (0) and *neg_fast* (5) are stored in the first two bytes. This is followed by a byte containing $FE which separates the input antecedents from the output consequents. The next byte contains 14, the offset of *pos_high* in the *inout_array*. This is followed by another $FE which separates the last consequent offset from the first antecedent offset of the next rule. A byte containing $FF marks the end of the rules. This rule encoding scheme will allow any number of inputs and any number of outputs.

		inout_array	
Y→	neg_far 0	- -	weight_pos[]
	neg_close 1	- -	
	zero_pos 2	- -	
	pos_close 3	- -	
	pos_far 4	- -	
	neg_fast 5	- -	weight_speed[]
	neg_slow 6	- -	
	zero_speed 7	- -	
	pos_slow 8	- -	
	pos_fast 9	- -	
	neg_high 10	0	Out[]
	neg_low 11	0	
	zero_m 12	0	
	pos_low 13	0	
	pos_high 14	0	

	rules	
X→	0	x1 is neg_far
	5	x2 is neg_fast
	FE	
	15	y is pos_high
	FE	
	0	x1 is neg_far
	6	x2 is neg_slow
	FE	
	15	y is pos_high
	FE	
	11	
A = $FF	FF	end of rules

Figure 11.8 Setup required for REV instruction

The declaration of the *inout_array*[ ] is shown in Listing 11.1a and the definition of the complete *rule*[ ] array is shown in Listing 11.1b. The index numbers associated with each rule can easily be seen in Fig. 11.9 where we have redrawn the fuzzy K-map from Fig. 11.4 and included the corresponding index numbers from the *inout_array*[ ].

		ball_position				
		neg_far 0	neg_close 1	zero_p 2	pos_close 3	pos_far 4
ball_speed	pos_fast 9	zero_motor 12	neg_low 11	neg_high 10	neg_high 10	neg_high 10
	pos_slow 8	pos_low 13	zero_motor 12	neg_low 11	neg_high 10	neg_high 10
	zero_speed 7	pos_high 14	pos_low 13	zero_motor 12	neg_low 11	neg_high 10
	neg_slow 6	pos_high 14	pos_high 14	pos_low 13	zero_motor 12	neg_low 11
	neg_fast 5	pos_high 14	pos_high 14	pos_high 14	pos_low 13	zero_motor 12

Figure 11.9 Fuzzy K-map inout_array[] indicies

In addition to initializing *X* and *Y* as shown in Fig. 11.8, accumulator *A* must be set to $FF and the *out*(*k*) array must be initialized to zero before the *REV* instruction is executed.

The *REV* instruction will then process all of the rules and fill the *out*(k) array following the pseudocode shown in Fig. 11.7.

You may wonder how the *REV* instruction can tell the difference between the $FE at the end of the antecedents and the $FE at the end of the consequents. The answer is that it uses the overflow bit *V* in the condition code register as a flag to tell the difference. This bit is automatically set to zero when the statement *LDAA #$FF* is executed. The *REV* instruction then toggles this bit to 1 when it encounters the $FE at the end of the antecedents are clears it to zero by reloading accumulator *A* with $FF when it encounters the $FE at the end of the consequents.

The C function *fire_rules(...)*

We have written an assembly language routine that is called by the C function *void* ***fire_rules***(*unsigned char* inout_array, unsigned char* rules, unsigned char* out, int numout*) that will first clear the out array. It then points to the *rules*[ ] array with index register *X* and to the *inout_array*[ ] with index register *Y*, sets accumulator *A* to $FF and calls the *REV* instruction. At this point the *out*[ ] array is filled with the appropriate output weights based on the entire list of fuzzy rules.

11.4 Output defuzzification – WAV and *calc_output(...)*

We will always use singleton fuzzy sets for the output represented by the centroids, $cent^k$. We will also use the MIN-MAX inference rule described in Appendix E. It should be clear from Fig. E.11 in Appendix E that in this case the centroid y_0 will still be given by Eq. (E.11) where W^k is now the output array, *out(k)*, shown in Fig. 11.8 and computed by the function *fire_rules*(...) described in the previous section.

Once the function *fire_rules*(...) has filled the output weight array *out*(k) the function *find_output*(...) will calculate the centroid y_0 using Eq. (E.11) in Appendix E. The pseudocode for the function *find_output*(...) is given in Fig. 11.10. The centroids of the Q output membership functions are stored in the array $cent^k$.

```
find_output()
numer = 0;
denom = 0;
for k = 1, Q
    if out[k] != 0
       {
       numer = numer + out[k]*cent[k];
       denom = denom + out[k];
       }
y0 = numer/denom;
```

Figure 11.10 Pseudocode for *find_output*(...)

The HCS12 WAV Instruction

The values of *numer* and *denom* in Fig. 11.10 can easily be calculated using the HCS12 *WAV* instruction. If index register *X* points to *cent*[*k*], index register *Y* points to *out*[*k*], and accumulator *B* contains the number of output membership functions, *Q*, then the HCS12 WAV instruction will compute a 24-bit value for *numer* and store the result in *Y:D* and compute a 16-bit value for *denom* and store this result in *X*. Therefore, if the *WAV* instruction is followed by the instruction *EDIV* (see Appendix C) then the centroid value y_0 will be left in *Y*.

We have written an assembly language routine that is called by the C function *unsigned char* ***calc_output***(*unsigned char* out, unsigned char* cent, int numout*) that will return the crisp output by using the WAV instruction as described above.

The complete while loop for the fuzzy controller is shown in Listing 11.1c. The functions *get_position*( ) and *get_speed*( ) are user-defined functions for reading the position and speed of the ping-pong ball. The position can be measured using an ultrasonic transducer. The speed can be computed by subtracting two successive position measurements.

After calling *fill_weights*(...) for both inputs, *fire_rules*(...), and *calc_output*(...), the word *adjust_motor*(*y*) is a user-defined word that will set the speed of the fan according the value of the output centroid *y*.

11.5 Under the Hood – Fuzzy Control Assembly Routines

In the previous sections of this chapter we have used the following three C function calls to design a fuzzy controller.

void ***fill_weights***(*unsigned char* weight, unsigned char* membx, int num_mem_fncs, char x*)

void ***fire_rules***(*unsigned char* inout_array, unsigned char* rules, unsigned char* out, int numout*)

unsigned char ***calc_output***(*unsigned char* out, unsigned char* cent, int numout*)

The three assembly language subroutines that are executed by these three C functions are given in Listing 11.2. The subroutine *fill_weights* receives pointers to the weight and membership arrays and the number of membership functions (5) on the stack and gets the input value *x* in accumulator *B*. After setting up these values as shown in Fig. 11.6, the instruction *MEM* is called five times. Note that when *MEM* is called, the number of membership functions is stored in *B* and the instruction *dbne B,fw1* will decrement *B* and branch not equal to *fw1*, i.e., to the *MEM* instruction.

The subroutine *fire_rules* shown in Listing 11.2 receives pointers to the *inout*, *rules*, and *out* arrays on the stack and gets the number of outputs in accumulator *D* (*B*). The subroutine first clears the *out* array and then sets up the registers for the *REV* instruction as shown in Fig. 11.8.

The subroutine *calc_output* shown in Listing 11.2 receives pointers to the *out* and *cent* arrays on the stack and gets the number of outputs in accumulator *D* (*B*). The subroutine first sets up the registers for the *WAV* instruction, which expects index register *X* to point to *cent*[*k*], index register *Y* to point to *out*[*k*], and accumulator *B* to contain the number of output membership functions. Then the *WAV* instruction will compute a 24-bit value for *numer* (shown in Fig. 11.10) and store the result in *Y:D* and compute a 16-bit value for *denom* and store this result in *X*. The *WAV* instruction is followed by the instruction *EDIV*, which will leave the quotient (centroid value y_0) in *Y*. This value is transferred to *D*, which will return the 8-bit output in *B* to the C program.

Listing 11.2 *Fuzzy Control* Assembly Language Subroutines from *main.asm*

```
; Fuzzy Control routines
; void fill_weights(unsigned char* weight, unsigned char* membx, int
   num_mem_fncs, char x)
fill_weights:
            pshb                    ; save x
            ldd    3,sp             ; B = num_mem_funcs
            ldx    5,sp             ; X -> membx
            ldy    7,sp             ; Y -> weight
            pula                    ; A = x
fw1:        mem                     ; fuzzy membership grade
            dbne   B,fw1
            rts

; void fire_rules(unsigned char* inout_array, unsigned char* rules,
   unsigned char* out, int numout)
fire_rules:
            ldy    2,sp             ;Y -> out array
fr0         clr    1,Y+             ;clear out array
            dbne   B,fr0            ;B = numout
            ldx    4,sp             ;X -> rules
            ldy    6,sp             ;Y -> inout array
            ldaa   #$FF             ;must set A = $FF
            rev                     ;rule evaluation
            rts

; unsigned char calc_output(unsigned char* out, unsigned char* cent, int
   numout)
calc_output:                        ;B = numout
            ldx    2,sp             ;X -> cent array
            ldy    4,sp             ;Y -> out array
            wav
            ediv                    ;Y = quotient
            tfr    Y,D              ;D = quot A = 0, B = output
            rts
```

PROBLEMS

11.1 Run the program in Listing 11.1 using the simulator mode. Set a breakpoint at the first *get_slopes*(...) function and single-step through the instructions of each function call. Observe the contents of the *inout_array*[ ] and note how the output centroid value is calculated.

11.2

a. Implement the floating ping-pong ball fuzzy control problem described in this chapter. Use an ultrasonic transducer to measure the distance to the ping-pong ball. The difference between two consecutive distance measurements can be used to represent the ball speed. A muffin fan at the bottom of the Plexiglas cylinder is used to maintain the ping-pong ball at a fixed height within the cylinder.
b. Add a dial that you can use to set the height of the ping-pong ball.
c. Add a mode that has the ping-pong ball move between two different heights every 10 seconds.
d. Use a second ultrasonic transducer to measure the distance from the floor to your hand. Use the serial port to send this distance to your ping-pong ball setup. Have the ping-pong ball float at the height of your hand above the floor. As you move your hand up and down, the ping-pong ball should follow!

11.3 A fuzzy controller is used to maintain the idle speed of an automobile engine. The idle speed can be controlled by varying both the throttle position and the spark advance. In this problem we will consider only the throttle position. The two inputs will be

x1: the RPM error (current RPM - desired RPM)

x2: the change in RPM error from one measurement to the next

The output, *y*, will be a signal to a stepper motor that changes the throttle position. All input and output values are scaled from 0 - 255. The membership functions for the two inputs are given in the following tables.

Input x1	u1	u2	u3	u4
NM_1	0	0	20	100
NS_1	0	100	100	120
Z_1	100	128	128	156
PS_1	136	156	156	255
PM_1	156	235	255	255

Input x2	u1	u2	u3	u4
NS_2	0	0	64	128
Z_2	64	128	128	192
PS_2	128	192	255	255

The output, *y*, will have the five centroid values, 10, 80, 128, 176, and 245, corresponding to *NM_y*, *NS_y*, *Z_y*, *PS_y*, and *PM_y*.

a. Make plots of the membership functions for the two inputs, *x1* and *x2*, and the output, *y*.
b. Make up a list of rules that seem sensible to you. For example, one rule might be

IF $x1$ is NS_1 and $x2$ is Z_2 THEN y is PS_y

Make a fuzzy K-map of your rule set similar to the one shown in Fig. 11.9.

c. Write a fuzzy control program for this problem by following the format in Listing 11.1.

11.4 Suggest how you might design a fuzzy control system for each of the following applications:

a. An auto-focusing camera.
b. The braking system of a truck.
c. A washing machine
d. A rain-dependent variable-speed windshield wiper.
e. An electric oven.
f. Acceleration and deceleration control of a train.
g. A robot manipulator.

Appendix A

CodeWarrior Tutorial
DRAGON12-Plus-USB

The latest free version of CodeWarrior – *Special Edition: CodeWarrior for S12(X) Microcontrollers V5.1* is available from www.freescale.com.
To use V5.1 of CodeWarrior begin by storing the folder *LBE_DRAGON12_Plus* available from http://www.lbebooks.com in the folder
Program Files\Freescale\CW S12v5.1\(CodeWarrior_Examples)\HCS12X

In this tutorial you will execute the program in Example 1a.

1. Start the program by double-clicking the CodeWarrior IDE icon on the desktop.

2. When you run CodeWarrior V5.1 (IDE.exe) you get this startup dialog.

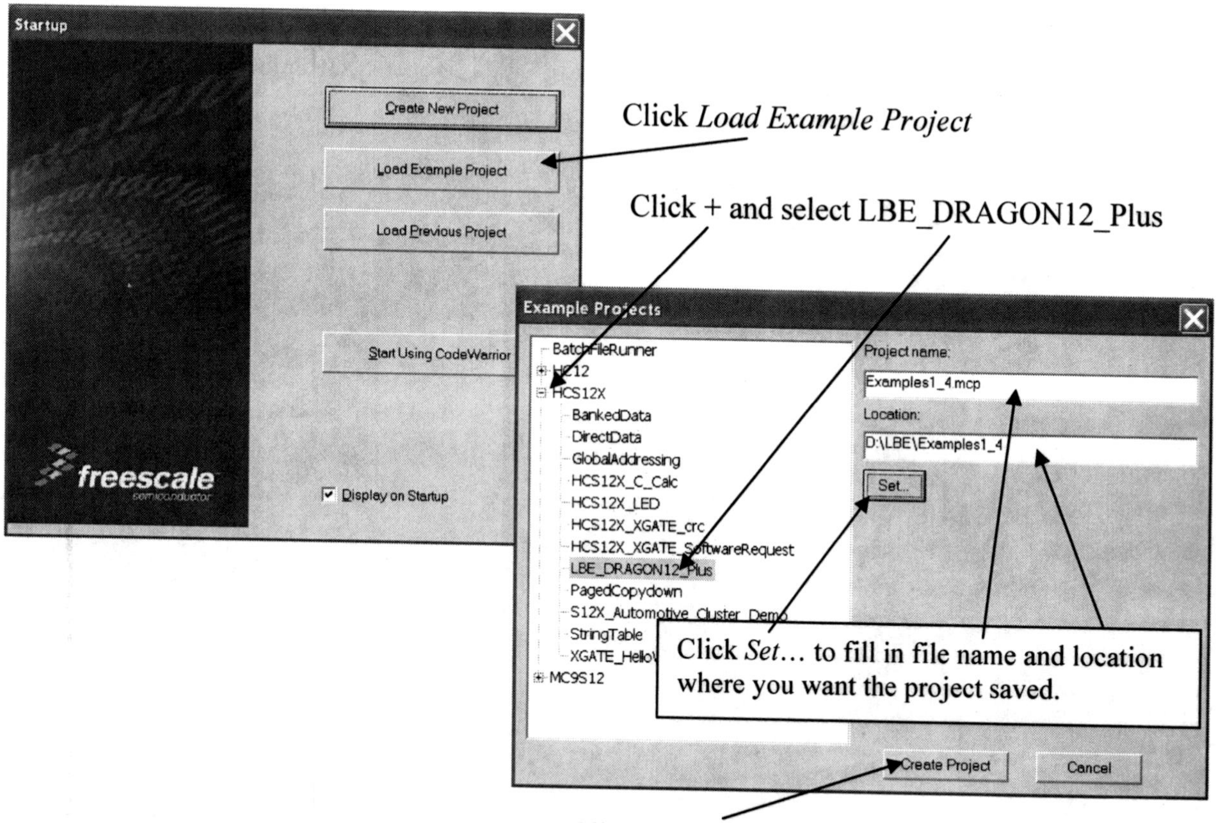

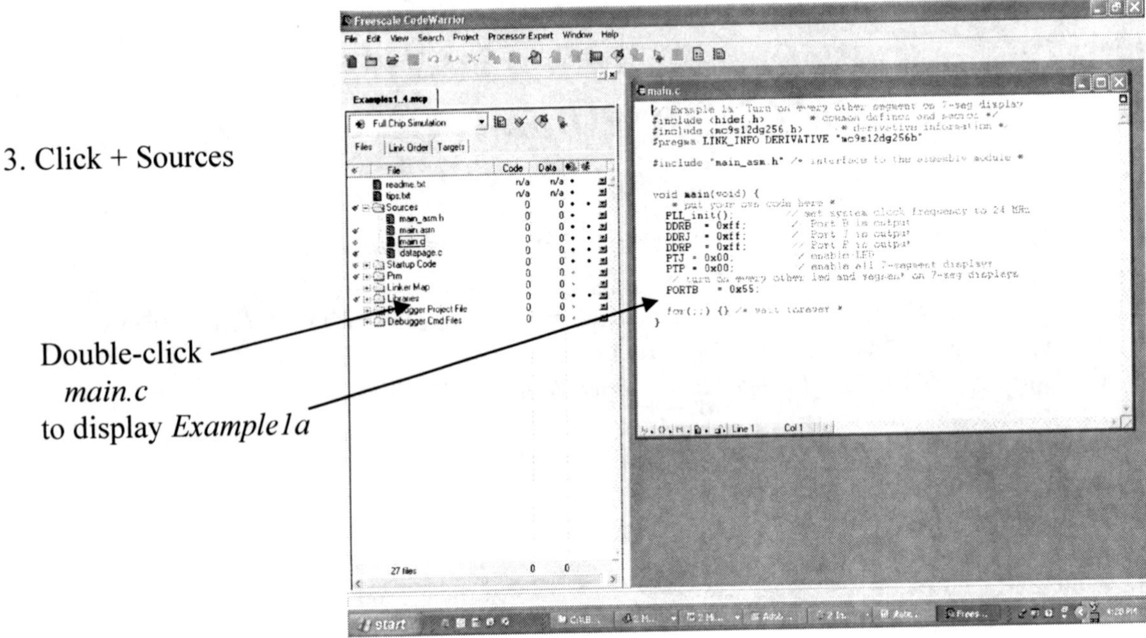
3. Click + Sources
Double-click
main.c
to display Example1a

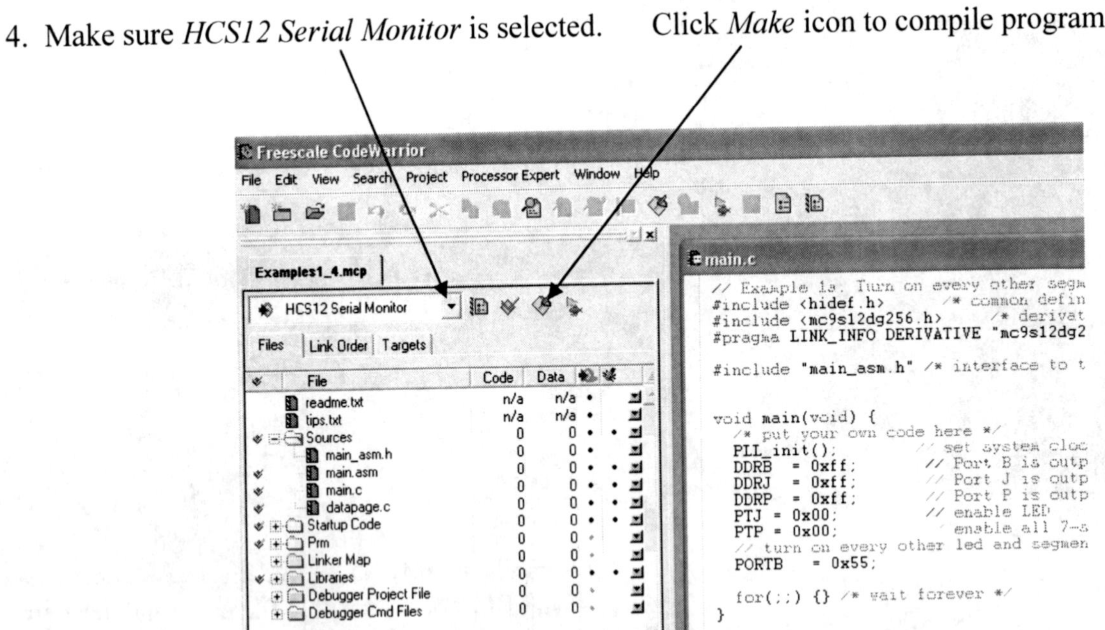
4. Make sure HCS12 Serial Monitor is selected.
Click Make icon to compile program.

5. Make sure slide switch is in the *down LOAD* position

Make sure that the USB cable is connected here

and the plug transformer is connected here

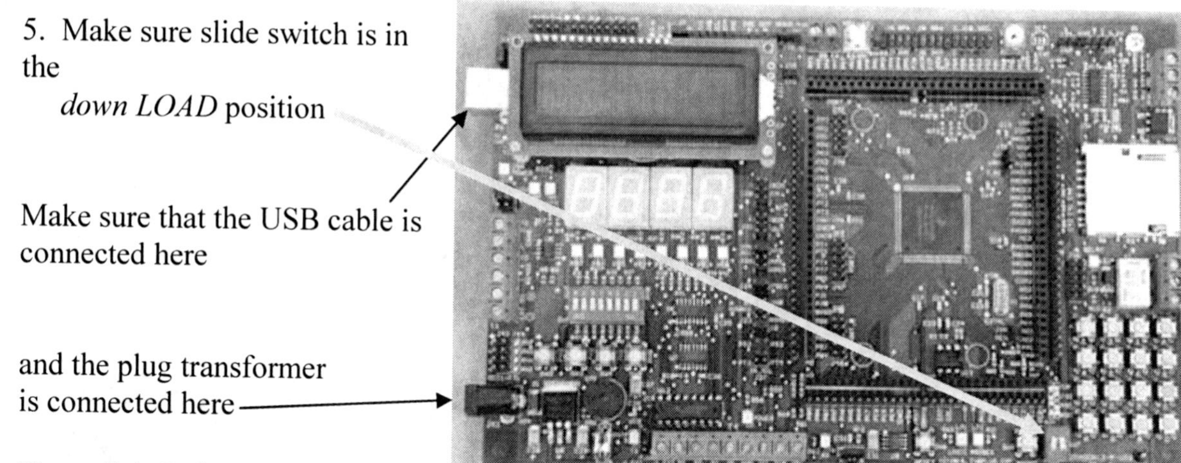

Then click *Debug* icon

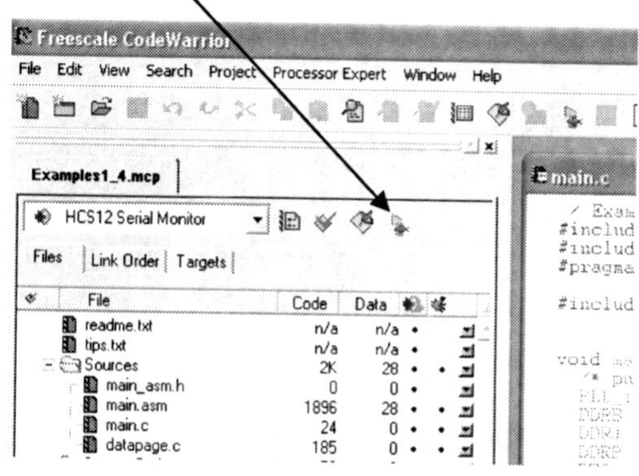

This will erase the flash memory (excluding the 2K bytes of protected flash containing the Serial Monitor) and bring up the following Debug window.

6. Click the *Start/Continue (F5)* icon to run the program.

Every other LED and segments a, c, e, and g of all 7-segment displays should be lit.

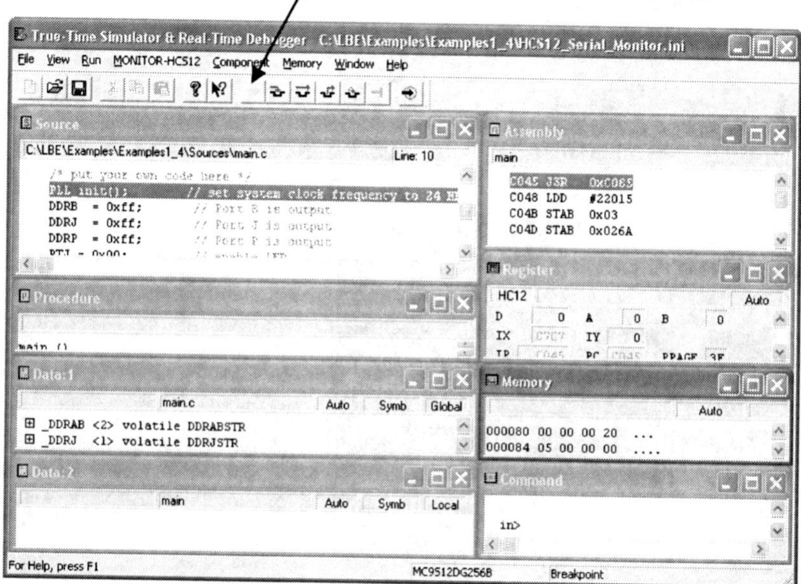

7. Press the reset button (the LEDs and 7-segment displays should go out)

8. Now move the slide switch up to the RUN mode

9. Press the reset button again. Your program is running in flash memory on the board and the LEDs and 7-segment displays should come back on.

10. Now move the slide switch right back to the LOAD mode and press the reset button. The Serial Monitor is running on the board (the 7-segment display will go out) and you are ready to download a new program.

11. Close the Debug window

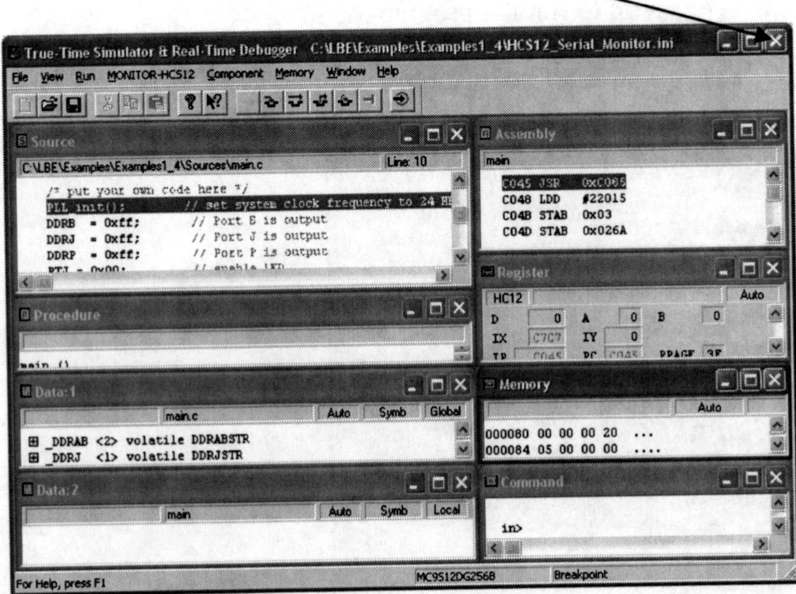

Example 1b – Read Example 1

At this point you could create a completely new project by following steps 2 and 3 above and edit *main.c* to be some new program. Instead we will keep the same project and just keep changing *main.c* to be Example1b – Example4b.

12. Select *File* → *Open...* Locate and open the file *Copy of Example 1b main.c.*

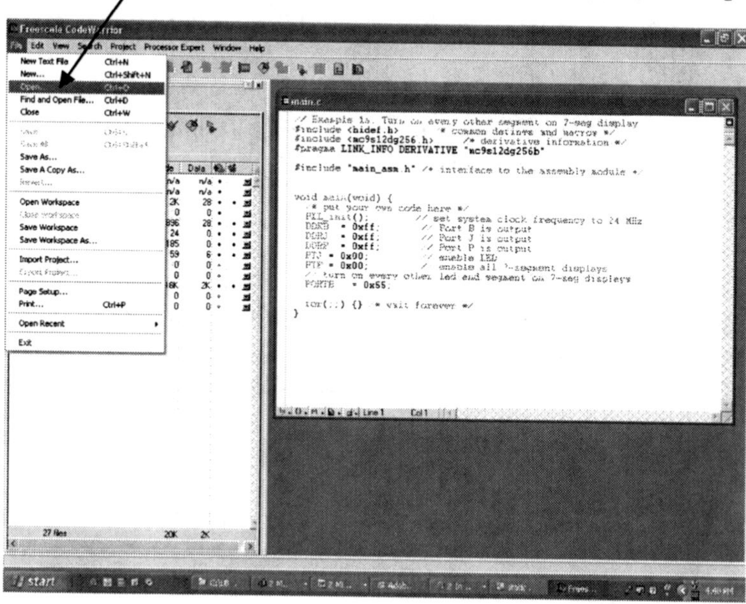

13. Select all of *Copy of Example 1b main.c* and copy it to the clipboard.

14. Select all of *main.c* and paste *Copy of Example 1b main.c* in its place

15. Save the file *main.c*

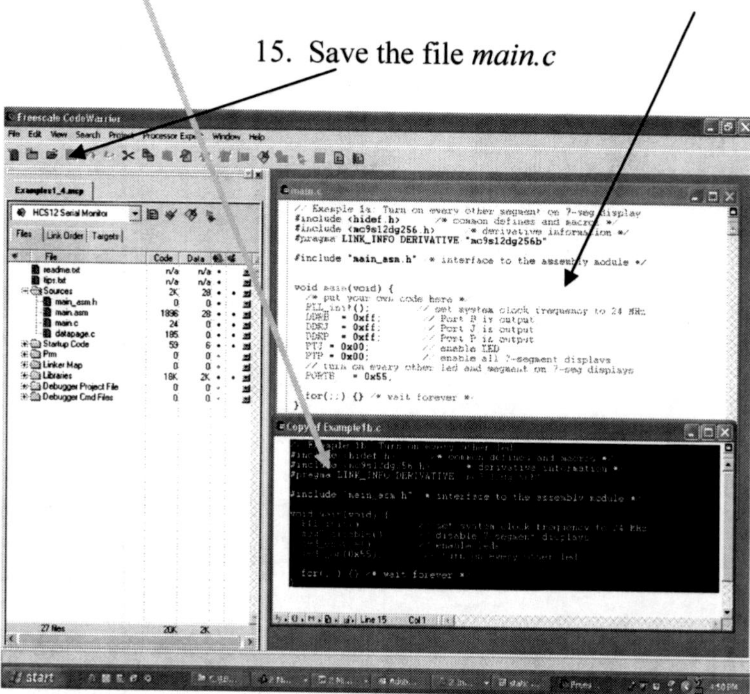

Repeat steps 4 – 11 for Example 1b.

Repeat steps 4 – 11 for Example 1c.

Read Example 2: Repeat steps 12 – 13 for *Copy of Example 2a main.c*.

Repeat steps 12 – 13 for *Copy of Example 2b main.c*.

Read Example 3: Repeat steps 12 – 13 for *Copy of Example 3a main.c*.

Repeat steps 12 – 13 for *Copy of Example 3b main.c*.

Read Example 4: Repeat steps 12 – 13 for *Copy of Example 4a main.c*.

Repeat steps 12 – 13 for *Copy of Example 4b main.c*.

Appendix B

HCS12 Assembly Language Essentials

B.1 The HCS12 Registers

The programming model of the HCS12 is identical with that of the 68HC11 and 68HC12. It consists of the set of registers shown in Figure B.1. We will refer to these as the CPU12 registers. The HCS12 also contains a register block that is associated with the various I/O operations of the HCS12.

In this section we will describe the CPU12 registers and illustrate how data can be moved into and out of these registers using some of the HCS12 instructions and addressing modes.

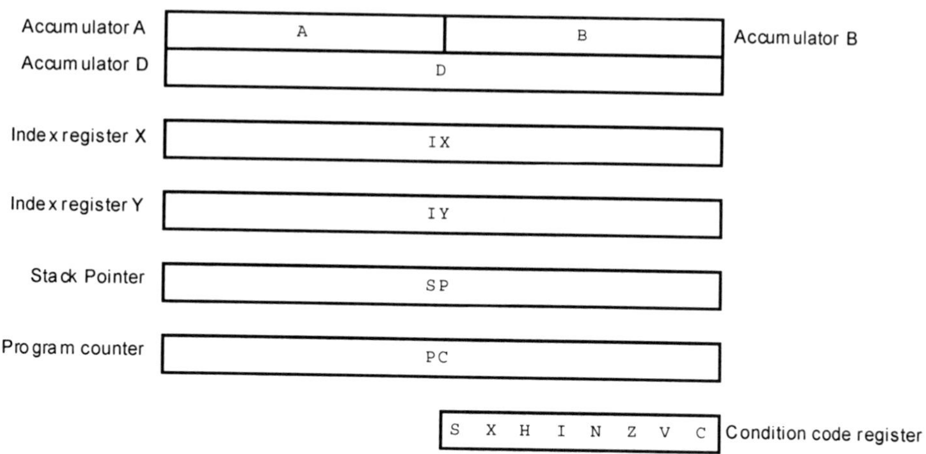

Figure B.1 The HCS12 Registers

B.1.1 The HCS12 Accumulators

The HCS12 has two 8-bit accumulators, *A* and *B*, that can be combined into the single 16-bit accumulator *D*. That is, *A* is the upper 8-bits of *D* and *B* is the lower 8-bits of *D*. The accumulators are used for storing intermediate results and for performing arithmetic and logical operations. The following are some of the instructions involving accumulators A, B, and D.

Load and Store Instructions:

LDAA	Load A from memory
LDAB	Load B from memory
LDD	Load D from memory
STAA	Store A to memory
STAB	Store B to memory
STD	Store D to memory

Transfer and Exchange Instructions:

TAB	Transfer A to B
TBA	Transfer B to A
EXG A,B	Exchange A and B

Addition and Subtraction Instructions:

ABA	Add B to A
ADDA	Add memory to A
ADDB	Add memory to B
ADCA	Add memory with carry to A
ADCB	Add memory with carry to B
ADDD	Add memory to D
SBA	Subtract B from A
SUBA	Subtract memory from A
SUBB	Subtract memory from B
SBCA	Subtract memory with borrow from A
SBCB	Subtract memory with borrow from B
SUBD	Subtract memory from D

Decrement and Increment Instructions:

DECA	Decrement A
DECB	Decrement B
INCA	Increment A
INCB	Increment B

Compare and Test Instructions:

CBA	Compare A to B
CMPA	Compare A to memory
CMPB	Compare B to memory
CPD	Compare D to memory
TSTA	Test A for zero or minus
TSTB	Test B for zero or minus

Boolean Logic Instructions:

ANDA	AND A with memory
ANDB	AND B with memory
EORA	Exclusive OR A with memory

EORB	Exclusive OR B with memory
ORAA	OR A with memory
ORAB	OR B with memory

Clear, Complement, and Negate Instructions:

CLRA	Clear A
CLRB	Clear B
COMA	One's complement A
COMB	One's complement B
NEGA	Two's complement A
NEGB	Two's complement B

Shift and Rotate Instructions:

LSLA	Logic shift left A
LSLB	Logic shift left B
LSLD	Logic shift left D
LSRA	Logic shift right A
LSRB	Logic shift right B
LSRD	Logic shift right D
ASLA	Arithmetic shift left A
ASLB	Arithmetic shift left B
ASLD	Arithmetic shift left D
ASRA	Arithmetic shift right A
ASRB	Arithmetic shift right B
ROLA	Rotate left A through carry
ROLB	Rotate left B through carry
RORA	Rotate right A through carry
RORB	Rotate right B through carry

Stacking Instructions:

PSHA	Push A
PSHB	Push B
PSHD	Push D
PULA	Pull A
PULB	Pull B
PULD	Pull D

Some of the instructions in the above list describe an operation involving a memory location. Where in memory the data resides is determined by the addressing mode. In general, several different addressing modes can be used with each memory access instruction. We will discuss addressing modes in more detail in Section B.2.

B.1.2 Index Registers, X and Y

The index registers *X* and *Y* are 16-bit registers that are used for several different purposes. They can be used in a manner similar to the accumulators for temporary storage when moving 16-bit data to and from memory. The following are some of the instructions involving index registers *X* and *Y*.

Load and Store Instructions:

LDX	Load X from memory
LDY	Load Y from memory
STX	Store X to memory
STY	Store Y to memory
LEAX	Load effective address into X
LEAY	Load effective address into Y

Transfer and Exchange Instructions:

EXG X,Y	Exchange X and Y
XGDX	Exchange D and X
XGDY	Exchange D and Y

Addition and Subtraction Instructions:

ABX	Add B to X
ABY	Add B to Y

Decrement and Increment Instructions:

DEX	Decrement X
DEY	Decrement Y
INX	Increment X
INY	Increment Y

Compare and Test Instructions:

CPX	Compare X to memory
CPY	Compare Y to memory

Stacking Instructions:

PSHX	Push X
PSHY	Push Y
PULX	Pull X
PULY	Pull Y

The main use of the index registers *X* and *Y* is in conjunction with various modes of addressing. An addressing mode is what specifies where a particular data item is to be found. For example, the instruction *LDAA #$10* is an example of the *immediate addressing mode*. This means that the data $10 immediately follows the opcode in memory. The $ sign means that 10 is a hexadecimal value. The # sign means that it is immediate addressing.

One of the most important addressing modes associated with the index registers *X* and *Y* is indexed addressing. For example, the instruction

```
LDAA 0,X
```

means load into accumulator *A* the byte in memory at the address that is in index register *X*. We say that *X* is pointing to a byte in memory. The zero in the above instruction is a displacement that gets added to the value of *X*. For example, the instruction *LDD 4,X* will load two bytes of memory into accumulator *D* (*A:B*). The byte at address *X*+4 will be loaded into accumulator *A* and the byte at address *X*+5 will be loaded into accumulator *B*.

B.1.3 Stack Pointer, SP

The stack is a region of memory that is set aside for storing temporary data. The stack pointer, *SP*, is a 16-bit register that contains the address of the top of the stack. The stack is used by the HCS12 to save the return address when a subroutine is called. It is also used to save register values when an interrupt occurs.

The stack can be used to save the contents of registers *A*, *B*, *X*, and *Y* using the instructions *PSHA*, *PSHB*, *PSHX*, and *PSHY*. These values are removed from the stack using the instructions *PULA*, *PULB*, *PULX*, and *PULY*.

The following are some of the instructions involving the stack pointer, *SP*.

Load and Store Instructions:

LDS	Load SP from memory
STS	Store SP to memory
LEAS	Load effective address into SP

Transfer and Exchange Instructions:

TSX	Transfer SP to X
TSY	Transfer SP to Y
TXS	Transfer X to SP
TYS	Transfer Y to SP
EXG X,SP	Exchange X and SP

Decrement and Increment Instructions:

DES	Decrement SP
INS	Increment SP

Compare and Test Instructions:

CPS	Compare SP to memory
CPY	Compare Y to memory

B.1.4 Program Counter, PC

The program counter, *PC*, is a 16-bit register that contains the address of the next instruction to be executed. When an instruction is executed the program counter is automatically incremented the number of times needed to point to the next instruction. HCS12 instructions may be from one to six bytes long. Therefore, the program counter may be incremented by 1 to 6 depending upon the instruction being executed.

Some instructions cause the program counter to change to some new value rather than simply be incremented. These include the branching, jump, and subroutine instructions. We will discuss subroutines in Section B.3 and branching instructions in Section B.4.

B.1.5 The Condition Code Register

The HCS12 has a condition code register (CCR) that contains five status flags or condition codes and three control flags. The five status flags are the carry flag *(C)* , the zero flag (*Z*), the negative flag (*N*), the overflow flag (*V*), and the half carry flag (*H*). The three control flags are the interrupt mask flag (*I*), the X-interrupt mask flag (*X*), and the stop disable flag (*S*). Each flag is one bit in the condition code register. The location of each flag is shown in Figure B.2.

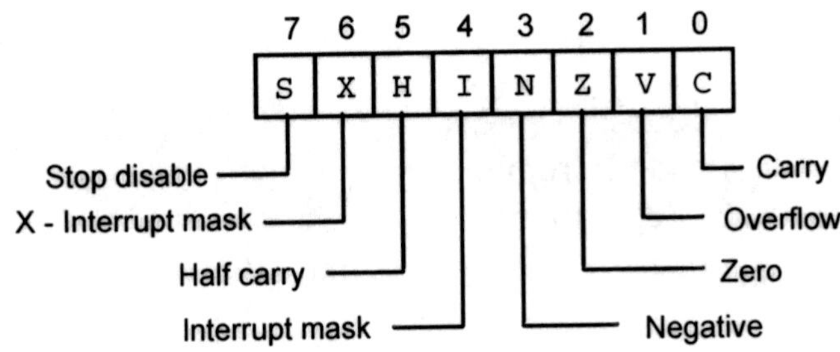

Figure B.2 The 68HC12 Condition Code Register

Any of the bits in the condition code register (with the exception of the *X* bit) can be set using the HCS12 instruction *ORCC*. This instruction will perform a logical OR of the CCR with a byte mask in memory (immediate addressing) containing a 1 in the bit locations to be set. Any of the bits in the condition code register can be cleared using the HCS12 instruction *ANDCC*. This instruction will perform a logical AND of the CCR with a byte mask in a memory containing a 0 in the bit locations to be cleared.

We will now look at the meaning of each bit in the condition code register.

Carry (C)

The carry flag is bit 0 of the condition code register. It can be considered to be an extension of a register, or memory location operated on by an instruction. The carry bit is changed by three different types of instructions. The first are arithmetic instructions. These include the addition instructions *ADDA*, *ADDB*, *ADDD*, *ADCA* (add with carry), *ADCB*, and *ABA* (add *B* to *A*), the subtraction instructions *SUBA*, *SUBB*, *SUBD*, *SBCA* (subtract with carry from *A*), *SBCB*, and *SBA* (subtract *B* from *A*), and the compare instructions *CMPA*,

CMPB, *CBA*, *CPD*, *CPX*, and *CPY*. The carry bit is also changed by the multiplication instructions, *MUL*, *EMUL*, and *EMULS*, the five division instructions, *IDIV*, *IDIVS*, *EDIV*, *EDIVS*, and *FDIV*, the negate instructions, *NEG*, *NEGA*, and *NEGB*, and the decimal adjust instruction, *DAA*.

The second group of instructions that can change the carry bit are the shifting and rotating instructions such as *ASL*, *ASLA*, *ASLB*, *ASR*, *ASRA ASRB*, *LSL*, *LSLA*, *LSLB*, *LSR*, *LSRA*, *LSRB*, *LSRD*, *ROL*, *ROLA*, *ROLB*, *ROR*, *RORA*, and *RORB*.

Finally, the carry bit can be set to 1 with the instruction *SEC* (set carry), and cleared to zero with the instruction *CLC* (clear carry). These instructions which are valid for the 68HC11 get translated to the HCS12 instructions *ORCC #$01* and *ANDCC #$FE* respectively.

Zero Flag (Z)

The zero flag is bit 2 of the condition code register. This flag is set to 1 when the result of an instruction is zero. If the result of an instruction is not zero, the *Z* flag is cleared to zero. This *Z* flag is tested by the branching instruction *BEQ* (branch if equal to zero, $Z = 1$) and *BNE* (branch if not equal to zero, $Z = 0$). These branching instructions are described in Section B.4.

Negative Flag (N)

The negative flag is bit 3 of the condition code register. Negative numbers are stored in HCS12 computers using the two's complement representation. In this representation a negative number is indicated when bit 7 (the left-most bit) of a byte is set to 1. When the result of an instruction leaves the sign bit set (bit 7 of a byte or bit 15 of a word), the *N* flag is set to 1. If the result of an instruction is positive, (the sign bit is 0), the *N* flag is cleared to 0. The *N* flag is tested by the branching instruction *BMI* (branch if minus, $N = 1$) and *BPL* (branch if plus, $N = 0$). These branching instructions are described in Section B.4.

Overflow Flag (V)

The overflow flag is bit 1 of the condition code register. It is set any time the result of a signed (two's complement) operation is out of range. The *V* flag is tested by the branching instructions *BVS* (branch if overflow set, $V = 1$) and *BVC* (branch if overflow clear, $V = 0$).

Half Carry (H)

The half carry flag is bit 5 of the condition code register. It contains the carry from bit 3 to bit 4 resulting from an 8-bit addition or subtraction operation. The half carry flag is used by the microprocessor when performing binary-coded decimal (BCD) addition. As a programmer you normally don't need to worry about the half-carry flag.

Interrupt Mask Flag (I)

The interrupt mask flag is bit 4 of the condition code register. When it is set to 1, hardware interrupts are masked and the HCS12 will not respond to an interrupt. When the *I* flag is cleared to 0, interrupts are enabled and the HCS12 will service hardware interrupts.

The *I* flag is set to 1 with the instruction *SEI* (set interrupt mask) and is cleared to zero with the instruction *CLI* (clear interrupt mask). The 68HC12 translates these two instructions to *ORCC #$10* and *ANDCC #$EF* respectively. A more detailed discussion of interrupts will be given in Section B.5.

X-Interrupt Mask Flag (X)

The *X*-interrupt mask flag is bit 6 of the condition code register. This bit is set to 1 by a hardware reset at which point hardware interrupts entering the *XIRQ* pin of the microprocessor are masked. The *X* flag can be cleared to 0 with the instruction *ANDCC #$BF* after which *X*-interrupts are enabled. The 68HC11 can use to instruction TAP (which gets translated to *TFR A,CCR* in the HCS12) to clear the *X* flag. The *X*-interrupt mask can not be set by software. Therefore, once the *X* bit has been cleared to zero the *XIRQ* is essentially a non-maskable interrupt. A more detailed discussion of interrupts will be given in Section B.5.

Stop Disable Flag (S)

The stop disable flag is bit 7 of the condition code register. If this bit is set to 1 the STOP instruction is disabled. If this bit is cleared to 0 the STOP instruction is enabled. When this bit is set the STOP instruction is treated as a no operation (NOP) instruction. The STOP instruction is used to conserve power by stopping the internal clocks. An external interrupt is needed to start the clocks again.

B.3 Addressing Modes

Addressing modes determine the address where the data associated with instructions are located. This address is called the *effective address*. All of the HCS12 addressing modes are listed in Table B.1. Only the first six addressing modes in Table B.1 are available on the 68HC11. (On the 68HC11 the relative addressing and indexed addressing use only 8-bit offsets.)

The 68HC12 and HCS12 have added the seven new addressing modes shown in the bottom half of Table B.1. In addition, the 68HC12 and HCS12 allow 5-bit, 9-bit, and 16-bit constant offsets in the indexed addressing mode. The constant offset is added to *X*, *Y*, *SP*, or *PC* to compute the effective address. For example, if *X* contains the value $1234, then the instruction *LDD -2,X* will store the value in *D* at address $1234 minus 2 or $1232. This will store the contents of *A* at $1232 and the contents of *B* at $1233. Similarly, the instruction *JSR 0,Y* will jump to a subroutine at the address stored in *Y*.

The pre-decrement indexed addressing mode computes the effective address by first decrementing *X*, *Y*, or *SP* by a value of 1 to 8. For example, if *X* contains the value $1234 then the instruction *STAA 1,-X* will first decrement *X* by 1 to $1233 and then store the value of *A* at address $1233.

As a second example, consider the *MOVW* instruction which is of the form

```
MOVW  source,dest
```

and moves a word (16-bits) from the effective address *source* to the effective address *dest*. (There is also a *MOVB* instruction which moves an 8-bit byte.) The addressing mode for *source* can be either immediate, extended, or indexed, and the addressing mode for *dest* can be either extended or indexed.

For example, suppose that *X* contains the value $1234 and the word $5678 is stored at address $1234 as shown in Figure B.3. Then after executing the instruction *MOVW 0,X,2,-X* the value at address $1234 (0,*X*) will be copied to address $1232 (2,-*X*) and *X* will now be equal to $1232 as shown in Figure B.3.

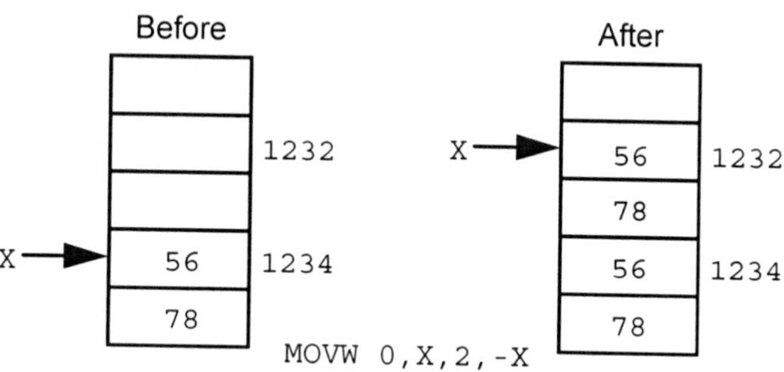

Figure B.3 Effect of executing the instruction *MOVW 0,X,2,-X*

Table B.1 HCS12 Addressing Modes

Addressing Mode	Description	Examples
Inherent	Data location is inherent in instruction	INX DECB
Immediate	Data immediately follows the opcode	LDAA #$2C LDD #$1234
Direct	Data is on page zero given by an 8-bit address ($00-$FF)	STAA $FC STD $34
Extended	Data is in memory given by a 16-bit address ($0000-$FFFF)	STAB $1234 STX $0848
Relative	Opcode is followed by an 8-bit or 16-bit relative offset from PC	BNE -$2B LBEQ $0452
Indexed (constant offset)	5-bit, 9-bit, or 16-bit constant offset from X, Y, SP, or PC	LDD -2,X JSR 0,Y
Indexed (pre-decrement)	Auto pre-decrement X, Y, or SP by 1 - 8	STAA 1,-X MOVW 0,X,2,-X
Indexed (pre-increment)	Auto pre-increment X, Y, or SP by 1 - 8	LDAB 1,+Y STD 2,+X
Indexed (post-decrement)	Auto post-decrement X, Y, or SP by 1 - 8	STD 2,X- LDAA 4,Y-
Indexed (post-increment)	Auto post-increment X, Y, or SP by 1 - 8	LDD 2,X+ STAA 1,X+
Indexed (accumulator offset)	Add contents of A, B, or D to X, Y, SP, or PC	ADDA B,X STX D,Y
Indexed-Indirect (16-bit offset)	Address of data located at 16-bit constant offset from X, Y, SP, or PC	LDAA [0,Y] JSR [0,Y]
Indexed-Indirect (D accumulator offset)	Address of data located at X, Y, SP, or PC plus the value in D	ADDA [D,X] JSR [D,Y]

The pre-increment indexed addressing mode computes the effective address by first incrementing *X*, *Y*, or *SP* by a value of 1 to 8. For example, if *Y* contains the value $1234 then the instruction *LDAB 1,+Y* will first increment *Y* by 1 to $1235 and then store the value of *B* at address $1235.

The post-decrement indexed addressing mode computes the effective address by using the value in *X*, *Y*, or *SP* (equivalent to *0,X*, for example) and then decrementing *X*, *Y*, or *SP* by a value of 1 to 8. For example, if *X* contains the value $1234 then the instruction *STD 2,X-* will store the value of *D* at address $1234 and then decrement *X* by 2 to $1232.

The post-increment indexed addressing mode computes the effective address by using the value in *X*, *Y*, or *SP* (equivalent to *0,X*, for example) and then incrementing *X*, *Y*, or *SP* by a value of 1 to 8. For example, if *X* contains the value $1234 then the instruction *LDD 2,X+* will load the value at address $1234 into *D* and then increment *X* by 2 to $1236.

The accumulator offset indexed addressing mode computes the effective address by adding the value of *A*, *B*, or *D* to *X*, *Y*, *SP*, or *PC*. For example, if *X* contains the value $1234 and *B* contains the value $12 then the instruction *ADDA B,X* will add the byte at address $1246 (*X+B*) to the value in *A* and leave the sum in *A*.

The 16-bit constant offset indexed indirect addressing mode adds a 16-bit constant offset to *X*, *Y*, *SP*, or *PC* to compute the address that contains the effective address. For example, if *Y* contains the value $1234 and if the value $5678 is stored at address $1234 then the instruction *LDAA [0,Y]* will load *A* with the byte at address $5678.

The *D* accumulator offset indexed indirect addressing mode adds the value in *D* to *X*, *Y*, *SP*, or *PC* to compute the address that contains the effective address. For example, consider the instruction *ADDA [D,X]*. If *X* contains the value $1234 and *D* contains the value $2345, then the value at $3579 ($1234+$2345) will contain the address of the byte that is added to accumulator *A*.

B.3 Subroutines and Stacks

B.3.1 The System Stack

The stack is a group of memory locations in which temporary data can be stored. A stack is different from any other collection of memory locations in that data is put on and taken from the *top* of the stack. The process is similar to stacking dinner plates on top of one another, where the last plate put on the stack is always the first one removed from it. We sometimes refer to this as a *last in-first out* or LIFO stack. In this section we will describe the HCS12 system stack.

The memory address corresponding to the top of the stack (the last full location) is stored in the stack pointer, *SP*. When data are put on the stack, the stack pointer is *decremented.* This means that the stack grows *backward* in memory. As data values are put on the stack they are put into memory locations with lower addresses. Data can be put on and taken off the stack using the *push* and *pull* instructions given in Table B.2.

When pushing one of the 8-bit registers, *A*, *B*, or *CCR*, on the stack the following operation takes place:

1) the stack pointer *SP* is decremented by 1.
2) the contents of the 8-bit register are stored at the address in *SP*.

When pushing one of the 16-bit registers, *D*, *X*, or *Y*, on the stack the following operation takes place:

1) the stack pointer *SP* is decremented by 2.
2) the contents of the 16-bit register are stored at the address in *SP*. (The high byte is stored at *SP* and the low byte is stored at *SP*+1.)

When pulling (sometimes referred to as popping) one of the 8-bit registers, *A*, *B*, or *CCR*, off the stack the following operation takes place:

1) the value at the address stored in *SP* is loaded into the 8-bit register.
2) the stack pointer is incremented by 1.

When pulling one of the 16-bit registers, *D*, *X*, or *Y*, off the stack the following operation takes place:

1) the value at the address stored in *SP* is loaded into the 16-bit register. (The byte at *SP* is loaded into the high byte and the byte at *SP*+1 is loaded into the low byte.)
2) the stack pointer is incremented by 2.

Table B.2 Push and Pull Instructions

Mnemonic	Function
PSHA	Push A
PSHB	Push B
PSHC	Push CCR
PSHD	Push D
PSHX	Push X
PSHY	Push Y
PULA	Pull A
PULB	Pull B
PULC	Pull C
PULD	Pull D
PULX	Pull X
PULY	Pull Y

As an example, suppose that the stack pointer, *SP*, contains the value $0A00 and the *D* register contains the value $1234. After executing the instruction *PSHD* the value $1234 will be stored at address $09FE as shown in Figure B.4. If the two instructions *PULB* and *PULA* are now executed in that order, then *B* will end up containing $12, *A* will end up containing $34 and the stack pointer, *SP*, will contain $0A00 again.

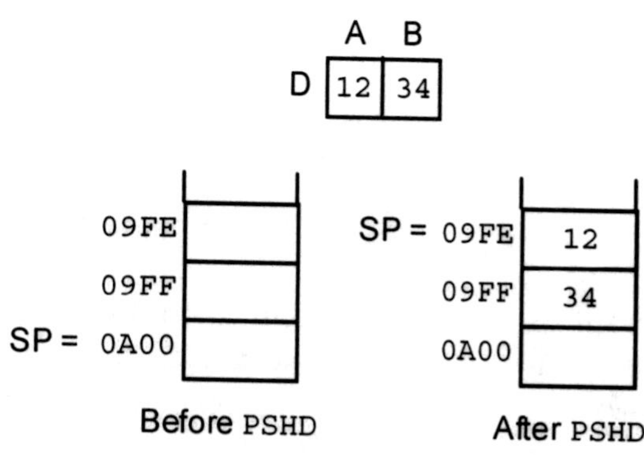

Figure B.4 Pushing D on the stack

B.3.2 Subroutines

A subroutine is a segment of code that is normally written to perform a particular function or task. A subroutine is called by executing a *JSR* (jump to subroutine) or *BSR* (branch to subroutine) instruction. A subroutine is exited by executing a *return from subroutine* (*RTS*) instruction. This will cause the program to return to the instruction following the *JSR* or *BSR* instruction that called the subroutine.*

The computer knows where to go when an *RTS* instruction is executed because it stored the return address on the stack when the *JSR* or *BSR* instruction was executed. The *RTS* instruction just pops the value on top of the stack into the program counter.

The *BSR* instruction uses relative addressing. It is a 2-byte instruction in which the second byte is a relative (two's complement) offset that gets added to the address of the next instruction to compute the subroutine address. This means that the address of the subroutine must be within ±128 bytes from the location of the *BSR* call. As a result the *BSR* instruction can only be used when calling nearby subroutines.

Several different addressing modes can be used with the *JSR* instruction. In the extended addressing mode the 16-bit address of the subroutine follows the opcode. For example, if in an assembly language program the label of a subroutine is *SUB1*, then the instruction *JSR SUB1* will be assembled using this extended addressing mode in which the address of *SUB1* will follow the *JSR* opcode.

As another example, if you want to jump to a subroutine whose address is in index register *Y*, you can execute the instruction *JSR 0,Y*. This is an indexed addressing mode in which the effective address is computed by adding a signed 5-bit offset (0 in this case) to the value in index register *Y*.

A program segment that calls a subroutine may be using a certain register, say *B*, for a particular purpose, such as a counter. If the subroutine changes the value of *B* then an error will occur in the calling program. To prevent this from happening a subroutine should save the values of registers that it modifies by pushing them on the stack at the beginning of the subroutine. Then they must be popped from the stack, in reverse order, at the end of the subroutine before the *RTS* instruction is executed as shown in Fig. B.5.

```
; subroutine example
subname
        pshb            ; save B
        pshx            ; save X
        ----
        ----            ; instructions that
        ----            ; change B and X
        ----
        pulx            ; restore X
        puxb            ; restore B
        rts
```

Figure B.5 Saving and restoring registers in a subroutine

It is important to remember that the return address is on the stack and this is the address that is popped by the *RTS* instruction. Therefore, the same number of bytes must be popped from the stack at the end of a subroutine as were pushed onto the stack at the beginning of the subroutine.

* The 68HC12 also has a CALL instruction that calls a subroutine in expanded memory. To return from such a subroutine one uses the RTC (return from call) instruction.

B.4 Branching Instructions

The HCS12 has a large number of branch instructions. There are two major categories, short branch and long branch instructions. When writing assembly language programs you would normally use the short branch instructions. We will first look at short conditional branch instructions that test only a single bit in the condition code register. We will then explore the difference between unsigned and signed branch instructions.

B.4.1 Short Conditional Branch Instructions

The instructions shown in Table B.3 test the state of one of the flags in the condition code register. Other branching instructions, that will be described in later sections, test some combination of the status flags.

A branching instruction will cause a branch to occur if the branch test is *true*. For example, the branching instruction *BEQ* (branch if equal zero) will cause a branch in the program if the *Z* flag in the condition code register is 1. This will be the case if the result of the previous instruction produced a result of zero.

Table B.3 Simple Short Conditional Branch Instructions

Operation	Mnemonic	Branch Test
Branch if equal zero	BEQ	Z = 1
Branch if not equal zero	BNE	Z = 0
Branch if plus	BPL	N = 0
Branch if minus	BMI	N = 1
Branch if carry clear	BCC	C = 0
Branch if carry set	BCS	C = 1
Branch if overflow set	BVS	V = 1
Branch if overflow clear	BVC	V = 0

The conditional branch instructions shown in Table B.3 are all two bytes long. The first byte is the opcode and the second byte is the *relative displacement* of the branch destination. This is the two's complement number that must be added to the value of the program counter + 2 (the address of the next instruction) to obtain the address of the instruction to be executed if the branch test is *true*. If the branch test is *false*, then the instruction following the branch instruction is executed. This is illustrated in Fig. B.6. Note that if *Z* = 1 when the *BEQ* instruction is executed, the program will branch to the address formed by adding the displacement (06) to the address of the next instruction (5014); that is, to address 501A = 5014 + 06.

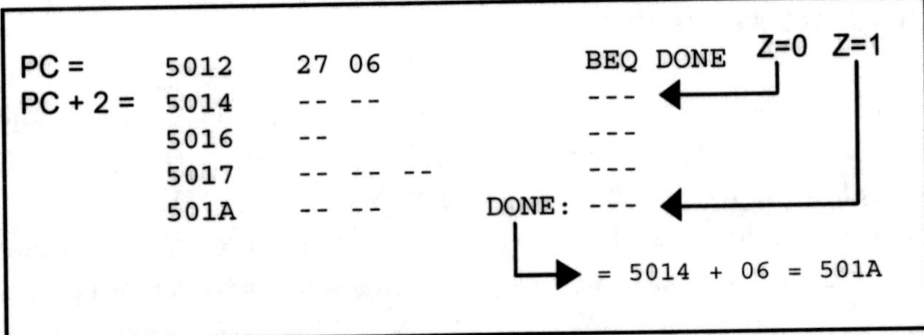

Figure B.6 The displacement (06) in a branch instruction is added to the program counter + 2 to obtain the destination address of the branch.

If a branching instruction branches backward in memory, the displacement must be negative. It is just the two's complement of the number of bytes between the address of the next instruction (*PC* + 2) and the branch destination address. These displacements are automatically calculated by the assembler.

As an example of calculating a branch displacement, suppose a branch instruction is to branch backward –8 bytes from the address of the next instruction. Since –8 is represented as a two's complement hexadecimal number by $F8, the branch displacement will be F8 as shown in Fig. B.7. Note that this subtraction is done by subtracting the address of the next instruction (*PC* + 2) from the destination address. The result, $FFF8, is the 16-bit hexadecimal representation of -8_{10}. When a two's complement, 8-bit hexadecimal number such as $F8 is stored as a 16-bit number, the sign bit (1 in this case) is extended to the left through the high order byte. Thus, $F8 and $FFF8 both represent the negative number -8_{10}. When using a short branch instruction, the displacement $F8 is used; when using a long branch instruction, the displacement $FFF8 is used.

```
           500C   --          LOOP1: ---
           500D   -- --              ---
           500F   -- -- --           ---
PC =       5012   26 F8              BNE LOOP1
PC + 2 =   5014   -- --              ---
           5016   -- -- --

                               500C   LOOP1
                              -5014   IP + 2
                               FFF8
```

Figure B.7 Negative branches can be found by subtracting the address of the next instruction from the destination address

Note that since the branch displacement for the short branch instructions given in Table B.3 is a single 8-bit byte, a short branch instruction can only branch forward a maximum of 127 bytes ($7F) and backward a maximum of -128 bytes ($80). The counting of these bytes always begins at the address of the instruction *following* the branch instruction.

At first this may seem like a serious limitation. Actually it is not. In fact, the 68HC11 has only short branch instructions. Well written assembly language programs should not need to branch conditionally more than ±127 bytes. Branches should take place within small program segments or subroutines. If you need to perform lots of instructions within a loop, for example, you should use subroutine calls to make the program more modular. This will make the program much easier to debug and maintain.

In the unlikely event that you do need to branch conditionally more than ±127 bytes you can use the HCS12 long branch instructions. Each of the instructions in Table B.3 has a long branch equivalent. For example, the instruction *LBEQ* (long branch if equal to zero) uses the test $Z = 1$ just as the instruction *BEQ* does. However, this instruction uses a 16-bit signed displacement rather than an 8-bit displacement. This means that the branching displacement can range from -32,769 ($8000) to +32,767 ($7FFF). The opcodes for the long branch instructions are two bytes long so that these long branch instructions use a total of four bytes and execute slower than the short branch instructions.

B.4.2 Unconditional Branch and Jump Instructions

The instructions in Table B.3 are *conditional* jump instructions that may or may not cause a branch to occur depending upon the value of one of the bits in the condition code register. Sometimes you may want to jump no matter what. This is called an unconditional branch or jump. Three different versions of unconditional branch and jump instructions are shown in Table B.4.

The short *BRA* (branch always) instruction has an 8-bit displacement as an operand. This is the same two's complement displacement described above for conditional branch instructions. It will allow an unconditional jump a maximum of 127 bytes forward or -128 bytes backward.

If you need to jump a farther distance you can use the long branch always instruction, *LBRA*. This requires a two-byte operand which represents a 16-bit two's complement number that must be added to the address of the next instruction to obtain the destination address.

Table B.4 Unconditional Branch and Jump Instructions

Operation	Mnemonic	Operand
Short Branch Always	BRA	8-bit displacement
Long Branch Always	LBRA	16-bit displacement
Jump	JMP	<effective address>

Both the short and long *branch always* instructions in Table B.4 use a *relative* displacement in the instruction. Since this is the number that is *added* to the address of the following instruction, it is independent of the destination offset address. This means that if the entire program is moved within the memory, this relative displacement does not change. The use of relative displacements for determining a destination address will allow you to write *position-independent code*. This means that a program can be moved to any location in memory and still run.

The *JMP* instruction shown in Table B.2 will jump uncondionally to the effective address determined by the particular addressing mode used in the operand. This could be an absolute address (extended addressing) or some form of indexed addressing.

B.4.4 Unsigned and Signed Branch Instructions

The conditional branch instructions given in Table B.3 are the ones most commonly used. In fact, you can write any program using only these. However, sometimes it is convenient to use the additional conditional branch instructions given in Tables B.5 and B.6. You must, however, be careful. It is very easy to make a mistake when using these conditional branch instructions. The instructions in Table B.5 must only be used when you are thinking about *unsigned* numbers; that is, 8-bit numbers with decimal values between 0 and 255 ($00-$FF), or 16-bit numbers with decimal values between 0 and 65,535 ($0000-$FFFF).

The branching instructions in Table B.6 must only be used when you are thinking about *signed* numbers; that is, 8-bit signed numbers with decimal values between –128 ($80) and +127, ($7F), or 16-bit signed numbers with decimal values between –32,768 ($8000) and +32,767 ($7FFF).

Table B.5 Conditional Jump Instructions to Use Following a Comparison of UNSIGNED Numbers

Operation	Mnemonic	Branch Test
Branch if Higher	BHI	C **or** Z = 0
Branch if Lower or Same	BLS	C **or** Z = 1
Branch if Higher or Same	BHS	C = 0
Branch if Lower	BLO	C = 1

Table B.6 Conditional Jump Instructions to Use Following a Comparison of SIGNED Numbers

Operation	Mnemonic	Branch Test
Branch if Greater Than or equal	BGE	N **xor** V = 0
Branch if Less Than	BLT	N **xor** V = 1
Branch if Greater Than	BGT	Z **or** (N **xor** V) = 0
Branch if Less than or Equal	BLE	Z **or** (N **xor** V) = 1

It is very easy to confuse the instructions in Tables B.5 and B.6. This can lead to execution errors that are sometimes hard to find. For example, suppose accumulator *B* is used as a counter and you want to go through a loop 200_{10} ($C8) times. You might think that the loop shown in Fig. B.8 will work.

```
        CLRB                ;set B = 0
LOOP    INCB                ;increment B
        CMPB    #$C8        ;compare B to C8H
        BLT     LOOP        ;loop if B < 200
```

Figure B.8 How many times is the instruction INCB exectued?

It won't! The branching instruction *BLT LOOP* will fail the first time. This is because the value of *B* is 1 and the value of \$C8 is not 200_{10} but is -56_{10}. Remember that the *BLT* instruction (and all the instructions in Table B.6) consider all numbers to be two's complement *signed* numbers. Inasmuch as 1 (the value of *B*) is greater than -56_{10} the instruction *BLT* will not branch.

The instruction you really want to use is *BLO* (branch if lower). This instruction, and all instructions in Table B.5 treat all numbers as unsigned numbers, so that \$C8 is considered to be 200_{10} and not -56_{10}.

In Table B.5 note that the instructions *BHS* and *BLO* test only the carry flag and are the same as *BCC* and *BCS* respectively. All other instructions in Tables B.5 and B.6 use branch tests that involve more than one flag in the condition code register.

B.4.5 Bit-Condition Branch Instructions

The HCS12 has two bit-condition branch instructions that are given in Table B.7. The *BRCLR* instruction will branch if selected bits in a particular memory location are zero. The bits are selected by setting corresponding bits in a mask to 1. The *BRCLR* instruction will then branch if the logical AND of the memory location with the mask is zero. The general form of the instruction is

```
BRCLR   opr,msk,rel
```

where *opr* is the addressing mode for the memory location to be tested, *msk* is the mask value, and *rel* is the label of the branch destination address.

Table B.7 Bit-Condition Branch Instructions

Operation	Mnemonic	Branch Test
Branch if Selected Bits Clear	BRCLR	`(M) & (mask) = 0`
Branch if Selected Bits Set	BRSET	`!(M) & (mask) = 0`

The *BRSET* instruction shown in Table B.7 will branch if selected bits in a particular memory location are 1. In this case the *BRSET* instruction will branch if the logical AND of the one's complement of the memory location with the mask is zero.

B.4.6 Decrement and Branch Instructions

The HCS12 has two decrement and branch instructions that are given in Table B.8. The *DBEQ* instruction will decrement a counter (A, B, D, X, Y, or SP) and branch if the counter is equal to zero. The *DBNE* instruction will decrement a counter (A, B, D, X, Y, or SP) and branch if the counter is not equal to zero. As an example the instructions

```
fw1:        mem                 ; fuzzy membership grade
            dbne   B,fw1
```

are used in the fuzzy control function *fill_weights(...)* in *main.asm* to execute the *MEM* instruction B times.

Table B.8 Decrement and Branch Instructions

Operation	Mnemonic	Operation
Decrement counter and branch if = 0 (cntr = A, B, D, X, Y, or SP)	DBEQ	`cntr -1 -> cntr` `branch if cntr = 0`
Decrement counter and branch if not = 0 (cntr = A, B, D, X, Y, or SP)	DBNE	`cntr -1 -> cntr` `branch if cntr not = 0`

B.5 HCS12 Interrupts

There are over fifty sources of interrupts on the MC9S12DP256B as shown in Appendix D. These interrupts are divided into two categories: non-maskable and maskable. The maskable interrupts can be masked by setting the I-bit in the condition code register. Non-maskable interrupts cannot be masked. We will discuss non-maskable interrupts in Section B.5.1 and maskable interrupts in Section B.5.2.

B.5.1 HCS12 Non-Maskable Interrupts

There are six HCS12 non-maskable interrupts shown in Table B.9. Each interrupt source has a 16-bit vector address that holds the address (interrupt vector) of the code to be executed when the interrupt occurs.

Table B.9 HCS12 Non-Maskable Interrupts

Vector Address	Interrupt Source
`$FFFE-$FFFF`	Reset
`$FFFC-$FFFD`	COP Clock Monitor Fail Reset
`$FFFA-$FFFB`	COP Failure Reset
`$FFF8-$FFF9`	Unimplemented Instruction Trap
`$FFF6-$FFF7`	SWI
`$FFF4-$FFF5`	XIRQ

The non-maskable interrupts shown in Table B.9 are listed in order of priority. If more than one interrupt occurs at the same time, the interrupt with the highest priority will be serviced first. We will briefly describe each of these non-maskable interrupts in turn.

Reset

When the *RESET* pin on a HCS12 goes low, normal microprocessor functions are suspended. When this pin returns high the microprocessor will set bits *X* and *I* in the condition code register and start executing instructions starting at the address stored at $FFFE-$FFFF. The HCS12 has a power-on reset (POR) circuit that causes the reset signal to be asserted internally after power has been applied to the processor.

It is necessary for addresses $FFFE-$FFFF to be in some type of non-volatile memory (ROM, EPROM, or Flash memory) so that a valid reset vector will be at that address. Of course, the memory it points to must also be in non-volatile memory so that some meaningful code will be executed when you turn on the processor.

COP (Computer Operating Properly)

The two COP (computer operating properly) interrupt sources shown in Table B.9 are used to help detect both hardware and software errors. When the clock monitor is enabled (by setting the *CME* bit in the *CRG PLL Control Register*, *PLLCTL*) special circuitry will produce a reset if the clock stops or its frequency falls below about 500 KHz.

The COP Failure Reset is a watchdog timer that will produce a reset if a special sequence ($55 followed by $AA) isn't written to the *CRG COP TimerArm/Reset Register* (*ARMCOP*) within a specified time. You would include this operation as part of your software when you know that certain portions of code must be executed within a certain time. A COP failure would be an indication that your software was not operating properly.

Unimplemented Instruction Trap

All 1-byte opcodes in the HCS12 are valid except $18 which requires a second byte to form the complete opcode. Only 54 of the 256 possible second bytes are valid. If your program tries to execute one of these invalid 2-byte opcodes, the program will trap to the address stored in $FFF8-$FFF9.

Software Interrupts (SWI)

A software interrupt occurs when you execute the *SWI* instruction. This will cause the instructions at the address stored in $FFF6-$FFF7 to be executed. Before this happens the return address (the address following the *SWI* instruction) is pushed on the stack together with registers *Y, X, A, B*, and *CCR* as shown in Fig. B.9. After pushing these values on the stack the interrupt mask, *I*, in the condition code register, *CCR*, is set to 1. This will prevent any maskable interrupts from being processed while in the software interrupt routine. The *I* bit can be cleared to zero by either executing the *CLI* (clear interrupt mask) instruction or by executing the *RTI* (return from interrupt) instruction. The *RTI* instruction is executed at the end of all interrupt service routines. It will pop from the stack all of the values shown in Figure B.9. This will include the *CCR* register which may have had the *I* bit cleared to zero if interrupts had been enabled before the *SWI* instruction was executed. A similar sequence occurs for maskable hardware interrupts which we will describe in Section B.5.2.

When the *RTI* instruction is executed the return address on the stack is popped into the program counter. The program will therefore continue at the point in the program where the interrupt occurred. For a software interrupt this would be the statement following the `SWI` instruction.

Non-maskable Interrupt Request (XIRQ)

The *XIRQ* is pin *PE0* on the HCS12. The *XIRQ* interrupt is a pseudo-non-maskable interrupt that is associated with the *X* bit in the *CCR*. After reset this bit is set which inhibits interrupts when the *XIRQ* pin goes low. However, software can clear the *X* bit in the *CCR* by using the instruction, *ANDCC #$BF*. Once this bit has been cleared it cannot be set to 1 again by software. Thus, at this point the interrupt becomes non-maskable.

When an *XIRQ* interrupt occurs by a high to low signal on pin *PE0* the current instruction is completed and then the registers shown in Figure B.9 are pushed on the stack. The return address will be the value in the program counter; i.e., the address of the instruction following the one being executed when the interrupt occurs. This will be the address returned to after the interrupt service routine is executed. The *XIRQ* interrupt service routine address is stored in the vector address $FFF4-$FFF5 (see Table B.9). After all registers shown in Fig. B.9 are pushed on the stack, both the *I* bit and the *X* bit in the *CCR* are set. This means that another *XIRQ* interrupt cannot occur during the execution of an *XIRQ* interrupt service routine. Executing the *RTI* instruction at the end of the interrupt service routine will pop the registers shown in Figure B.9 off the stack, including the *CCR* register which will have its *X* bit cleared. At that point a new *XIRQ* interrupt can occur.

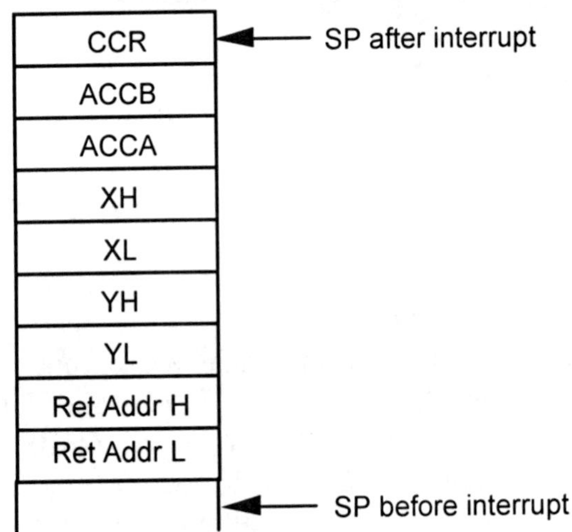

Figure B.9 Register stacking for interrupts

B.5.2 68HC12 Maskable Interrupts

All of the interrupts shown in Appendix D with vector numbers between 6 and 57 are maskable interrupts that are inhibited when the *I* bit in the *CCR* is set (using the *SEI* instruction). To enable all of these maskable interrupts you must clear the *I* bit in the *CCR* by executing the *CLI* instruction. In addition, each interrupt source will have a local enable bit that must be set in one of the I/O registers in order to enable that particular interrupt. For example, to enable pin *PE1* as an IRQ interrupt, you must set bit *IRQEN* (bit 6) in the *Interrupt Control Register, INTCR*.

The interrupts shown in Appendix D are listed in order of priority. If more than one interrupt occurs at the same time, the interrupt with the highest priority will be serviced first.

When maskable interrupts occur the same process of pushing the registers on the stack occurs as described above for software interrupts.

Appendix C

Summary of C Function Calls to *main.asm*

Chapter 2: C function calls for turning on the 7-segment display

C Function Call	Meaning
`led_enable();`	Sets DDRB and DDRJ to outputs, clears DJ1 to 0, and turns off all LEDs by clearing all bits of PORTB
`leds_on(int);`	Stores the lower 8 bits of the integer *int* in Port B
`led_disable();`	Sets DDRJ to outputs and sedts DJ1 to 1
`leds_off();`	Turn off all LEDs by clearing Port B
`seg7_enable();`	Sets DDRB and DDRP to outputs, clears the lower 4 bits of Port P, and clears all bits of PORTB
`seg7_disable();`	sets the lower 4 bits of Port P to 1
`seg7_on(int s, int b);`	Display the segments *s* on the 7-segment digit no. *b*
`seg7s_off();`	Turn off all 7-segment displays by clearing Port B

Chapter 2: C function call delaying *n* milliseconds

C Function Call	Meaning
`ms_delay(int n);`	Delay *n* milliseconds

Chapter 2: C function calls for turning on or off a single bit of PORTB

C Function Call	Meaning
`led_on(int b);`	Sets bit *b* of PORTB high
`led_off(int b);`	Sets bit *b* of PORTB low

Chapter 2: C function call for 7-segment displays

C Function Call	Meaning
`seg7_enable();`	Enables the 7-segment displays
`seg7_disable();`	Disables the 7-segment displays
`seg7_on(int s, int b);`	Display the segments *s* on the 7-segment digit no. *b*
`seg7dec(int i, int b);`	Display the hex value *i* on the 7-segment digit no. *b*

Chapter 3: C function calls for reading switches SW1 – SW5

C Function Call	Meaning
`SW_enable();`	Enable switches SW1 – SW5
`SW1_dip();`	Returns 8-bit reading of SW1
`SW2_down();`	Returns **true** if SW2 is down
`SW3_down();`	Returns **true** if SW3 is down
`SW4_down();`	Returns **true** if SW4 is down
`SW5_down();`	Returns **true** if SW5 is down
`SW2_up();`	Returns **true** if SW2 is up
`SW3_up();`	Returns **true** if SW3 is up
`SW4_up();`	Returns **true** if SW4 is up
`SW5_up();`	Returns **true** if SW5 is up

Chapter 3: C function calls for reading a 4 x 4 keypad

C Function Call	Meaning
`keypad_enable();`	Enable the keypad
`int getkey();`	Waits to press key and returns value
`void wait_keyup();`	Waits until key is not being pressed
`int keyscan();`	Returns 16 if no key is being pressed Returns key value if key is being pressed

Chapter 4: C Function calls for LCD display

C Function Call	Meaning
`void lcd_init(void);`	Initialize LCD display (clears display)
`void set_lcd_addr(char);`	Set cursor address (see Fig. 6.3)
`void data8(char);`	Write ASCII character to display at cursor location
`void instr8(char);`	Write instruction to display (see Table 6.1)
`void clear_lcd(void);`	Clear LCD display
`void hex2lcd(char);`	Write hex digit (0 – F) to LCD display
`char hex2asc(char);`	Convert hex digit (0 – F) to ASCII code
`void type_lcd(char*);`	Display ASCIIZ string on LCD display at cursor location

Chapter 4: C function calls for writing integers to the LCD

C Function Call	Meaning
`void write_int_lcd(int);`	Display a 16-bit integer right-justified in a field of 5 digits
`void write_long_lcd(long);`	Display a 32-bit integer right-justified in a field of 10 digits

Chapter 4: C Function call for converting ASCII number string to binary

C Function Call	Meaning
`long number(char* ptr);`	Return 32-bit binary number equal to ASCII number string

Chapter 5: C Function calls for the real-time interrupt

C Function Call	Meaning
`void RTI_init(void);`	Initialize real-time interrupts every 10.24 ms
`void clear_RTI_flag(void)`	Clear the RTI flag
`void RTI_disable(void)`	Disable real-time interrupts

Chapter 6: C Function calls for the A/D converters

C Function Call	Meaning
`void ad0_enable(void);`	Enable ATD0 for 10 bits
`int ad0conv(char ch#);`	Return the average of 4 successive readings of channel *ch#*
`void ad1_enable(void);`	Enable ATD1 for 10 bits
`int ad1conv(char ch#);`	Return the average of 4 successive readings of channel *ch#*

Chapter 7: C function calls for controlling the speed of a DC motor

C Function Call	Meaning
void **motor0_init**(void);	Initialize PWM0 with 10 ms period
void **motor1_init**(void);	Initialize PWM1 with 10 ms period
void **motor2_init**(void);	Initialize PWM2 with 10 ms period
void **motor3_init**(void);	Initialize PWM3 with 10 ms period
void **motor4_init**(void);	Initialize PWM4 with 10 ms period
void **motor5_init**(void);	Initialize PWM5 with 10 ms period
void **motor6_init**(void);	Initialize PWM6 with 10 ms period
void **motor7_init**(void);	Initialize PWM7 with 10 ms period
void **motor0**(int speed);	Set speed of motor0 (0 – 255)
void **motor1**(int speed);	Set speed of motor1 (0 – 255)
void **motor2**(int speed);	Set speed of motor2 (0 – 255)
void **motor3**(int speed);	Set speed of motor3 (0 – 255)
void **motor4**(int speed);	Set speed of motor4 (0 – 255)
void **motor5**(int speed);	Set speed of motor5 (0 – 255)
void **motor6**(int speed);	Set speed of motor6 (0 – 255)
void **motor7**(int speed);	Set speed of motor7 (0 – 255)

Chapter 7: C function calls for controlling the position of a servo

C Function Call	Meaning
void **servo54_init**();	Initialize PWM5 with 20 ms period
void **servo76_init**();	Initialize PWM7 with 20 ms period
void **set_servo54**(int width);	Set position of servo5 (3300 – 5700)
void **set_servo76**(int width);	Set position of servo7 (3300 – 5700)

Chapter 8: C Function calls for the SCI port

C Function Call	Meaning
void **SCI0_init**(int b);	Initialize SCI0 with baud rate *b*
char **inchar0**(void);	Wait for character in SCI0 and return char
void **outchar0**(char c);	Output character *c* out SCI0 TxD pin
void **SCI1_init**(int b);	Initialize SCI1 with baud rate *b*
char **inchar1**(void);	Wait for character in SCI1 and return char
void **outchar1**(char c);	Output character *c* out SCI1 TxD pin

Chapter 8: C Function calls for the SCI port with interrupts

C Function Call	Meaning
void **SCI0_int_init**(int b);	Initialize SCI0 with interrupts and baud rate *b*
char **read_SCI0_Rx**(void);	Read character received in SCI0 Rx port
void **outchar0**(char c);	Output character *c* out SCI0 TxD pin
void **SCI1_int_init**(int b);	Initialize SCI1 with interrupts and baud rate *b*
char **read_SCI1_Rx**(void);	Read character received in SCI1 Rx port
void **outchar1**(char c);	Output character *c* out SCI1 TxD pin

Chapter 8: C Function calls for using the character queue in queue.c

C Function Call	Meaning
void **initq**(void);	initialize the queue
void **qstore**(char);	store character in queue
int **qempty**(void);	return 0 if queue is not empty
char **getq**(void);	read character from queue

Chapter 9: C Function calls for the SPI ports

C Function Call	Meaning
`void SPI0_init(void);`	Initialize SPI0 with baud rate of 250 KHz
`char send_SPI0(char c);`	Send character *c* out SCI0; returns character shifted in
`void SS0_HI(void);`	Set SS0 (PS7, pin 95) HI
`void SS0_LO(void);`	Set SS0 (PS7, pin 95) LO
`void SPI1_init();`	Initialize SPI1 with baud rate of 250 KHz
`char send_SPI1(char c);`	Send character *c* out SCI1; returns character shifted in
`void SS1_HI(void);`	Set SS1 (PP3, pin 1) HI
`void SS1_LO(void);`	Set SS1 (PP3, pin 1) LO
`void SPI2_init();`	Initialize SPI2 with baud rate of 250 KHz
`char send_SPI2(char c);`	Send character *c* out SCI2; returns character shifted in
`void SS2_HI(void);`	Set SS2 (PP6, pin 110) HI
`void SS2_LO(void);`	Set SS2 (PP6, pin 110) LO

Chapter 10: C Function calls for generating a pulse train

C Function Call	Meaning
`void ptrain6_init(void);`	initialize pulse train interrupts on PT6 timer clock = 1.5 MHz
`void ptrain6(int period, int pwidth);`	update TC6 and TC7 in timer 6 interrupt routine
`void sound_init(void);`	initialize pulse train interrupts on PT5 (speaker) timer clock = 1.5 MHz
`void sound_on(void);`	Turn sound on by enabling timer and interrupts
`void sound_off(void);`	Turn sound off by disabling timer and interrupts
`void tone(int pitch);`	Set pitch value of sound by updating TC5 and TC7 in timer 5 interrupt routine

Chapter 10: C Function calls for measuring pulse widths on Channel 1

C Function Call	Meaning
`void HILO1_init(void);`	initialize input capture interrupts on both edges of channel 1 timer clock = 1.5 MHz
`void HILOtimes1(void);`	update HI – LO times in input capture interrupt routine
`int get_HItime1(void);`	return latest HI time of input pulse train
`int get_LOtime1(void);`	return latest LO time of input pulse train

Chapter 11: C function calls for a fuzzy controller

C Function Call	Meaning
`void fill_weights(unsigned char* weight, unsigned char* membx, int num_mem_fncs, char x);`	Given a crisp input *x* and membership functions, *membx*, fill the corresponding *weight* array.
`void fire_rules(unsigned char* inout_array, unsigned char* rules, unsigned char* out, int numout);`	Given *inout_array* containing *weight* arrays and a set of *rules*, fire all rules and fill the *out* array.
`unsigned char calc_output(unsigned char* out, unsigned char* cent, int numout);`	Calculate crisp output given the *out* array and the output membership singletons, *cent*.

Appendix D

MC9S12DP256B Interrupt Vectors

Vector Number	Interrupt Source	Vector Address
0	Reset	$FFFE-$FFFF
1	Clock Monitor Fail Reset	$FFFC-$FFFD
2	COP Failure Reset	$FFFA-$FFFB
3	Unimplemented Instruction Trap	$FFF8-$FFF9
4	SWI	$FFF6-$FFF7
5	XIRQ	$FFF4-$FFF5
6	IRQ	$FFF2-$FFF3
7	Real-Time Interrupt	$FFF0-$FFF1
8	Timer Channel 0	$FFEE-$FFEF
9	Timer Channel 1	$FFEC-$FFED
10	Timer Channel 2	$FFEA-$FFEB
11	Timer Channel 3	$FFE8-$FFE9
12	Timer Channel 4	$FFE6-$FFE7
13	Timer Channel 5	$FFE4-$FFE5
14	Timer Channel 6	$FFE2-$FFE3
15	Timer Channel 7	$FFE0-$FFE1
16	Timer Overflow	$FFDE-$FFDF
17	Pulse Accumulator A Overflow	$FFDC-$FFDD
18	Pulse Accumulator Input Edge	$FFDA-$FFDB
19	SPI0	$FFD8-$FFD9
20	SCI 0	$FFD6-$FFD7
21	SCI 1	$FFD4-$FFD5
22	ATD0	$FFD2-$FFD3
23	ATD1	$FFD0-$FFD1
24	Port J	$FFCE-$FFCF
25	Port H	$FFCC-$FFCD
26	Modulus Down Counter Underflow	$FFCA-$FFCB
27	Pulse Accumulator B Overflow	$FFC8-$FFC9
28	CRG PLL lock	$FFC6-$FFC7
29	CRG Self Clock Mode	$FFC4-$FFC5
30	BDLC	$FFC2-$FFC3
31	IIC Bus	$FFC0-$FFC1
32	SPI1	$FFBE-$FFBF
33	SPI2	$FFBC-$FFBD

34	EEPROM	$FFBA-$FFBB
35	FLASH	$FFB8-$FFB9
36	CAN0 wake-up	$FFB6-$FFB7
37	CAN0 errors	$FFB4-$FFB5
38	CAN0 receive	$FFB2-$FFB3
39	CAN0 transmit	$FFB0-$FFB1
40	CAN1 wake-up	$FFAE-$FFAF
41	CAN1 errors	$FFAC-$FFAD
42	CAN1 receive	$FFAA-$FFAB
43	CAN1 transmit	$FFA8-$FFA9
44	CAN2 wake-up	$FFA6-$FFA7
45	CAN2 errors	$FFA4-$FFA5
46	CAN2 receive	$FFA2-$FFA3
47	CAN2 transmit	$FFA0-$FFA1
48	CAN3 wake-up	$FF9E-$FF9F
49	CAN3 errors	$FF9C-$FF9D
50	CAN3 receive	$FF9A-$FF9B
51	CAN3 transmit	$FF98-$FF99
52	CAN4 wake-up	$FF96-$FF97
53	CAN4 errors	$FFA4-$FF95
54	CAN4 receive	$FF92-$FF93
55	CAN4 transmit	$FF90-$FF91
56	Port P Interrupt	$FF8E-$FF8F
57	PWM Emergency Shutdown	$FF8C-$FF8D
	Reserved	$FF80-$FF8B

Appendix E

Introduction to Fuzzy Control

Fuzzy logic has been applied successfully to a wide variety of difficult control problems. The input and output control variables are members of fuzzy sets that admit varying degrees of membership. In this appendix we will introduce the basic ideas of fuzzy sets. We will then describe how a fuzzy controller works and present an overall approach to implementing a fuzzy controller on a microcontroller. The HCS12 has some special instructions which simplify the implementation of a fuzzy controller. We define some C functions in Example 20 that use these HCS12 instructions to implement a fuzzy controller.

E.1 Fuzzy Sets

Lotfi Zadeh introduced the term *fuzzy sets* in 1965.* In normal "crisp" logic the basic assumption is that assertions, or statements, are either *true* or *false*. But this assumption leads to paradoxes. For example, is the sentence in Figure E.1 true or false? If the sentence is true, then it must be false; but if it is false, then it must be true. There are many such paradoxes in which it appears that true must be equal to false.

The sentence on the other side of the line is false
The sentence on the other side of the line is false

Figure E.1 Is this sentence *true* of *false*?

Fuzzy logic does not require that everything be either true or false. In normal "crisp" set theory an element either belongs to the set, or it doesn't. However, a little

* L. Zadeh, "Fuzzy Sets," Inform. and Contr., Vol. 8, pp. 338-353, 1965.

reflection should convince you that most things in the world aren't that black and white. For example, is a given person *young*? We can consider *young* to be a fuzzy set in which we use membership functions to define the degree of membership (between 0 and 1) in the set.

A membership function for the fuzzy set *Young* is shown in Figure E.2. People who are younger than age *a1* are definitely young (with a degree of membership equal to 1) while people who are older than age *a2* are definitely not young (with a degree of membership equal to 0). However, people with ages between *a1* and *a2* are young to some degree determined by the membership function shown in Figure E.2.

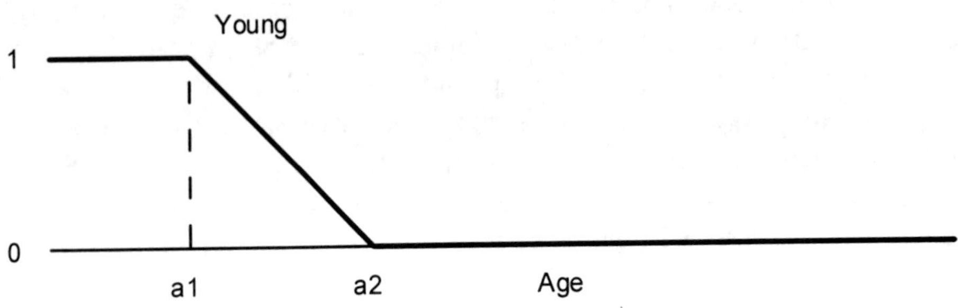

Figure E.2 Membership function for the fuzzy set *Young*

When applied to fuzzy sets the logic operations *NOT*, *AND*, and *OR* are defined as shown in Table E.1. These are not the only possible definitions but they are the ones most commonly used. Note that they reduce to the crisp case when *A* and *B* have the binary values 0 and 1.

Table E.1 Fuzzy Logic Operations

Logic Operation	Fuzzy Logic Operation
`NOT a`	`1 - a`
`a AND b`	`MIN(a,b)`
`a OR b`	`MAX(a,b)`

If we apply the *NOT* operation to the fuzzy set *Young* we obtain the fuzzy set *NOT Young* shown in Figure E.3. In a similar way we could define the fuzzy sets *Old* and *NOT Old* as shown in Figure E.4.

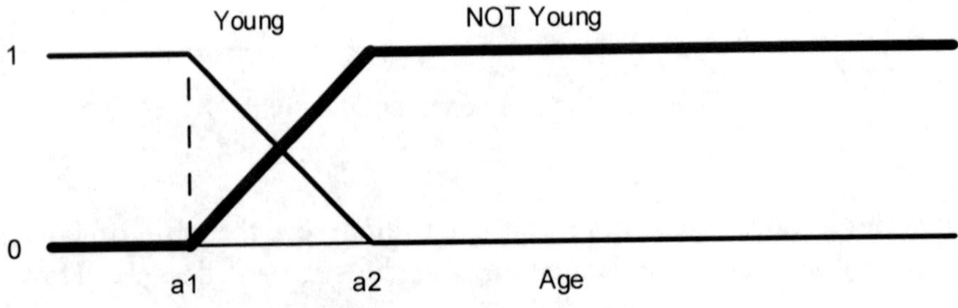

Figure E.3 *NOT Young* = 1 - *Young*

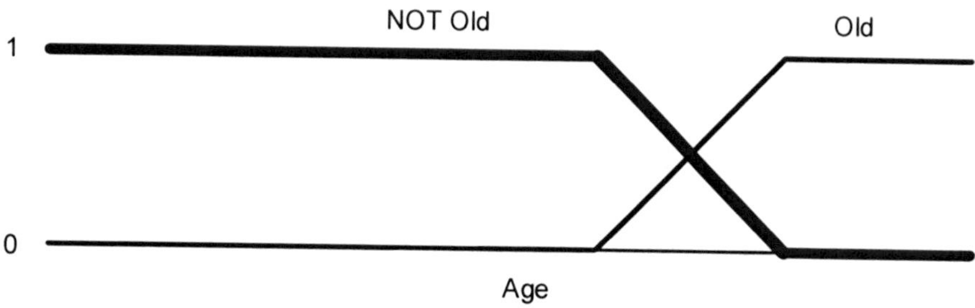

Figure E.4 Membership functions for the fuzzy sets *Old* and *NOT Old*

We can use the *AND* operation given in Table E.1 to define new fuzzy sets. For example, we might define *Middle Age* as *NOT Young AND Not Old.* Taking the minimum of the membership functions for *NOT Young* and *NOT Old* will produce the membership function for *Middle Age* as shown in Figure E.5.

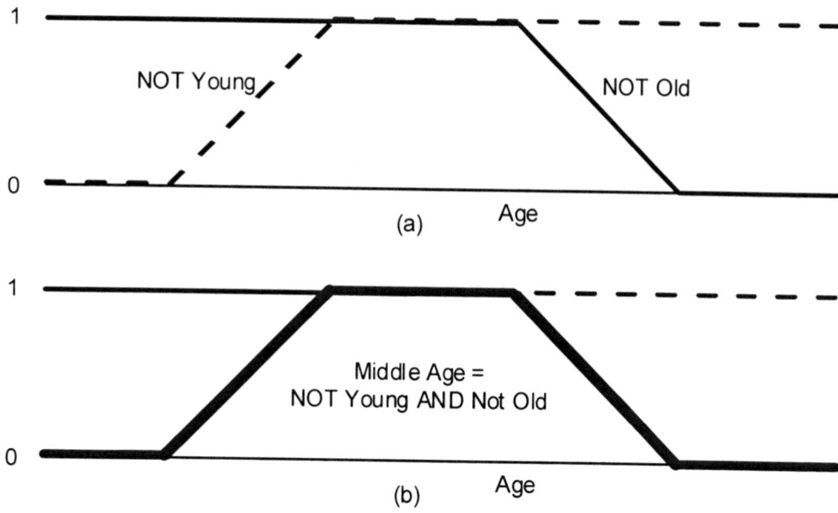

Figure E.5 Deriving the membership function for *Middle Age*

E.2 Design of a Fuzzy Controller

In this section we will show how fuzzy logic can be applied to the control of physical systems. The design process begins by associating fuzzy sets with the input and output variables. These fuzzy sets are described by membership functions of the type shown in Figure E.6. These fuzzy set values are labeled *NM* (negative medium), *NS* (negative small), *Z* (zero), *PS* (positive small), and *PM* (positive medium). For example, if an input variable is temperature, the five membership functions might be labeled *COLD*, *COOL*, *MEDIUM*, *WARM*, and *HOT*. The shape of the membership functions are, in general, trapezoids that may have no top (triangles) or may have vertical sides as shown in Figure E.6.

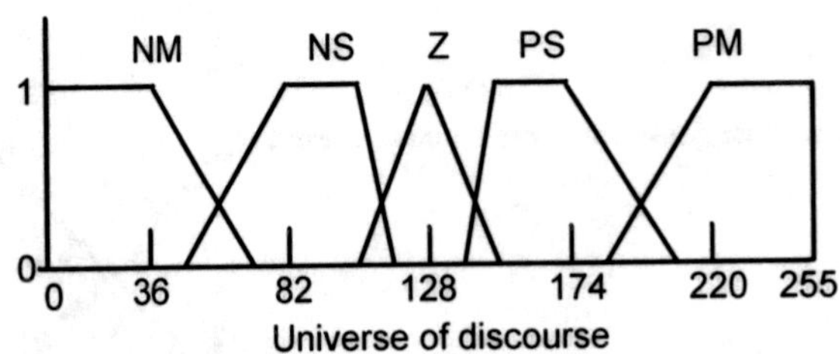

Figure E.6 Example of fuzzy membership functions

A functional diagram of a fuzzy controller is shown in Figure E.7. The inputs to a fuzzy controller are assigned to the fuzzy variables with a degree of membership given by the membership functions. For example, in Figure E.6 an input value of 140 would have a degree of membership of 0.25 in *Z* and a degree of membership of 0.5 in *PS*. On the other hand, an input value of 85 would belong to *NS* with a degree of membership of 1.0. In general, an input value will belong to all fuzzy sets with different degrees of membership (including zero).

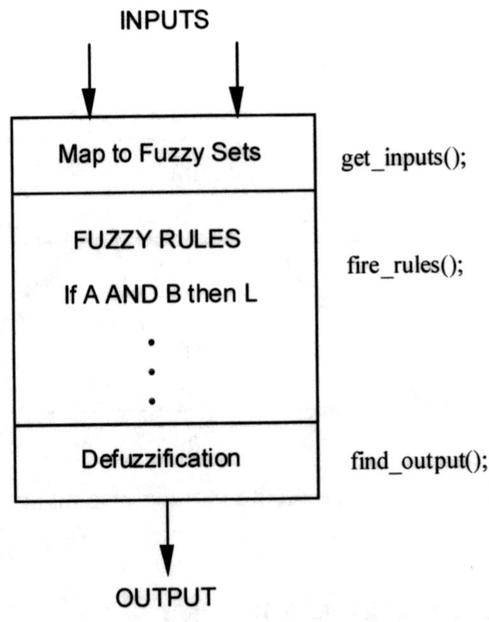

Figure E.7 Functional diagram of a fuzzy controller

The fuzzy controller itself consists of a set of fuzzy rules of the form *if* x_1 *is PM AND* x_2 *is Z, then y is NM*, where x_1 and x_2 are inputs, *y* is the output, and *PM*, *Z* and *NM* are fuzzy sets of the type shown in Figure E.6. For example, a fuzzy rule for an air conditioner might be *if temperature is WARM AND change in temperature is ZERO, then motor speed is FAST*. Note that *WARM*, *ZERO*, and *FAST* are fuzzy sets. After applying all of the fuzzy rules to a given set of input variables, the output (motor speed in this case) will, in general, belong to more than one fuzzy set with different weights. The weighted output fuzzy sets are combined in a manner to be described below and then a centroid defuzzification process is used to obtain a single crisp output value.

The fuzzy controller shown in Figure E.7 consists of three parts: the fuzzification of inputs, the processing of rules, and the defuzzification of the output. The overall algorithm of a fuzzy controller is shown in Figure E.8 where each function represents the three parts of the controller shown in Figure E.7. We will consider each of these parts separately.

```
do_forever
        {
        get_inputs();
        fire_rules();
        find_output();
        }
```

Figure E.8 Overall algorithm of a fuzzy controller

E.3 Fuzzification of Inputs

For each crisp input x_i a set of weights w_j^i are computed for each membership function such as those shown in Figure E.6. In general, each input will have a different set and number of membership functions. For input number i the weight w_j^i can be stored in a vector $weight_i[j]$, $j = 1, M_i$ where M_i is the number of membership functions for input i. Each value in the weight vector is a weight value between 0 and 1 given by the shape of a particular membership function. Typically for a given input the weight vector will contain up to two non-zero entries in adjacent cells.

The purpose of the function *get_inputs()* is to read each input value x_i and fill the weight vector $weight[M_i]$ with the degree of membership of x_i in each input fuzzy set. The pseudo-code for *get_inputs()* is shown in Figure E.9. In this figure M_i is the number of membership functions for input i.

```
get_inputs()
for i = 1, num_inputs
        {
        get_x(i);
        fill_weight(xi, Mi);
        }
```

Figure E.9 Pseudocode for *get_inputs()*

The function *get_x(i)* is problem dependent and will consist of reading the input values x_i, $i = 1$, *num_inputs*. The function *fill_weight*(x_i, M_i) will fill the weight vector $weight[M_i]$ with the degree of membership of x_i in each of the M_i membership functions for input i.

E.4 Fuzzy Inference

The heart of a fuzzy controller is the list of fuzzy rules. Fuzzy logic inference is used to find a fuzzy output, given a fuzzy input and a list of fuzzy rules. In a fuzzy controller the inputs are normally crisp, non-fuzzy values that must first be fuzzified in the first step of Figure E.7 as described in Section E.3. The output also needs to be a crisp value used to control some device. Therefore, the fuzzy output resulting from processing the fuzzy rules must be defuzzified as described in the next section. The way fuzzy rules are processed is illustrated in Figure E.10 where fuzzy sets are represented by their membership functions *m*.

Fuzzy inference involves a set of fuzzy rules of the form

if x_1 is A_1 and x_2 is B_1 then y is L_1 rule 1

if x_1 is A_2 and x_2 is B_2 then y is L_2 rule 2

Given the fact that

x_1 is A' and x_2 is B' fact

the problem is to find the conclusion

y is L' conclusion

In this representation of the problem, A_1, A_2, B_1, B_2, A', and B' are input fuzzy sets and L_1, L_2, and L' are output fuzzy sets. Fuzzy reasoning would form the union of the intersection of A' and A_1. This is interpreted as being the maximum (union) of the minimum (intersection) of the membership functions A' and A_1. In Figure E.10 A' is taken to be the singleton fuzzy set $x_1 = a$. In rule 1, the maximum of the intersection (minimum) of this singleton with A_1 is the value w_1 shown in Figure E.10. Similarly, the maximum of the intersection (minimum) of the singleton $x_2 = b$ with B_1 is the value w_2 shown in Figure E.10. The fact $x_1 = a$ *and* $x_2 = b$ applied to the antecedent x_1 *is* A_1 *and* x_2 *is* B_1 is interpreted as the intersection (minimum) of w_1 and w_2, i.e. w_2 for rule 1 in Figure E.10. The conclusion of rule 1, y *is* L_1, is found by taking the intersection (T-norm) of w_2 with L_1. This is normally the minimum operation which would truncate L_1 to the height w_2. However, for fuzzy control it is sometimes advantageous to use a product T-norm for this intersection which would have the effect of multiplying L_1 by w_2 as shown in rule 1 in Figure E.10. Thus, rule 1 in Figure E.10 will contribute the fuzzy set w_2*L_1 to the conclusion fuzzy set L'. Similarly, rule 2 in Figure E.10 will contribute the fuzzy set w_1*L_2 to the conclusion fuzzy set L' because w_1 is the minimum of w_1 and w_2 for rule 2. Note that if L_1 and L_2 are singletons (as is normally the case) then there will be no difference in using the minimum T-norm or the product T-norm.

The conclusion fuzzy set L' is found by forming the T-conorm of w_2*L_1 and w_1*L_2. This is normally the maximum operation. However, sometimes better results are obtained by taking the sum of w_2*L_1 and w_1*L_2 as shown in Figure E.10. The difference between these two approaches is shown in Figure E.11.

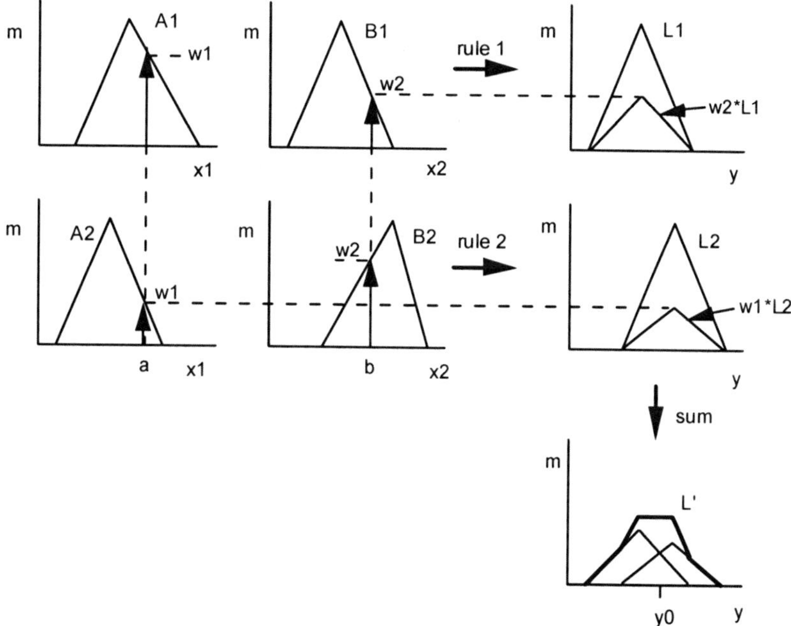

Figure E.10 Fuzzy inference

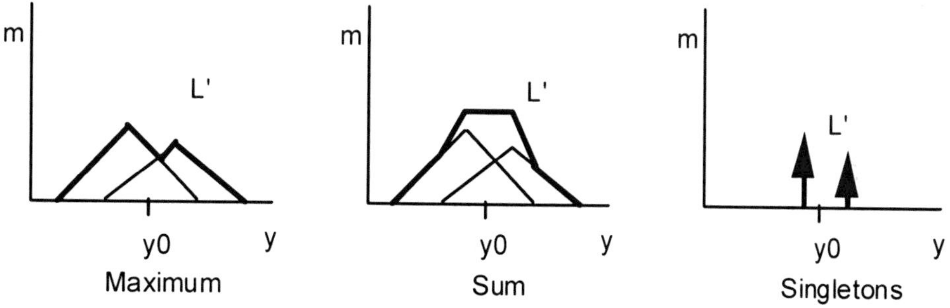

Figure E.11 Comparing the MAX rule and the SUM rule

If L_1 and L_2 are singletons (the normal case) then taking the maximum or sum of the two rules shown in Figure E.10 will be the same as shown in Figure E.11. In general, they won't be the same if more than one rule contribute to the same output fuzzy set L_i. In this case the maximum rule will keep only the maximum value while the sum rule will add the contributions of each.

The conclusion output L' is a fuzzy set shown by the bold line membership function in Figures E.10 and E.11. To obtain a crisp output some type of defuzzification process is required. The most common method is to compute the centroid of the area of L'. We will see that using the sum rule will be helpful in analyzing centroid defuzzification in Section E.5.

E.5 Centroid Defuzzification

The last step in the fuzzy controller shown in Figure E.7 is defuzzification. This involves finding the centroid of the net output fuzzy set L' shown in Figures E.10 and E.11. Although we have used the MIN-MAX rule in the previous section we will begin by deriving the centroid equation for the sum rule shown in Figure E.11. This will illuminate the assumptions made in deriving the defuzzification equation that we will actually use in the fuzzy controller.

Let $L_i(y)$ be the original output membership function associated with rule i where y is the output universe of discourse (see Figure E.10.). After applying rule i this membership function will be reduced to the value

$$m_i(y) = w_i L_i(y) \tag{E.1}$$

where w_i is the minimum weight found by applying rule i. The sum of these reduced output membership functions over all rules is then given by

$$M(y) = \sum_{i=1}^{N} m_i(y) \tag{E.2}$$

where N is the number of rules.

The crisp output value y_0 is then given by the centroid of $M(y)$ from the equation

$$y_0 = \frac{\int y M(y) dy}{\int M(y) dy} \tag{E.3}$$

Note that the centroid of membership function $L_i(y)$ is given by

$$c_i = \frac{\int y L_i(y) dy}{\int L_i(y) dy} \tag{E.4}$$

But

$$I_i = \int L_i(y) dy \tag{E.5}$$

is just the area of membership function $L_i(y)$. Substituting (E.5) into (E.4) we can write

$$\int y L_i(y) dy = c_i I_i \tag{E.6}$$

Using Eqs. (E.1) and (E.2) we can write the numerator of (E.3) as

$$\int yM(y)dy = \int y \sum_{i=1}^{N} w_i L_i(y)\, dy$$

$$= \sum_{i=1}^{N} \int y w_i L_i(y)\, dy$$

$$= \sum_{i=1}^{N} w_i c_i I_i \qquad \text{(E.7)}$$

where (E.6) was used in the last step.
Similarly, using (E.1) and (E.2) the denominator of (E.3) can be written as

$$\int M(y)dy = \int \sum_{i=1}^{N} w_i L_i(y)\, dy$$

$$= \sum_{i=1}^{N} \int w_i L_i(y)\, dy$$

$$= \sum_{i=1}^{N} w_i I_i \qquad \text{(E.8)}$$

where (E.5) was used in the last step. Substituting (E.7) and (E.8) into (E.3) we can write the crisp output of the fuzzy controller as

$$y_0 = \frac{\sum_{i=1}^{N} w_i c_i I_i}{\sum_{i=1}^{N} w_i I_i} \qquad \text{(E.9)}$$

Eq. (E.9) says that we can compute the output centroid from the centroids, c_i, of the individual output membership functions.

Note in Eq. (E.9) the summation is over all N rules. But the number of output membership functions, Q, will, in general, be less than the number of rules, N. This means that in the sums in Eq. (E.9) there will be many terms that will have the same values of c_i and I_i. For example, suppose that rules 2, 3, and 4 in the sum all have the output membership function L^k as the consequent. This means that in the sum

$$w_2 c_2 I_2 + w_3 c_3 I_3 + w_4 c_4 I_4$$

the values c_i and I_i are the same values c^k and I^k because they are just the centroid and area of the kth output membership function. These three terms would then contribute the value

$$(w_2 + w_3 + w_4)c^k I^k = W^k c^k I^k$$

to the sum, where

$$W^k = (w_2 + w_3 + w_4)$$

is the sum of all weights from rules whose consequent is output membership function L^k. This means that the equation for the output value, y_0, given by (E.9) can be rewritten as

$$y_0 = \frac{\sum_{k=1}^{Q} W^k c^k I^k}{\sum_{k=1}^{Q} W^k I^k} \tag{E.10}$$

If the area of all output membership functions, I^k are equal, then Eq. (E.10) reduces to

$$y_0 = \frac{\sum_{k=1}^{Q} W^k c^k}{\sum_{k=1}^{Q} W^k} \tag{E.11}$$

Eqs. (E.10) and (E.11) show that the output crisp value of a fuzzy controller can be computed by summing over only the number of output membership functions rather than over all fuzzy rules. Also, if we use Eq. (E.11) to compute the output crisp value, then we need to specify only the centroids, c^k, of the output fuzzy membership functions. This is equivalent to assuming singleton fuzzy sets for the output.

For more information on fuzzy control you can consult the many books on this topic including

Fuzzy Logic and Control: Software and Hardware Applications, Vol. 2, by M. Jamshidi, N. Vadiee, and T. Ross, Prentice-Hall, Upper Saddle River, NJ, 1993.

Applications of Fuzzy Logic: Towards High Machine Intelligence Quotient Systems, by M. Jamshidi, A. Titli, L. Zadeh, and S. Boverie, Prentice-Hall, Upper Saddle River, NJ, 1997.

Appendix F

Phase Locked Loop

A *phase locked loop* (PLL) is used to produce a higher output frequency than the oscillator frequency generated by the crystal on the board. A block diagram of the PLL that is in the Freescale MC9S12DG256 microcontroller is shown in Fig. F.1. The registers used to program this phase locked loop are shown in Fig. F.2. The lower four bits of the REFDV register are used to divide the oscillator frequency, *OSCCLK*, by a value from 1 to 16, producing a signal with frequency f_1. The phase difference between this signal and a second signal with frequency f_2 is measured by the phase detector. The loop filter converts this phase difference into an analog voltage that is the input to a *voltage controlled oscillator* (VCO). The output of the VCO is a clock signal with a frequency that is proportional to the input voltage to the VCO. If the input voltage to the VCO increases, the output frequency will increase. If the input voltage to the VCO decreases, the output frequency will decrease. If you want the output frequency f_3 to be N times the reference frequency f_1, then the loop programmable divider will divide the output frequency f_3 by N to produce the frequency f_2, which will end up being the same frequency as f_1. If f_2 starts out at a lower frequency than f_1, then the output of the phase detector and loop filter will be positive, causing the frequency f_3 (and therefore f_2) to increase. On the other hand, if f_2 starts out at a higher frequency than f_1, then the output of the phase detector and loop filter will be negative, causing the frequency f_3 (and therefore f_2) to decrease. After a short time, the two frequencies f_1 and f_2 will become *locked* (equal) and therefore the phase difference will remain constant, and the output frequence f_3 will be constant and N times the frequency of f_1.

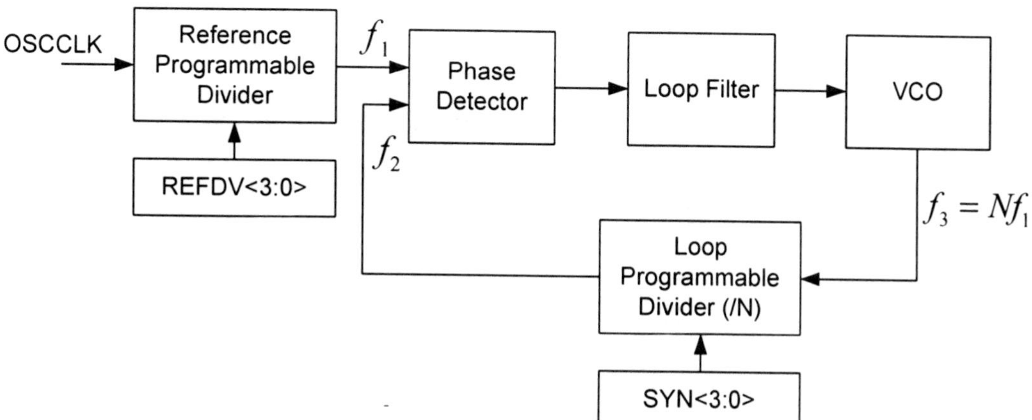

Figure F.1 Block diagram of the phase locked loop

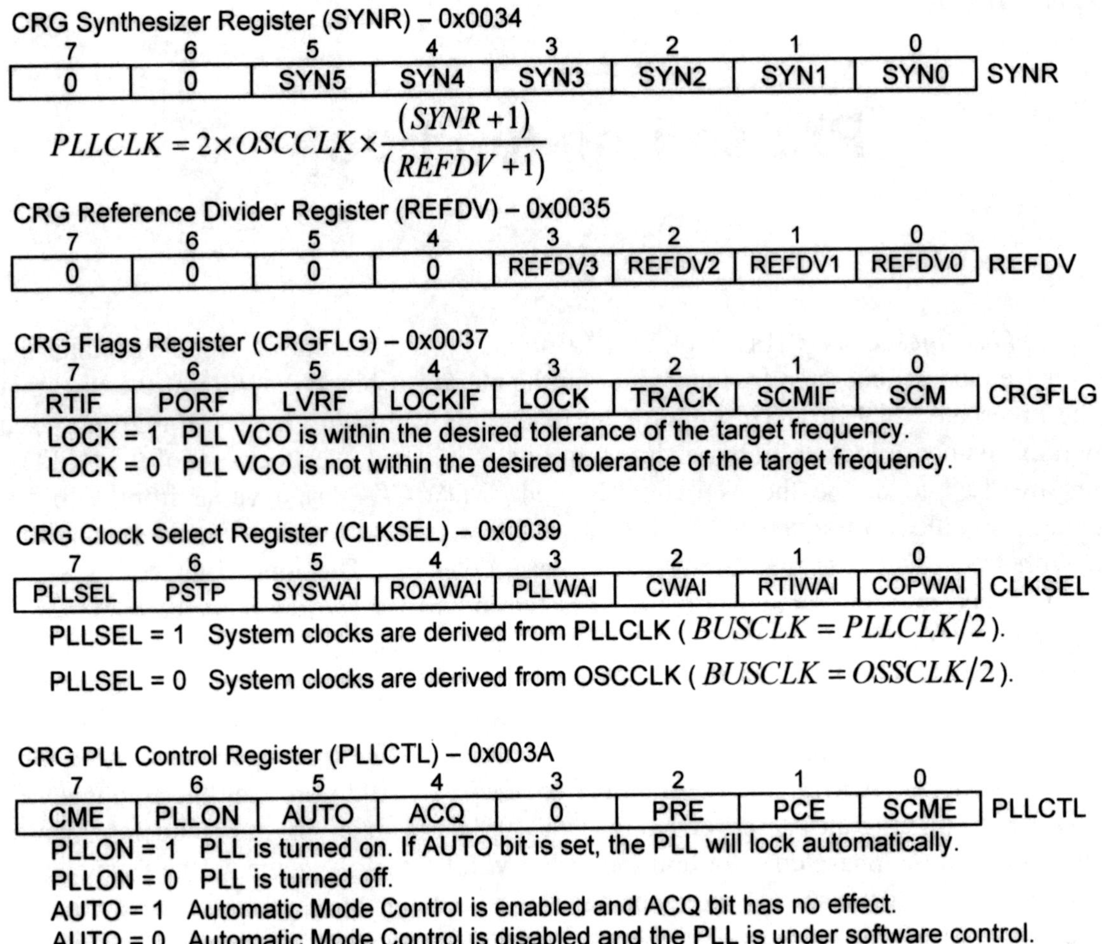

CRG Synthesizer Register (SYNR) – 0x0034
7 6 5 4 3 2 1 0
0 0 SYN5 SYN4 SYN3 SYN2 SYN1 SYN0 SYNR
$PLLCLK = 2 \times OSCCLK \times \frac{(SYNR+1)}{(REFDV+1)}$
CRG Reference Divider Register (REFDV) – 0x0035
7 6 5 4 3 2 1 0
0 0 0 0 REFDV3 REFDV2 REFDV1 REFDV0 REFDV
CRG Flags Register (CRGFLG) – 0x0037
7 6 5 4 3 2 1 0
RTIF PORF LVRF LOCKIF LOCK TRACK SCMIF SCM CRGFLG
LOCK = 1 PLL VCO is within the desired tolerance of the target frequency.
LOCK = 0 PLL VCO is not within the desired tolerance of the target frequency.
CRG Clock Select Register (CLKSEL) – 0x0039
7 6 5 4 3 2 1 0
PLLSEL PSTP SYSWAI ROAWAI PLLWAI CWAI RTIWAI COPWAI CLKSEL
PLLSEL = 1 System clocks are derived from PLLCLK ($BUSCLK = PLLCLK/2$).
PLLSEL = 0 System clocks are derived from OSCCLK ($BUSCLK = OSSCLK/2$).
CRG PLL Control Register (PLLCTL) – 0x003A
7 6 5 4 3 2 1 0
CME PLLON AUTO ACQ 0 PRE PCE SCME PLLCTL
PLLON = 1 PLL is turned on. If AUTO bit is set, the PLL will lock automatically.
PLLON = 0 PLL is turned off.
AUTO = 1 Automatic Mode Control is enabled and ACQ bit has no effect.
AUTO = 0 Automatic Mode Control is disabled and the PLL is under software control.

Figure F.2 Registers associated with the phase locked loop

The C function call *PLL_init*( ) that we have been using at the beginning of all of our C programs calls the assembly language subroutine given in Listing F.1.

Listing F.1 *PLL_init( )* Assembly Language Subroutine from *main.asm*

```
PLL_init:
          movb    #$02,SYNR           ;PLLCLK = 48 MHz
          movb    #$00,REFDV
          clr     CLKSEL
          movb    #$F1,PLLCTL
pll1:     brclr   CRGFLG,#$08,pll1    ;wait for PLL to lock
          movb    #$80,CLKSEL         ;select PLLCLK
          rts
```

The first two instructions in Listing F.1 store a value of 2 in register *SYNR* and a 0 in register *REFDV*. The value of the oscillator frequency, *OSCCLK*, on the DRAGON12-Plus_USB is 8 MHz. Using the equation for *PLLCLK* in Fig. F.2, this will produce a *PLLCLK* frequency of

$$PLLCLK = 2 \times 8 \times 10^6 \times \frac{(2+1)}{(0+1)} = 48 \text{ MHz}$$

The next instruction in Listing F.1 will clear the register *CLKSEL*, which, from Fig. F.2, will clear bit *PLLSEL*. This means that the bus frequency, *BUSCLK*, will be

$$BUSCLK = OSSCLK/2 = 8 \times 10^6/2 = 4 \text{ MHz}$$

It is necessary to use this bus frequency because, at this point, the PLL is not locked. The one-instruction loop, *pll1:*, in Listing F.1 will wait for the PLL to lock by polling the *LOCK* bit in the *CRGFLG* register in Fig. F.2.

The last instruction in Listing F.1 will set the *PLLSEL* bit in the *CLKSEL* register in Fig. 5.2. This means that the bus frequency, *BUSCLK*, will now be

$$BUSCLK = PLLCLK/2 = 48 \times 10^6/2 = 24 \text{ MHz}$$

Thus, after calling the C function call *PLL_init*( ), the bus frequency will be 24 MHz.

Appendix G

C Quick Reference Guide

Category	Definition	Example
Identifer Names	Can contain any letter, digit, or underscore _ Can not begin with a digit or be a keyword Case sensitive	q3 SCI0_init val32
Integer Numbers	signed char (8 bit) -128 to + 127 unsigned char (8 bit) 0 to 255 short (16 bit) -32,768 to +32,767 unsigned short (16 bit) 0 to 65,535 int (16 bit) -32,768 to +32,767 unsigned int (16 bit) 0 to 65,535 long (32 bit) -2,147,483,648 to +2,147,483,647 unsigned long (32 bit) 0 to 4,294,967,295	char c unsigned char x3 short Jay unsigned short ticks int i unsigned int Green long var32 unsigned long Black
Real Numbers (floating point)	float (32 bits) 6 significant digits double (64 bits) 10 significant digits long double (64 bits) 10 significant digits	float radius double rose
Constants	Decimal Hexadecimal (Hex)	1234 55 0xFC 0xA4C9
Characters	char	char c

Constant character arrays	Used to build a table of constant values	const char seg7tbl[] = {
		0x3F,0x06,0x5B,0x4f,
		0x66,0x6D,0x7D,0x07,
		0x7F,0x6F,0x77,0x7C,
		0x39,0x5E,0x79,0x71
		};

Character strings	"This is a string"	**char*** q1; **char*** q2; q1 = "Programming"; q2 = "Microcontrollers";

Arrays	A named collection of values of a particular type.	**unsigned char** memb_speed[20]
		unsigned char cent[ ] = {
		5,65,128,175,220
		};
		memb_speed[j+2] = 0;
		x = cent[2];

Pointers	An address that points to some memory location.	**char*** ptr; **char*** plus; **char** kbuf[12]; ptr = kbuf; plus = "+ ";
Arithmetic operators	+ (addition) - (subtraction) * (multiplication) / (division) % (mod)	count = count + 1; count++

C Quick Reference Guide (cont.)

<table>
<tr><td>Relational operators</td><td>==, !=, >, <, >=, <=, ===, !==</td><td>while(a <= b);
if(clr == 1)</td></tr>
<tr><td>Logic operators</td><td>! (Logical negation)
&& (Logical AND)
|| (Logical OR)
& (Bitwise AND)
| (Bitwise OR)
^ (Bitwise Exclusive OR)</td><td>while((i < 16) && (found == 0)){
    if((data & mask) == 0){
        found = 1;
        key = keytbl[i];
    }
    else {
        mask >>= 1;
        i++;
    }
}</td></tr>
<tr><td>Shift operators</td><td><< (shift left)
>> (shift right)</td><td>speed = val >> 2;
data = data << 8;</td></tr>
<tr><td>Shorthand operators</td><td>++ (increment)
-- (decrement)
+= a += b same as a = a + b
-=, *=. /= %=
<<=. >>=, ^= &=, |=</td><td>ticks++;
i--;
a += 5;
data |= c;
PTH &= 0xFE;
mask >>= 1;</td></tr>
<tr><td>Functions</td><td>return_type function_name(param1, ...parmN){
local_declarations;
statements;
}</td><td>void qstore(char c){
  rear++;
  if(rear > max)
    rear = min;
  if(rear == front){
    rear--;
  if(rear < min)
    rear = max;
  }else
    qbuff[rear] = c;
}
char getq(void){
  front++;
  if(front > max)
    front = 0;
  return qbuff[front];
}</td></tr>
<tr><td>Main program</td><td>preprocessor statements

void main(void) {
    declarations;
    statements;
}</td><td>void main(void) {
    PLL_init();
    DDRH = 0xff;
    PTH = 0x55;
    while(1) {
    }
}</td></tr>
<tr><td>if statement</td><td>if(expression){
    statement;
else
    statement;
}</td><td>if(readback == keycodes[i]){
    key = i;
    found = 1;
}
else
    i++;</td></tr>
<tr><td>for loop</td><td>for(initial_index; terminal_index; increment)
    statement;</td><td>for(i = 0; i < 16; i++){
    PORTB = seg7tbl[i];
    delay();
}</td></tr>
<tr><td>while loop</td><td>while(expression)
    statement;</td><td>while(SW1_down()){
    seg7dec(1);
}</td></tr>
</table>

C Quick Reference Guide (cont.)

<table>
<tr><td>switch statement</td><td><pre>
switch(expression) {
    case alternative1:
        statements;
        break;
    case alternative2:
        statements;
        break;
    default:
        statements;
        break;
}
</pre></td><td><pre>
switch(c){
  case 0xE:
    set_lcd_addr(0x40);
    while(qempty() != 0){
        data8(getq());
    }
    set_lcd_addr(0x00);
    type_lcd(blanks);
    wait_keyup();
    set_lcd_addr(0x00);
    break;
  case 0xF:
    clear_lcd();
    wait_keyup();
    break;
  default:
    break;
}
</pre></td></tr>
<tr><td>static storage class</td><td>A static local variable will retain its value from call to call.
A static global variable is not visible to other program files.</td><td><pre>
static char qbuff[QMAX];
static int front;
static int rear;
</pre></td></tr>
<tr><td>Interrupts</td><td>void interrupt <vector_number> int_name() {
statements;
}</td><td><pre>
void interrupt 7 handler(){
   ticks++;
   clear_RTI_flag();
}
</pre></td></tr>
</table>

Index

CPSIA information can be obtained
at www.ICGtesting.com
Printed in the USA
FFOW03n1650160216
21549FF